P9-DXM-721

The Canal Builders

THE STORY OF CANAL ENGINEERS THROUGH THE AGES

Pierre Stephen

by Robert Payne

627.13

THE MACMILLAN COMPANY · NEW YORK · 1959

79746

© Robert Payne 1959

All rights reserved—no part of this book may be reproduced in any form without permission in writing from the publisher, except by a reviewer who wishes to quote brief passages in connection with a review written for inclusion in magazine or newspaper.

First Printing

Library of Congress catalog card number: 59-5635

The Macmillan Company, New York
Brett-Macmillan Ltd., Galt, Ontario

Printed in the United States of America

for

NINA, SALLY and ALAN

with love

Contents

Illustrations

Invitation to the voyage

At the beginning of human history stands a man with a hoe digging in the soft earth on the banks of a silt-laden river somewhere in Egypt or Mesopotamia. A small man, burned by the sun, he works slowly and laboriously, and sometimes he pauses and dries the sweat from his brows with the edge of a flaxen loincloth, and looks across the river to the many channels teeming with fish and the wild fowl in the reed brakes, and then to the high ground where his village lies—a small village of reed huts clustered around the temple of his gods, the god of the storm and the god of the flooding rivers and the corn goddess who presides over the germinating seeds planted in the scratched furrows. He works on in the broiling heat, digging his long trench slantwise to the river, creeping closer and closer to the water, until at last there is only a frail wall of earth separating the trench from the river. Then with one last dramatic blow and a shout of triumph he destroys the wall and stands back to watch the river boil into the trench, filling it to the brim. At this moment civilization was born.

We shall never know the name of the man who built the first irrigation ditch, nor exactly where he built it, nor the names of the gods he worshiped, nor what thoughts passed through his mind as he stood there in the first morning of the world and marveled at his triumph. Innumerable consequences were to flow from his discovery that he could tame the river or at least imprison part of it and place it at his service. This mastery of water was the beginning of his mastery of the earth. And looking down at the quivering, glinting water trapped in his trench, he may have guessed at the fearful responsibility he had undertaken, for this was only the beginning. Beyond lay fabulous explorations. Soon he would learn to dig deeper and more complicated trenches. Soon he would find means to prevent the water from seeping away into the earth and from falling back into the river in times of drought. Out of the need for sharp digging instruments he would develop metallurgy, and out of the need for measuring the water in his canals would come mathematics, and from the stage towers he built to watch the advent of the spring floods would arise monumental and religious architecture. Now at last with the fertility of his fields secured by his control of the life-giving sweet waters ensuring an abundance of food, he had the leisure and the strength to set about populating the earth.

Soon there would arise further developments, all of them springing from that first trench. When the irrigation works expanded so that the canals served many communities, a ruling class of priests and irrigation experts came into existence to control the use of the canals and to establish a liturgy; and with the passing of the age of the nomadic farmers settled communities were established on the shores of the river, and as more and more communities amalgamated they formed a state. Because the canals must be safeguarded, armies arose to defend them. Because they must be inspected carefully, bureaucracy came into existence. Those who took more than their fair share of water had to be punished; therefore law courts were formed and the laws codified. In time powerful military establishments became the basis of authority, and a military caste took precedence over the priests and the irrigation experts, and the soldiers raided neighboring territory in order to control their canals, for the trenches filled with water were tangible assets, the greatest wealth in the world.

Out of canals, out of that first trench, arose the great theocratic and monolithic state—Ur, Lagash, Sumer, Babylon, Nineveh, Upper and Lower Egypt. Pharaoh controlled the flow of water:

from his bounty came the life flowing in the rivers and tamed at last in the neat checkerboard of canals on the banks of the Nile. To house the officials in charge of the innumerable canals he ordered the construction of the Labyrinth, at least five times larger than the Pentagon, and to house the dead Pharaoh pyramids arose surrounded by artificial lakes fed by a complex canal system. Empires arose on the work of the canal diggers, and when the empires perished the canals perished with them, leaving only shadowy traces on the desert sand. Sometimes the empires rose again, following a strange cyclic pattern, and once again canals were dug in places where no water had flowed for a thousand years.

Sometimes as we look back on those ancient canal diggers it is possible to guess at the emotions which moved them when they tamed the waters. For them, as for us, water was power, without which all life would cease from the earth. We too have watched the great rivers passing by and seen all their power, except for the small fraction which turns mill wheels and turbines or is channeled off to irrigate the fields, going to waste. For century upon century the rivers have fallen into the sea, and men have stood on the banks, dimly aware of the vast explosive forces locked within them.

Today we are in process of taming the rivers, but we are only a little closer to the heart of the mystery. The life-giving sweet water which falls from heaven as rain and which flows down in rivers or springs up from impenetrable sources deep in the earth is still a mystery. Why is it there? How does it give life to growing plants? By what miracle of photosynthesis do moisture and the sun's heat produce the waving corn? For the ancients it was even more mysterious, for they saw seeds and bulbs and the eggs of insects lying lifeless in the rich soil of the eastern Mediterranean lands until the rains came or the sluice gates were opened, and then they sprang into life. For them water was only another word for life. Colorless, scentless, shapeless, so powerful that it could break granite mountains apart, so frail that it could trickle through the fingers, assuming whatever shape men desired and reflecting all the colors around it, vanishing into steam when a fire was lit under it, turning into ice on the high mountains, it possessed a mysterious, ghostly presence. Sanctity lay in it, and the gods spoke from it. Thales said that water was the cause of all things—the ἀρχή, which is more than the cause: at once the final image and the great generator from which all things flow. Pindar said, more quietly: "Best of all things is water."

So for centuries men have lived out their lives in its ghostly presence, aware of its power to destroy and to save, aware of the impenetrable secrets locked in every silvery globule, the latent power, the lightning in the water drop. Inevitably those who could make water serve the community acquired something of the stature of gods. So we see in the earliest portrait of a canal builder a Pharaoh of Upper Egypt standing in a posture of relentless power, gazing impassively before him at the fields and the workmen and the standards of the tribes with the air of someone who knows perfectly well that he is performing a miracle. Moses striking water from the rock is not far removed from De Lesseps, who made water flow across the aimless desert. The faces of the canal builders are all faces of power, with stern mouths and deep-set eyes. Look, for example, at the face of Sesostris III and then at Agrippa, the power behind the throne of Augustus Caesar, and then at Leonardo, who built few canals in the earth but continued throughout his life to build them in his vast imagination. They are faces which seem to have been carved by water on the rocks, unyielding as granite, possessed of an inner calm and compassionate self-assurance. It is the same with the lesser canal builders—Pierre-Paul Ricquet, James Brindley, Thomas Telford, DeWitt Clinton, George Goethals. Unknown to each other, they yet form a brotherhood. It could hardly be otherwise, since of all the works of man canal building is the one that gives most life.

Sometimes, of course, the canal builders have been demonstrably evil, their only desire to write their names across the earth. So Nero attempted to dig a canal at the Isthmus of Corinth, and the mad Claudius tunneled through a mountain to dig a canal from

Lake Fucinus, and the wild Sennacherib at an earlier period built the great Jerwan aqueduct which conveyed water on an immense stone-paved causeway across the Gomer River to the gardens of Nineveh thirty miles southwest. The Pharaoh who built the Labyrinth may not have been entirely devoted to serving his people. Even De Lesseps suffered from occasional bouts of enervating gigantomania. It is in the nature of the beast that men should grow proud and reckless when they build great works; and sometimes they grow still more reckless when they only dream about them.

Normally, General Gordon was a man who held his passions in check. Almost single-handedly he had overthrown a vast conspiratorial insurrection in China, and then, returning to England, he retired from the army to devote himself to biblical researches in Jerusalem. It was a time when Britain was seriously considering the annexation of Egypt. One day, when he was poring over his maps in Jerusalem, it occurred to him that a great canal stretching from Haifa to the head of the Gulf of Aqaba in the Red Sea would have the advantage of effectively preventing Russian subversion in the Near East. In a mood of uncontrollable excitement he wrote to a friend in England:

> Such a canal would close all attacks from Russia upon Palestine, except upon the line between Haifa and Zerin, and strangely enough would force her to attack on Megiddo (Armageddon). It would prepare the way for a United Europe to put this thus isolated Palestine under a common ruler, and would bring about the true prophecy of the Scriptures. All nations would come here and colonize. As for the Jews, they do not exist in my mind, in those who call themselves so. I am a Jew a thousand times more than they are.[1]

It is a strange letter with uncomfortable overtones and a curious relevance to our own time—just such a canal was proposed recently at the time of the Suez crisis. But what is chiefly interesting in the letter is the glimpse of megalomania at work, the strident voice, the summons to the lesser manias to assist the greater, and

[1] H. E. Wortham, *Gordon* (London, Harrap, 1933), p. 267.

the terrible simplicity of the thing. Occasionally we detect the same strident voice in our own day, as men set about transforming the great rivers into navigable lakes. Perhaps, after all, the Chinese had reason on their side when they said that men should surrender to "the winds and the waters" (*feng shui*), and not attempt to dominate them.

Now, however, it is too late, and the course of human progress demands that we should dominate the forces of nature, or perish in the attempt. Once more the canal builders assume the role they assumed at the beginning of history—they are the creators of landscapes, the purveyors of vast wealth, the hieratic engineers of destiny. Where once there were virgin forests and granite outcrops, cities arise on the banks, industries are born, new civilizations come into being. When the great rivers of northern Russia are tamed and the St. Lawrence Seaway is completed, will Russia and America be the same as before? Almost inevitably the center of gravity of the United States will move northward, and the Russian center of gravity will be found in Central Asia.

Yet this is only the beginning. All over the world vast canal projects are on the drawing boards. In Iraq the ancient canals between the Euphrates and the Tigris are being reopened and reshaped, and the wandering tribesmen are being settled on the land, no longer obedient to the local sheikhs but to the central government which alone possesses the wealth to build the canals. Forty-six million Indians and Pakistanis live on the banks of the Indus and its snow-fed tributaries over an area of 200,000 square miles, more than four times the size of New York State. Now at last canals and storage dams are being built, and here again we can expect a prodigious increase in the population and a shift in centers of gravity. Since 1951, when the Federal Government of Mexico completed the Alvaro Obregón dam on the Yaquí River, the deserts of Sonora, irrigated with an intricate system of canals running off the dam, have been made to bloom. Recently the Israelis discovered in the deserted highlands of the western Negev evidence of a complex irrigation system built by the Nabataeans during the century before the birth of Christ, and now they plan to restore it. In time the Chinese may be able to canalize the Yangtze, that most bloodthirsty of rivers, which has been known to leap upward fifty feet in a single night. Once Achilles fought against the raging floods of the Scamander River, a river so unruly and so powerful that bulls were sacrificed to it and living horses were thrown into it. The flood hung over him and gripped him by the throat and would have overwhelmed him if Hephaestus of the Crooked Foot had not set the river on fire. The successors of Achilles on the plain of Troy had other means of taming the relentless river—they built canals. Today the visitor to the Troad sees the ancient Scamander wandering sluggishly across the plain, spreading canals to the right and left of it. So in time may all the other rivers of the earth be tamed.

I have told the story of the canals as a continuing history, but sometimes it has been necessary to allow the periods to overlap. I wish there had been space to describe the stone-walled canals of Tokyo, Yokohama, and Osaka, or those of Peru, built superbly before the white men came, or those which the Dutch built close to the western shores of Ceylon. There should have been a place for the flower-strewn canal between Mexico City and Xochimilco and the graceful Atlantic Intracoastal Waterway which wanders for twelve hundred miles between New Jersey and Florida. Something too should have been said about Dutch canals and especially of Canal Albert, that heavily fortified waterway which runs parallel to the border of the Netherlands for ninety-five miles. But men have built canals from the beginning of history and are likely to go on making them until history ends, and there was the danger that the book might go on for ever.

Here, the last word must go to Charles Baudelaire, who alone among major poets celebrated canals in his poem *L'Invitation au Voyage*. He describes first the charms of a mysterious Eastern land, but the final image is reserved for ships returning from the ends of the earth to bask at sunset in the calm waterways, as the light turns to hyacinth and gold:

Vois sur ces canaux
Dormir ces vaisseaux
Dont l'humeur est vagabonde;
C'est pour assouvir
Ton moindre désir
Qu'ils viennent du bout du monde.
—Les soleils couchants
Revêtent les champs,
Les canaux, la ville entière,
D'hyacinthe et d'or;
Le monde s'endort
Dans une chaude lumière.

Là, tout n'est qu'ordre et beauté,
Luxe, calme et volupté.

(Here there is only grace and measure,
Richness, quietness and pleasure.)

So might an ancient Egyptian have spoken on the banks of the reborn Nile, as he contemplated the water swinging past the sluice gates and flooding his quiet canals.

Scorpion and labyrinth

In the hot, arid land of Egypt, where a single river threads from the mountains of the south to empty itself in the Mediterranean, men fought for water to survive. For them water was life, a little thin thread of life flowing across the deserts, coming to flood in high summer, then ebbing away, reviving each year with wonderful and inexplicable regularity. They could not conceive why the Nile rose in June or July, but they knew it was so, and they were grateful for the prevailing winds from the north which allowed their ships to move against the current and for the reddish-brown mud which the Blue Nile washed down from the volcanic plateaus of Abyssinia—a strange life-giving mud, almost the color of blood. They knew that without the Nile they would die, for no rain falls in Upper Egypt, and only a few scattered showers fall over the Delta. For the Egyptians the Nile was life and food and gaiety, color and taste and sweetness, a highway to the present and perhaps a highway after death, for it was inconceivable to them that they could not find it again after their deaths. They saw themselves as people who were born out of the Nile and went back to the Nile again; and it would not have surprised them if the Nile spoke to them with a divine voice.

"Egypt," said Herodotus, "is the gift of the Nile." It is a good phrase, and very true, but it is unlikely that Herodotus invented it—similar phrases were used by priests worshiping in the temples.

And Herodotus, who came to Egypt when the great days of the Egyptian empires were already over and spent much time with priests, may have heard the words in the great cavernous temples, where emblems of the river were painted on the walls. The worship of Isis and Osiris was intimately connected with the rise and fall of the river. The ship of Isis sailed on the Nile in search of the body of Osiris, dismembered and thrown to the winds and made whole again by the sacred river and by the prayers men uttered on its banks.

For the Egyptians the Nile was sacred, and like all sacred things it laid heavy obligations on its worshipers. In those early days life crowded along the margins of the river, and the floods spread over the swamps and the riverine jungles teeming with game, and then over the surrounding desert, where the waters drained off quickly in the sands. Long before the Sumerians were learning to tame the Tigris and Euphrates, and before the Egyptians entered history, men were learning to capture and retain the waters, to dig wells and irrigation canals. The first recorded canal builder has no name and almost no history; we do not know where he built his capital, or what wars he fought, or exactly when he reigned. But we know that he built a canal, and we can watch him as he presides over the ceremonial opening somewhere in Upper Egypt at some time in the fourth millennium before Christ.

We know him as King Scorpion, only because the artist who carved the great imperial mace head now in the Ashmolean Museum at Oxford portrayed a scorpion hovering in the air in front of him, together with a seven-petaled lotus—the flower and the scorpion almost certainly formed his name. Wearing the tall white crown of Upper Egypt, he stands on the bank of the canal with a hoe in both hands, three times larger than the men around him, with a look of authority and power. In front of him a man holds up a basket, perhaps filled with seeds, and beyond him another holds some ears of corn. The king waits patiently, fanned by fan bearers, while the carved standards of the conquered tribes

Mace head of King Scorpion (Ashmolean Museum)

are displayed before him. Down below, the workmen are putting the last touches to the canal banks, two workmen on opposite sides, while a third is running up to assist them. In the right-hand lower corner we see a fence of matted reeds below a palm tree. Such fences may have been used to shore up the banks, but as the artist has depicted it, it looks surprisingly like a sluice gate. The artist has done his work well. We are aware of the frenzy of the workmen and the proud impassivity of the king with his feet firmly planted on the banks of the Nile, and there is no mistaking the power which emanates from his sharply carved features. He looks like a warrior, but also a good administrator, and he must have attached importance to this canal opening, for otherwise he would not have had it carved on his mace head.[1]

Of this mysterious King Scorpion, who comes at the beginning of history, we know very little. We know that he conquered part of the Delta and that he was one of the Servants of Horus, and some of his monuments bearing the characteristic "scorpion" sign have been found near Abydos on the site of the ancient Thinis. When we come to Menes, the first King of the First Dynasty, we are already in historical times.

King Menes conquered the whole Delta and unified the Valley of the Nile. He lived about 3000 B.C., and built his capital at Memphis. According to Herodotus, he dammed the Nile some twelve miles south of Memphis and diverted it into a new channel between two nearby hills, then built his city on the fertile bed of the Nile and excavated a lake to the north and west of the city. A new canal joined the lake to the Nile, and then the canal, the lake, and the river served as a moat to protect him from his enemies. The priests told Herodotus that of the 350 kings who followed Menes there was not one equal to him, and we can well believe them. Yet here and there, carved on the rocks of Egypt and painted on the walls of tombs, we find records to show that the Egyptians had not lost their skill in engineering.

In the Sixth Dynasty (about 2300–2180 B.C.), Pepi I sent expeditions to Nubia to secure gold and incense and to control the tribesmen. Accordingly he planned a series of short canals through the granite barriers of the First Cataract. Under the supervision of Uni, the governor of Upper Egypt, the canals were cut in the fifth year of the reign of Uni's son, Mernere. There were altogether five canals, and Uni claimed that he carved them all in a single year. He wrote on the walls above the canals an inscription which still survives:

His Majesty sent me to dig five canals in the South and to make three cargo boats and four tow-boats of acacia wood of Wawat. Then

[1] King Scorpion's mace head resembles a famous slate commemorative palette showing King Menes overpowering his enemies. Artistically, the Scorpion mace head is the greater work.

the dark-skinned chieftains of Yarrtt, Wawat, Yam and Mazoi drew timber for them, and I did the whole in a single year.[2]

Another record says that King Mernere himself appeared at the cataract to receive the homage of the southern chieftains.

The power and wealth of Egypt depended upon opening new canals, and every new dynasty introduced great public works. Achtoy IV, the most powerful of the Herakleopolitan kings, whom Manetho, the Egyptian chronicler, described as "more terrifying than any before him, the doer of evil to the people of Egypt," dug a canal fifty-five miles long from Herakleopolis to the old capital at Memphis. It was the longest canal dug up to this time. Then for three more dynasties the records are silent, or else they are still buried in the Egyptian sands. With the Middle Kingdom, which began about 2000 B.C., there appears to be a sudden change of direction. In the past canals had been dug for military purposes or on the arbitrary whim of a Pharaoh, but now vast stretches of uncultivated land were being put to the plow. Previously the Egyptians had learned to supplement the annual overflow of the Nile by an elaborate irrigation system. Now the marshlands were drained and artificial lakes were built to collect and hold the surplus water of the annual inundation. For the first time we are made aware of social advances and of an effort to use the land which had never been used before.

The Middle Kingdom was a time of rebirth, of great intellectual advances and social peace. Egypt was the greatest power in the world, ruled by gifted Pharaohs whose fame rests more on their monuments and on their cultivation of the arts than on their skill in war. The most outstanding of these Pharaohs was Amenemhet III, who ruled for nearly fifty years: a lean, grave, handsome man, with a peculiarly modern cast of features, and enormous ears. Long before the archaeologists had dug up the sculptural masterpieces of his reign, the classical historians were immortalizing his ambitious program of hydraulic engineering leading to the great agricultural and economic expansion of the Fayum, an immense marshy oasis

[2] J. H. Breasted, *Ancient Records of Egypt* (University of Chicago Press, 1906), I, 324.

west of the Nile and south of Memphis, still the most fertile region of Egypt.

Herodotus knew Amenemhet III as Moeris, and gaped at the great artificial lake called after him. It was even more wonderful than the great palace, which housed the temple and the water board, with its twelve immense courts and three thousands rooms, half of them underground. Herodotus was not allowed to see the underground rooms, which contained the tombs of many Pharaohs, but he was escorted through the labyrinthine upper chambers with their baffling and intricate passages leading to galleries and still more courtyards. This immense building was called the Labyrinth and rivaled the older Labyrinth of King Minos at Cnossus in Crete. Herodotus was overwhelmed by the exquisite whiteness of the marble and the paintings on the walls and the ceilings which were composed of vast stone slabs. This building, a monument to bureaucracy, was still standing in Strabo's time.[3] But Herodotus was still more amazed by the extent and grandeur of the artificial lake:

Still more marvellous and astonishing is the Lake of Moeris, which has a circumference of 3600 stades, or 60 *schoeni,* a distance of about 420 miles, equal to the length of the whole Egyptian coastline. The shape of the lake is elongated, running north and south, and the greatest depth is fifty fathoms. Now this immense lake is clearly artificial, for nearly in the middle of it there rise two pyramids, which stand 300 feet above the water, and there must be an equal depth below the surface; and each pyramid is surmounted by a stone carving of a man sitting on a throne. The water in the lake is not supplied by natural springs, for the country here is excessively dry, but is brought from the Nile by means of an artificial channel, which flows for six months of the year and pours back to the Nile for the other six months. While the water runs in, the lake pays the treasury a silver talent for the fish which are

[3] The ground plan of the Labyrinth was discovered by Sir Flinders Petrie by tracing out an immense bed of white limestone. All the stones had long since been removed, but he was able to measure out the exact dimensions. Herodotus had not exaggerated the size. "On that space," commented Sir Flinders Petrie, "could be erected the great hall of Karnak, and all the successive temples adjoining it; also the temple of Mut, and that of Khonsu, and that of Amenhotep III at Karnak; also the two great temples of Luxor; and still there would be room for the Ramasseum." See *Hawara, Biahmu and Arsinoe* (London, Field and Tuer, 1889), p. 5.

caught, but during the other half of the year only twenty *minae* are paid, which is only one third of a talent.[4]

Herodotus visited Egypt during the fifth century B.C., when Egypt was being ruled from Persia, but Diodorus Siculus, a Greek historian from Sicily, who visited Egypt during the first century B.C., was equally impressed. The sheer size of that great catch basin for the fast-moving waters of the Nile inundation fascinated him. He found himself continually asking himself how many men had worked on it, and how many years they worked, and at what cost of incredible toil. "No one," he said a little breathlessly, "can adequately commend the King's design, which brings such usefulness and advantage to all the inhabitants of Egypt."

It was clear to Diodorus Siculus that the lake and even the Labyrinth were triumphs of royal beneficence. Herodotus had heard the rumor that there was an underground tunnel leading from Lake Moeris to the Libyan Syrtis, but it was no more than rumor; and he has hardly begun to tell the story of the lake when he remembers a story of King Sardanapalus, and he is off hunting for hares. Diodorus Siculus is a little more explicit with an account of the canal and the cost of operating the sluice gates:

Since the Nile keeps to no definite bounds in its rising, and the fertility of the country depends upon regulating the river, the King dug the lake to accommodate the surplus water, so that the Nile should not flood the land unseasonably because of its strong current, forming swamps and marshes, and at the same time regulation is necessary to prevent the land from being parched by lack of water. So between the river and the lake the King dug a canal 80 stades long and 300 feet wide. He arranged that at certain times the water should be allowed to enter the canal, and at other times it was cut off, thus providing the peasants with water at the proper times. He opened and closed the gates scientifically, and at great expense. The sum of 50 talents had to be paid by anyone who wanted to open or shut the sluice-gate. Down to our own days the lake has continued to serve the Egyptian people—this lake, which is still named after the man who built it.[5]

[4] Herodotus, *History,* II, 140.
[5] Diodorus Siculus, *The Historical Library,* I, lii.

Diodorus Siculus is not always reliable, and one might boggle at his detailed description—there is something suspicious about the fifty talents which were paid whenever the gate was opened or closed—but Strabo, a far more reliable contemporary, declares that he saw the canal with his own eyes, and took careful observations on the regulators which control the inflow and outflow, though he unfortunately failed to describe them. It seems certain that the lake, the Labyrinth, and the canal were the work of several Pharaohs, and came to fruition during the reign of Amenemhet III, who built the two pyramids at Hawara at the entrance to the Fayum, one for himself, the other mysteriously left empty. We are accustomed to thinking of the pyramids as giant tombs left to molder in the sand. As usual, Herodotus puts these things in their proper perspective. Herodotus specifically mentions that he saw the pyramids rising from the lake when he visited the Labyrinth, and he speaks of a canal leading to the pyramid of Cheops. It is probable that all the pyramids were originally intended to rise out of artificial lakes supplied by canals from the Nile. There they were, gleaming white, bathed in the living waters, capped with the golden image of the Pharaoh, surrounded by quiet waters. So in death the Pharaoh was perpetually bathed in the sacred lake of his own mortuary temple, as in life he performed daily the ceremonies of purification, coming to life every day as the sun god came to life every morning by bathing in the Lake of Lilies before embarking on his journey across the heavens. It was a conception of fantastic grandeur, filled with continuing life and power, worthy of great kings.

For the Egyptians water was life, especially the quiet water of lakes and canals. The Nile was dreaded, a force almost beyond man's conception, and always to be placated. But a canal was the Nile made captive and humanized, a place of fructifying peace and quietness. So inevitably in *The Book of the Dead,* written during the time of the Middle Kingdom, we find men dreaming of an after-life spent on the shores of a canal. The chapters called *The Coming Forth by Day* recite the blessings of the soul in Paradise—he will break the bread of eternity and drink the beer of everlastingness and sow and reap and marry and sail for ever in a boat along those intricate canals where the reeds are continually bending in the heavenly wind. In the *Papyrus of Ani* we are even shown the boat of death with the passengers contentedly pulling themselves along a canal in a boat laden with all manner of delicacies. But it was not quite the canal the Egyptians knew when they were living. Says the *Papyrus of Ani:* "Mouth of the canal, a stream one thousand cubits long. Its length cannot be stated. No fishes of any kind live in it, nor are there serpents." [6] Along these canals men and women walk at leisure, with flowers in their hair and fans in their hands, in the shade of the palm trees. Many paintings and sculptures show Osiris, lord of life and judge of the dead, resting above the canal—the waters of the Nile boxed and circumscribed, and with an array of lotuses issuing from it.

The Pharaoh was the lord of the whole earth, lord of the sweet winds from the Mediterranean, lord of the Nile which he regulated, and also lord of canals and all irrigation works, because he regulated them doubly. To Pharaoh the Egyptians paid the tribute due to a god, but a still greater tribute was due to Osiris. According to a Hymn to Osiris composed in the Twelfth Dynasty, canals were sacred to him:

> As for thee, the Nile comes forth from the sweat of thy hands. Thou spewest out the wind that is in thy throat into the nostrils of men. When canals are dug, when houses and temples are built, when monuments are transported and fields are cultivated, it is thou who makest them. They are on thy back.[7]

So they paid their dues in flowers thrown into the canals, in hymns and special celebrations every year when the new waters rushed into the canals. It was a simple patriarchal life, and sometimes it seemed only a hairbreadth away from the other world, the beautiful "Amenti," where life flowed in the eternal noonday, and it was

[6] E. A. Wallis Budge, *The Book of the Dead* (New York, G. P. Putnam's Sons, 1913), p. 325.
[7] J. H. Breasted, *The Dawn of Conscience* (New York, Charles Scribner's Sons, 1939), p. 97.

always early autumn, the Nile at the flood and the canals filled to the brim.

From the great administrative building which stood on the north bank of the inflowing canal at the entrance to the Fayum, Pharaoh administered all the canals of Egypt. Presumably there were vast maps, hordes of officials, couriers running in all directions. According to Herodotus, a fever of canal making occurred during the reign of Sesostris III, who employed his prisoners of war to such advantage that the whole face of the country was changed. Because there were no more roads, only a vast network of interlocking canals, horses and carts vanished from the scene. They had been common in the past, but now there was no trace of them:

> All Egypt is level; yet from this time onwards it has been unfit for horses or wheeled traffic because of the innumerable canals running in all directions, cutting the country into small segments. It was the King's desire to supply water to the towns which lay inland at some distance from the river, for previously when the level of the Nile fell, the people went short and drank brackish water from the wells. It was this King also who divided the land into lots and gave everyone a square piece of equal size, and from the produce exacted an annual tax. Any man whose holding was damaged by the encroachment of the river could go and declare his loss before the King, who would send inspectors to measure the extent of his loss, in order that he might pay in future a proper portion of the tax at which he had been assessed. Perhaps this was the way in which geometry was invented.[8]

Perhaps; and it is likely enough that Herodotus discussed the matter with the Egyptians at length. It is an intriguing chain of argument: canals leading to the division of the land, and the division leading to geometry. According to Herodotus, Sesostris III was the greatest of canal builders. Menes and Moeris built canals, but Sesostris III is "he who made the canals." We know that the Pharaoh sent his viceroy Thure to reopen the canal at the first cataract. Thure left a record of his accomplishment in an inscription carved

[8] Herodotus, *History,* II, 109.

on the rocks of the Island of Sehel near Elephantine. The inscription, which was carved three times on the rocks, explains the purpose of the canal; it was to provide a direct waterway for the conquest of Nubia. The inscription reads:

> Year Eight under the Majesty of the King of Upper and Lower Egypt Khekure [Sesostris III] living for ever. His Majesty commanded to make the canal anew, the name of the canal being "Beautiful are the ways of Khekure living for ever." Through this canal His Majesty proceeded up-river, to overthrow the wretched Kush.[9]

From other records we learn a little more about this expedition against Kush, or Nubia. When the conquering armies returned, Sesostris III himself stood in the foremost ship, and from the ship's prow the body of the Nubian chieftain hung head downward. The canal was 260 feet long, 35 feet wide and 26 feet deep, carved out of the solid rock. Eight years later it was found to be choked up. It was frequently repaired, and was still in use in the New Kingdom. The wars against the Nubians continued. Thutmose I sailed through the canal at the head of his army, and the long-lived Thutmose III in the fiftieth year of his reign gave orders for the canal to be cleared again. He also ordered that the canal should be placed under the care of the fishermen of Elephantine, who were to clear it every year and report back to the king on whether it was navigable.

So the work of the Egyptians went on, with more and more waterways stretching over the country. Some time during the Middle Kingdom a canal was dug between the Red Sea and the eastern branch of the Nile at the Delta. Egyptian priests informed Herodotus that at one time the Red Sea and the Mediterranean were connected, and geographical and geological evidence suggests that the division occurred comparatively recently, perhaps only ten thousand years before the first of the Pharaohs ruled in Egypt. But we know nothing of the first canal between the Red Sea and the Mediterranean. The records, if there are any, lie buried still beneath the sands.

[9] J. H. Breasted, *Ancient Records of Egypt,* I, 647.

The work of making canals went on, because the Egyptians were obsessed with it. For them canals were life and breath, giving order and ritual to their daily lives. Quite early in their history they learned how to tame the floods and make the water work for them; and serenity came to them from the peaceful waters between the canal dikes. Meanwhile, a thousand miles away from Memphis across the Syrian deserts, other kingdoms had emerged, canals were being dug, wars were being fought over water rights, and men were pitting their wits against more ferocious floods than the Egyptians had ever seen. There was a world of difference between the calm of the Egyptians and the fierce vigor of the Sumerians. For the Egyptians water was peaceful, beneficent, fructifying. To the Sumerians living on the banks of the Tigris and Euphrates, it was violent and unpredictable, almost untamable, and one of the greatest of their gods was the Lord of the Storm.

No one knows where the Sumerians came from, but they may have come originally from beyond the Caspian and the Caucasus. A small vivid brilliant thin-boned people, they seem to have reached the Tigris-Euphrates plain about the time the kings of Upper Egypt were marching north toward the delta. They had few of the heaven-sent advantages of the Egyptians. In the spring when the snow melts in the Armenian mountains, the Euphrates and Tigris overflow their banks, and at the same time the tides in the Persian Gulf may rise to a height of eight or nine feet, banking up the rivers. The Sumerians coped with these difficulties as best they could, removing the coarse silt that came down with the fierce Tigris and maintaining a permanent watch on the rivers which gave them so much anxiety. It is possible that the high temples known as ziggurats with ascending terraces winding around them developed from the high stage towers they built to look down upon the approaching floods. The priests watched the stars and the rivers; and in the Mesopotamian sky, where the stars seem very close, it was not difficult to imagine that the heavens, too, were irrigated with complex canal systems.

The earliest surviving map is inscribed with a reed stylus on a clay tablet, and shows the two great canals flowing through the ancient city of Nippur which stood at the great fork of the Euphrates. Today the sand blows over the ruins of Nippur, and the Euphrates has long since carved another channel for itself to

Nippur—the earliest known map (Falcon's Wing Press)

the Persian Gulf, but the map shows Nippur in all its glory—the river flowing by, the quays, the harbors, and the temples. More significantly, the map shows the Nunbirdu Canal where Enlil, "the father of the gods, the king of heaven and earth, the king of all lands," saw the goddess Ninlil bathing. The wise old goddess Ninshebargunu warned her young and headstrong daughter against appearing unclothed in the canal, for the prying eyes of the greatest god of all might see her, and from seeing her beauty might be tempted to violate her. In *The Myth of Enlil and Ninlil* the old goddess is uttering a last warning:

> In the pure stream, O woman, in the pure stream do not bathe!
> In the pure stream, O Ninlil, in the pure stream, O woman, do not bathe!
> O Ninlil, do not climb onto the bank of the canal Nunbirdu.
> With his shining eyes will the Lord, with his shining eyes will he espy thee;
> With his shining eyes will he espy thee, the great mountain, father Enlil;
> With his shining eyes will espy thee, the . . . shepherd, the determiner of fates.
> Forthwith he will embrace thee, he will kiss thee! [10]

But Ninlil is too headstrong to pay attention to the warning. She climbs onto the canal bank, where Enlil finds her and ravishes her, leaving her pregnant with Sin, the moon god, whose cold clear light is like the waters of the canal. And this meeting between Enlil and Ninlil is only the beginning, for other gods were subsequently born to them when the young and beautiful goddess followed the father of the gods to Hades. There is nothing strange in an epiphany on the banks of a canal, for the Sumerians evidently regarded canals as sacred, made by the labor of men's hands but inspired by the gods.

Just as the earliest surviving map shows the high banks of two great canals, so the earliest Sumerian relief, known as the Stele of the Vultures, shows the victory of the *patesi* of Lagash in a war fought over a canal. It is the first of a long line of impressive battle scenes to be sculptured in Mesopotamia. Previously there had been long periods of peace, with the communities at the mouth of the Tigris and Euphrates trading quietly with one another. Surviving records of the reign of Ur-Nina, who lived about 2900 B.C., show him building temples and digging canals. His grandson Enneatum was made

[10] Henri Frankfort, *Before Philosophy* (Harmondsworth, Penguin Books, 1951), p. 166.

of sterner stuff. A powerful full-chested man, he led his soldiers against the neighboring city of Umma, which lay a few miles to the northwest across the plain on the other side of the canal known as "The Lion of the Plains," where the battle was fought. Enneatum's troops moved in close formation with ten-foot spears, protected by heavy leather shields provided with metal bosses and with iron helmets which fitted closely to their skulls. Enneatum called upon Ningursu, the god who presided over the fortunes of the city of Lagash, to grant him victory, and promised, if successful, to dig a new canal in honor of the god. His heavily armed troops advanced to the canal and beyond it, and set the soldiers of Umma to flight, and the vultures carried off the dead. Like the mace head of King Scorpion, the Stele of the Vultures shows the king at the supreme moment of climax, calmly regarding the action around him, as though from the infinite distance of his royal power. He stands there, holding a fly whisk, wearing a skirt of sheepskin, while below him one of his commanders hurls a spear clear across the canal. We see the dead lying in rows with the vultures floating over them, and from the expressions on the faces of the living we know the battle was hard-fought. Enneatum returned in triumph to Lagash, fulfilled his promise to dig a new canal in honor of the god, and then dug another canal separating the plain of Gu-edin from the territory of Umma to mark the limits of his own territory. On the Stele of the Vultures he caused to be written an account of his victory. "Over the people of Umma I, Enneatum, threw the great net of Enlil," he wrote, and he begged Ningursu to protect the new canal he had dug, saying, "O Ningursu, lord of the crown, give life to the canal Gu-edin." His success, however, was short-lived, for soon afterward the people of Umma arose and attacked Lagash, and during the fighting they came upon the Stele of the Vultures and smashed it into a hundred fragments. Today the fragments rest in the Louvre and in the British Museum, monuments to the first war fought over water rights.

All through the early history of Sumeria the wars continued. Songs and hymns describe the destruction on the banks of the canals, when the towpaths grew nothing but weeds, and only the wild goats, snakes, and scorpions inhabited them. Then, as now, goats are the enemies of canal banks, forever running up and down the slopes. We hear of ancient bankers speculating in canal buildings and in the sale of irrigated fields. From the making of canals and the division of the Egyptian land, Herodotus saw the birth of geometry: from canals too we can derive the birth of law in Sumerian times. Each irrigation ditch had a price and all were taxed, and all were sacred to the gods, and perhaps the first of all written commandments was one found on a clay tablet: "Uphold the banks."

Lagash was defeated, but only for a while. Enneatum's nephew, Entemanna, fought back, won a victory against the people of Umma, and restored the ancient boundaries. He built a vast network of strongly defended canals, and canalized part of the ancient course of the Tigris, conducting it through the plains to the lower Euphrates at Ur. This was the famous Shatt-el-hai, which can still be traced today. When Sumer and Akkad fell, the conquerors only continued the ancient customs. They built temples to their gods and linked the temples by canals, and inscribed on rock and clay the evidence of their benevolence.

The kings follow one another, and sometimes it seems that they spent all their time building canals. Some had more reason than others to build them. There was Sargon, who reigned for fifty-five years, rescued as a child by a canal builder from a reed basket in the Euphrates, and he too built them. Five hundred years later, about 1800 B.C., when the great Hammurabi after thirty years as ruler of the small city-state of Babylon led his troops against southern Mesopotamia, he continued the tradition and added Enlil, the storm god of the Sumerians, to the pantheon of the Babylonian gods.

Hammurabi, who called himself "the obedient and god-fearing prince," demanded absolute obedience from his subjects. His famous code of laws was no more than the codification of the laws of Sumeria and Babylon, and it contained, as one might expect, warnings against cultivators who opened sluice gates in such a way that the water flooded their neighbors' fields. According to clauses 53 and 54 of the code, the punishment for flooding a neighbor's field was the payment of a measure of grain exactly corresponding to the loss of yield. The king was constantly sending memoranda to his officials about canals. We find him writing to Sid-idinnam, one of his officials:

> Thus saith Hammurabi:
>
> The whole canal was dug, but it was not dug clear to Erech, so that water does not come into the city. Also, on the banks of the Duru the canal has fallen in. This labor is not too much for the people at thy command to do in three days. Directly upon receipt of this writing, dig the canal with all the people at thy command clear into the city of Erech within three days.

We know precise details of life on the canals during the reign of Hammurabi. Clay tablets preserve legal documents concerning litigation about water rights, about the opening and closing of canals and the management of sluices. There are even documents about poaching in canal waters. In the reign of Hammurabi's son Samsu-iluna, some fishermen went down in their boats to the village of Shakanin and caught fish there. Arrested and put on trial for fishing in a canal where they had no right to be, they defended themselves with a long list of precedents; and the interminable trial, written down on clay by a court reporter, has survived for nearly four thousand years. There are accounts of trials brought against those who polluted the waters, and others who were simply careless or disobedient. We hear of irrigation inspectors, and there are long lists of the fees paid for water rights. Prisoners were used to work on the canals, but nearly everyone in the state was also forced to work on them. In time the deep, soft, and yielding soil of Mesopotamia was crisscrossed with a complicated network of canals like the veins, capillaries, and arteries of the human body.

We do not know how they shored up the banks of their canals in those early days. Sometimes there must have been stone courses, and occasionally they may have used bitumen, which was found in large quantities in Ur. Herodotus describes the building of the great moat around Babylon with bricks, bitumen, and mats made of rushes. He is speaking of a time just before Cyrus invaded Assyria, but it is likely enough that important canals had been built in the same way for generations. Herodotus is describing how the soil dug out of the moat is used for building the wall:

> While the digging is going on, the earth which is shovelled out is formed into bricks, and as soon as there is a sufficient number, these are baked in ovens. With hot bitumen for mortar the workmen start to build parapets along each side of the moat, and then they go on to erect the actual wall, and they lay rush mats between every thirty courses of brick.[11]

Herodotus describes how the whole of Assyria was intersected with canals, and the largest of them, which had to be crossed in boats, ran in a southeasterly direction from the Euphrates to the Tigris. He observed one pronounced difference between Egyptian and Assyrian canals: in Egypt the canals were filled by the natural flooding of the river; in Assyria they were filled by the use of hand pumps, probably *shaddufs,* buckets swinging on the end of poles balanced by counterweights, which are still used today.

Herodotus knew Babylon when it was the capital of the wealthiest province of the Persian Empire, producing more wheat than all Egypt. Cyrus had captured the city by the simple ruse of digging a diversion canal which drained off the Euphrates. The river flowed through the heart of the city, and suddenly on a night when the Babylonians were feasting, the Persian soldiers crept along the bed of the river, which was so low that it only reached up to the middle of their thighs. No one suspected the ruse, and by the time the soldiers had penetrated the center of the city it was too late. There was a short, bitter fight between the Persians and the Assyrian guards, and then it was all over. Cyrus was merciful. He put an end to the slaughter, kept the king a prisoner, worshiped in the great towered temple of Esagila, where offerings were made to the Canal Star, and called himself "Cyrus, king of all worlds, great king, mighty king, king of Babylon."

[11] Herodotus, *History,* I, 193.

Other kings were not so merciful. Exactly one hundred and fifty years before, in 689 B.C., Sennacherib destroyed Babylon so completely that no one could have expected it would ever rise again. It was an act of unprincipled barbarism, comparable to the Roman destruction of Carthage. First he put the city to the flames, then he dammed the Euphrates, then dug canals through the burned city, and then let loose the flood. It gave him particular pleasure to topple the immense temple to Esagila into a canal, thus drowning the Canal Star god in a canal sacred to him. He wrote, or caused to be written, an account of his exploit:

I destroyed, I burned with fire the city and the houses, the foundations and the walls. The walls and the outer-walls, the temples and the gods, all the temple towers of brick and earth, as many as there were, I razed and dumped and cast into the Arakhtu Canal. In the midst of the city I dug canals, and the earth thereof I overwhelmed with water. I destroyed it with water, so that it became a swamp, so that in days to come the very site of the city and its temples and gods might not be remembered.

So Babylon was destroyed, only to come to life again a little later, when Nebuchadnezzar rebuilt it, restoring the Arakhtu Canal and the towered temple of Esagila as an act of piety. The rebuilt city survived the Persians and Alexander's Greeks and the tides of Islam, dying at last in the twelfth century about the time of the First Crusade.

Sennacherib built his capital at Nineveh far to the north, on the banks of the Tigris. It had been his father's capital, and he set about fortifying it with huge walls. He built triple-arched gateways flanked with winged, human-headed bulls, brilliant with glazed tiles; he laid out parks and orchards; and, not content with the muddy waters of the Tigris, he sought a clear mountain spring. He found one nearly fifty miles away at Bavian, dammed it, built a stone-paved canal as wide as an arterial road, and for the rest of his life —he was assassinated eight years after he destroyed Babylon—he tasted the sweet waters of Bavian. This fifty-mile canal, with its aqueducts flying over ravines, was perhaps the greatest of all his accomplishments.

Until recently all trace of the canal was lost. In 1932 a Danish archaeologist, working with the American expedition at Khorsabad, found the *mukhtar* of a village nearby sitting on a stone which bore an Assyrian inscription. The archaeologist could decipher the word for "bridge," but nothing else. Suspecting that the inscription referred to an aqueduct, he returned the next year and began excavating. He found the bridge in an almost perfect state of preservation. It was 900 feet long, 70 feet wide, and 23 feet high at the center. He calculated that over two million blocks of stone were employed to build the bridge. The water flowed over a concrete bed twenty inches thick. Enormous trouble was taken to grade the surface accurately. This astonishing aqueduct, built almost entirely of limestone, with five pointed arches, was an accomplishment of the first magnitude. Recently, with the help of inscriptions on the rock sculptures near the village of Hinnes, archaeologists have been able to piece together the story of its construction. The canal was built during the year of the destruction of Babylon, or perhaps a year or two previously. The whole fifty-mile canal was constructed in fifteen months. When the bridge was nearly completed, Sennacherib gave gifts to the gods of the springs and rivers. In spite of these gifts, a minor catastrophe occurred: the waters broke through the sluice gate and flooded the canal, damaging it. Repairs were made, and Sennacherib seems to have been proud of the fact that he built the canal with the help of only a few men, for he concludes his account with the words: "By Assur, my Great God, I swear that with these few men I dug the canal, and in a year and three months I completed it."

The archaeologists were unusually lucky. They uncovered the whole bridge and were able to trace the stone-paved canal bridge through half a dozen villages almost to the gates of Nineveh, where they also found remains of the dam which had once deflected the water into orchards and gardens round the city. Finally they found the complete text of Sennacherib's inscription, of which only the single word "bridge" was known previously. It was one of the happiest, and simplest, of inscriptions. It read:

I caused a canal to be dug to the meadows of Nineveh. Over deep-cut ravines I spanned a bridge of white stone blocks. These waters I caused to pass over it.[12]

In the reign of Sennacherib's son Esarhaddon, Assyrian power reached out over Egypt. The princes of Sais in the western delta were established as vassals. Among these princes was one called Necho, known to Herodotus as Necos, son of Psammetichos, who began to build the canal which Darius afterward completed from the eastern Delta along the Wady Tumilat to Suez. Herodotus, who saw the canal in full working order, described it in detail, giving its exact course as though reading from a map. He claimed that Necho was the first to attempt the construction of a canal to the Red Sea, but failed to complete it in deference to an oracle which warned him that he was laboring only for the barbarians. Here is Herodotus's account with all its remarkable detail:

This Prince was the first to begin the construction of a canal to the Arabian gulf, a work afterwards completed by Darius the Persian. It was four days' sail, and so wide that two triremes could be rowed abreast. The water comes from the Nile, which the canal leaves a little above Bubastis, then it runs past the Arabian town of Patumus, and so to the Red Sea. The first part of its course is along the Arabian side of the Egyptian plain, a little to the northward of the chain of hills opposite Memphis, where the plain comes to an end and where there are great stone quarries. Then it skirts the base of the hills running from west to east, and then turns and enters a narrow gorge, afterwards moving generally in a southerly direction until it enters the Red Sea. The shortest distance from the Mediterranean, or Northern Sea, to the Southern Sea—or Indian Ocean—namely from Mount Casius between Egypt and Syria to the Arabian gulf, is exactly a thousand *stades,* or about 125 miles. This is the most direct route, but the canal follows a wandering course and is considerably longer.

The construction of the canal in the reign of Necos cost the lives of 120,000 Egyptians, who perished during the excavations.[13] In the end

[12] Seton Lloyd, *Ruined Cities of Iraq* (New York, Oxford University Press, 1945), p. 40. Seton Lloyd took part in the excavations which uncovered the canal.

[13] In July 1956, President Gamal Abdel Nasser claimed that 120,000 Egyptians perished during the construction of the Suez Canal by De Lesseps. He was in error by more than twenty-five centuries.

Stele of Darius recording construction of Nile-Red Sea Canal

Necos put a stop to the work in consequence of an oracle, which warned him that his labor was all for the advantage of the "barbarian," as the Egyptians call anyone who does not speak their language. He then turned his attention to war, built triremes, some on the Mediterranean coast and others on the Arabian gulf, where the docks can still be seen.[14]

Necho's brief reign—he ruled for only sixteen years—was an unusually vigorous one. He made a great raid across Syria and cap-

[14] Herodotus, *History,* II, 158.

tured Carchemish, restored Egyptian influence in Arabia, and sent one of his ships sailing around Africa. Herodotus, who tells the story, adds: "On their return the sailors reported (others may believe them but I will not) that in sailing from east to west around Africa they had the sun on their right hand."

Until comparatively recently there was some doubt whether Darius had in fact completed the canal which Necho nearly a century before had attempted and abandoned. Then in 1866, when De Lesseps was forging ahead with the construction of the Suez Canal, eighteen fragments of a red granite stele inscribed with a cartouche of Darius were found in the sand. When the fragments were put together, they were seen to form a solemn record of the canal opening in four languages—the three cuneiform languages, Persian, Median, and Assyrian on one side, and Egyptian on the other. As one might expect, the Egyptian version contains fulsome praise of the Persian conqueror, who ruled in Egypt under the reign name of Stitu-Re. The Nile grants to the king "all life, fortune and health, all joy, all offerings, all food, every good thing, and all the lands and foreign countries lie in adoration before him." The Persian inscription makes even greater boasts, but with Persian incisiveness:

> A great god is Ahura Mazda, who created the sky, who created this earth, who created the welfare of man, who bestowed the kingdom on King Darius—a kingdom which is great, rich in horses, rich in men.
>
> I am Darius, the great king, king of kings, king of lands of many races, king of this wide earth, son of Hytaspes, the Achaemenian.
>
> Saith King Darius: "I am a Persian. From Persia I conquered Egypt. I ordered this canal to be dug from the river called the Nile which flows in Egypt to the sea which goes from Persia. So this canal was dug, as I commanded, and ships went from Egypt to Persia, according to my desire.[15]

Darius was the great conqueror. Xerxes, his successor, was a smaller man, doomed to failure, too much in love with his own aristocratic nature to leave more than a mere trace of his existence

[15] Arthur Upham Pope, *A Survey of Persian Art* (Oxford University Press, 1938), I, 341.

on the earth. He wanted, says Herodotus, to show his power and leave something to be remembered, but most of his plans were futile and he was assassinated at last by the eunuchs in his own magnificent palace.

He, too, built a canal, but it was far smaller than Darius's. There was no particular reason why he should have built the canal on the Isthmus of Mount Athos. A Persian fleet had come to grief against the towering cliffs, but when he ordered the canal to be dug he seems to have been actuated by spite, by the desire to punish the mountain, as later he punished the raging seas of the Hellespont by ordering them to be whipped. Herodotus describes how Xerxes cut the canal, and since they were contemporaries, Herodotus may have received the information from eyewitnesses. The Isthmus of Mount Athos was about a mile and a half long, level except for some low hills. Xerxes ordered a straight line to be drawn across the isthmus and divided it into portions, one portion to be dug by Egyptians, another by Phoenicians, another by Greeks from the neighborhood. The deepest cutting was about fifty feet. When they reached the bottom, they continued digging, passing up basketfuls of earth to men on ladders above them, who then passed them to others, who dumped the earth on the side of the canal. It was cut with sheer sides, with the inevitable result that the sides kept falling in. Herodotus noted that only the Phoenicians, skilled at making earthworks, failed to make this mistake: they had the good sense to make a trench double the size prescribed by Xerxes, then they filled in the sloping sides in safety. Herodotus came to the conclusion that no purpose was served by the canal, and Xerxes could have hauled his ships across the isthmus, as the Corinthians hauled their ships over the Isthmus of Corinth, with far less trouble. "I conclude that he dug the canal out of a desire for ostentation," said Herodotus. No one knows whether Xerxes actually led his ships through the canal. In 1932 my father and another naval officer from H.M.S. *Queen Elizabeth* hunted for signs of the old canal. All they could find was "a tiny groove, which may never have been more than seven feet wide and three feet deep." But they also noted that it was a land of earthquakes, and they were not surprised to find the traces of the canal obliterated.

In revenge against the destruction wrought by Xerxes, Alexander the Great led his armies against the successors of Xerxes. Hydraulic works fascinated him. His engineers drained the lakes of Boeotia, and accompanied him in all his travels. He made Babylon, with its extensive system of canals, the capital of his empire. He liked to sail in the placid waters of these canals, and like the Assyrian and Persian kings before him, gave orders that they should be kept constantly cleared. One day, when he went sailing along a canal, the wind carried away his diadem and hung it on some reeds growing on the crumbling tomb of an ancient king. A sailor swam after it and, afraid of letting it get wet, held it high above his head as he swam back to the boat. Alexander's companions were horrified. It seemed to them that the sailor must inherit the throne because he had held the diadem above his own head. They talked of killing the sailor at once, but Alexander gave the man a silver talent and thanked him, and never traveled on the canals of Babylon again. A few days later he died, on a day of high summer, perhaps of malarial fever caught while sailing on the canals.

Darius completed Necho's canal to the Red Sea, but the shifting sands choked it up. In 285 B.C. Ptolemy II, a grandson of Philip of Macedon and therefore the nephew of Alexander, restored the canal from the Nile near Heliopolis to the Red Sea near Suez. Strabo says he constructed locks with movable gates so that boats could enter and leave the canal whenever they pleased, thus anticipating by about seventeen centuries the invention of the lock gate in Italy. Pliny says the canal was 100 feet wide, 40 feet deep and 37 miles long, but though he describes it at length, he throws some doubt on whether the Ptolemaic canal was ever completed. It may have been abandoned or partially closed by the shifting sands at an early period. Three hundred years later, when Anthony and Cleopatra were running before the fleet of Augustus Caesar after the battle of Actium, they thought of conveying their ships across the isthmus "which separates the Red Sea from the Sea of

Egypt." By this time all the waters of the Ptolemaic Canal had vanished in the desert sands. Anthony and Cleopatra had neither the time nor the desire to haul their ships overland, and so they died. At various times an Egyptian, a Persian, and a Greek opened a seaway to the Indian Ocean, but the sands claimed all the canals they carved with so much difficulty across the desert. Not until De Lesseps cut the Suez Canal in 1869 was the seaway opened again, and this too in time may vanish away.

For the extraordinary thing about the great canals is how vulnerable they are. Most of the imperial canals joining the Euphrates and Tigris have vanished without a trace, as the rivers themselves have long ago vanished from their original beds. The Itchen Dike, which cut across England, has vanished. Of the original Erie Canal, which joined the Hudson River to the Great Lakes and brought untold wealth to the Empire State, there remain barely fifteen miles of scattered ditches, now stagnant and covered with green slime. Here and there we can trace the limestone walls and follow the tow paths where the patient mules once trod, and see the crumbling lock gates which will never again swing open for the passing ships. It is the little irrigation ditches which go on for ever—the capillaries go on living long after the veins and the arteries have died. Two thousand years ago Strabo watched the canal boats bobbing in the innumerable channels of the Delta, and they are still there.

The great canals, like the civilizations that brought them into being, are mortal. An earthquake could toss all the waters of the Suez Canal into the sea and leave only dry sand. An abnormally dry season could put an end to Madden Lake and make the Panama Canal unpassable. The winds blow over Sennacherib's conduit, and only the faintest spider-web markings in the sand suggest the triumphal progress of some of the Babylonian canals. Hubris leaves its mark on all the great undertakings of man. As we contemplate the great new canals in Russia and on the St. Lawrence River, there is always the nagging suspicion that in time they may suffer the same fate.

The ancient waterways

Plato says the Egyptians looked upon the Greeks as children, too young and innocent to be the creators of great things. The Greeks had no pyramids, no vast administrative buildings like the Labyrinth, no kings as splendid as the Pharaohs, no luxuriant Nile flowing at the foot of the Acropolis. In their ancient wisdom the Egyptians were not so much contemptuous of the Greeks as indifferent; and it seems never to have occurred to any Pharaoh that Greece was worth conquering.

But if the Greeks were children, they were the most vigorous children who have ever lived. The clear blue skies, the wine-dark seas around them, the fierce earth they lived on—all these gave them poise and dignity and cunning and the sense of adventure which had long since died in Egypt. Greece possessed advantages denied to Egypt—regular rainfall, innumerable rivers, wine, barley, and beans in abundance. The Greeks adored sailing the sea, while the Egyptians hated it, and like the English they had the sea in their blood. Aphrodite and Poseidon emerged from the sea, and their earliest hymns celebrate all "moist and gleaming things." They were a people in love with water, but they made almost no waterworks, because there was so little need for them.

The Egyptians never sent their armies against Greece, but their civilization was the oldest and most stable of its time, and inevitably their influence was far-reaching. It penetrated Crete and

Mycenae, and it was especially prevalent in the island of Samos, which lies off the shore of Asia Minor near Ephesus. The people of Samos were traders and seamen, fiercely intelligent, the leaders of Ionian culture. At one time they had a fleet of a hundred fifty-oared galleys, and in Herodotus's day Samos with its wide harbor and magnificent marble temples under the towering hills was regarded as one of the finest cities of the world.

Herodotus devotes several pages of his history to the story of Samos, and apologizes, twice in the same chapter, for doing so, because "they are responsible for three of the greatest building and engineering feats in the Greek world." The first of these was a tunnel nearly a mile long, eight feet wide and eight feet high, driven clean through the base of a hill nine-hundred feet high. Within the tunnel was a cutting three feet deep and three feet wide through which water was conducted to the city.[1] The engineer was Eupalinus of Megara. The second engineering feat for which the Samians were justly proud was an artificial harbor enclosed by a breakwater a quarter of a mile long, and the third was the largest of all Greek temples. Herodotus thought that these three works gave Samos a special place in Greek history, but it is at least possible that the great tunnel owed a good deal to Egyptian or Persian engineers. For centuries the Persians had carved underground canals called *qanats,* cutting them below the surface of the earth so that little water would be allowed to evaporate. But it was only very much later that the Persians carved through mountains.

The most formidable hydraulic feat on the Greek mainland was the draining of the Copais Lake in prehistoric times. This lake in Boeotia received the streams flowing from Parnassus and Helicon. A great mountain-girdled basin, some fourteen miles by ten miles, seems to have been drained by the prehistoric Minyae, who possessed a citadel on the lake island of Gla and were ruled by the Kings of Orchomenos, whose magnificent tombs, discovered by Heinrich Schliemann, showed that they possessed engineering skill

[1] The tunnel was rediscovered in 1878. It was narrower than Herodotus described it, and had a pointed ceiling with smooth sloping stones.

at least as great as that of their contemporaries in Mycenae. To prevent the basin from becoming a lake, a system of ditches was built on the lake bottom to conduct the waters to the *katavothra,* or "swallows," which consisted of some natural and some artificial tunnels in the hills. Sometimes there were rockfalls and the tunnels choked up, and then throughout the winter there would be a great expanse of water, and in summer a marsh crowded with the Copaic eels, which were the delight of epicurean Athenians.

The Copais Lake is a monument to prehistoric engineering. We can trace the two successive ways in which men attempted to drain it. First, there was the ingenious system of ducts leading the lake waters to the *katavothra* and to the lower lake of Likeri and the Epirus. Secondly, by a combination of dikes, canals, and embankments around the lake, they attempted to increase the cultivable areas. It is possible that at the time of the Orchomenian kings the whole lake area was cultivated. The riches of Orchomenos vied with the treasures of Delphi and Egyptian Thebes: wealth, manpower, and skilled mechanics were available. By the time of Alexander the Great it was a lake again; and the shafts which he sank, to be connected in due course to the main drainage tunnels, can still be seen. Alexander put his chief engineer, Crates, in charge of the operation, but strife broke out among the Boeotians and the work was never completed. So the lake remained a flood in winter and an evil-smelling marsh in summer until the nineteenth century when a French company undertook to drive another drainage tunnel through the limestone hills, with surprising results, for the great mass of vegetable matter lying at the bottom of the lake burst into flame by spontaneous combustion—the lake was on fire! Even today this land, which was last cultivated by the people of Orchomenos, burns and smolders. It is the richest land in all Greece, and succulent eels still come from it.

Today, with the lake drained by a great tunnel through the hills, we can see the extent of the prehistoric constructions. The lowering of the water level has disclosed three lines of drainage canals extending the entire length of the lake, with numerous branches, forming a complete drainage system. Some of these canals are simply excavations; others are earthen dikes strengthened by Cyclopean walls, which once collected the water and led it to the "swallows." More than anything else these extensive works prove the high standard of Mycenaean civilization.

Here and there in Mycenaean cities we come upon traces of the work of hydraulic engineers. Recently at Tiryns it was discovered that a stream threatening the lower town had been canalized and turned into a new course. The stones speak, but Homer is silent. Homer tells of how the Greeks of the Heroic Age banked up the streams against the winter floods, but offers no details. The description of the flood in the famous twenty-first book of the *Iliad* may conceivably be read as a plea for extensive canal works, but it remains as enigmatic as the biblical deluge. Virgil, too, mentions the damming of streams only in passing. *Claudite jam rivos, pueri; sat prata biberunt.* "Dam up the streams, slaves; the meadows have drunk enough." It is as near as he ever comes to canals, but there is nothing surprising in this. The Egyptians and Sumerians regarded canals as divine, but the more practical Romans regarded them quite simply as technical problems to be surmounted by human ingenuity. Henceforth canals were to be described only in prose, and their openings were to be celebrated by orators impervious to poetry.

From the beginning of their history the Romans, living in their hill forts on the banks of a goat marsh, dug canals. Tarquinius Superbus, the seventh King of Rome, who reigned in the sixth century B.C., was the reputed builder of the great drainage tunnel called the Cloaca Maxima, which emptied itself into the Tiber. Herodotus thought the temple of Hera, the harbor, and the great tunnel at Samos to be among the greatest things ever produced; Livy declared that the greatest works of the early Romans were the Circus Maximus and the Cloaca Maxima, which was navigable by boats and followed the course of one of the original streams. Much improved and restored, the roof in some places topped with concrete, the Cloaca Maxima is still an important drainage sewer, though no longer navigable by boats.

Throughout the early history of Rome the work of draining the marshes went on, and left few records. As Roman power swept over Italy, surveyors and drainage experts were sent out to remote areas. So it happened that in Rieti, the ancient Sabine capital, the consul Manius Curius Dentatus drained the marshes by constructing a canal to carry off the waters of the Velino till they emptied themselves in the Nera. The canal was nearly a mile long, and much of it was carved out of rock. Quite deliberately the consul arranged that the canal should lead to a sheer precipice overlooking the Nera: the canal and the great waterfall remain to this day.

Manius Curius Dentatus was one of the great heroes of the Roman Republic, the conqueror of Pyrrhus, and a man of formidable gentleness. When the Samnites sent an embassy with costly presents, they found him sitting at the hearth and roasting turnips. He rejected their presents, saying that he preferred to rule over the possessors of gold than to possess it himself. Long after his death men remembered vividly the year when he undertook a vast program of public works.

Marcus Vipsanius Agrippa was a man of the same temper, slow to anger, devoid of all malice, completely lacking in Roman ruthlessness. Born of an obscure Illyrian family, he became the childhood friend of Octavius, who became the Emperor Augustus, and in the critical period following the assassination of Julius Caesar, Agrippa was the closest adviser to the emperor. In 34 B.C. he was appointed to the office of *Curator Aquarum,* in charge of all the hydraulic projects in Rome. Previously he had commanded the battle fleet against Pompey in the Sicilian War, and still later he was to command the battle fleet at Actium. He married the emperor's only daughter, and his sons were marked out to become the successors to the throne. In the intervals between writing and commanding the fleet and completing a map of the world, he built a canal between Lake Avernus and Lake Lucrinus, and opened a seaway so that ships could take shelter in a lake anchorage.[2] The appointment of Agrippa as the first permanent *Curator Aquarum* shows the importance attached to hydraulic engineering under the Empire.

Among the canals administered by Agrippa was one joining the seaside resort of Tarracina and Appii Forum across the Pontine marshes. Passengers would embark at Tarracina in the evening, spend the night on the canal, and then travel by coach or horseback along the Appian Way to the gates of Rome. The poet Horace once spent a miserable night on the canal. He remembered the slaves cursing while the drunken boatman collected the fares and harnessed the wretched mules which would drag the boat along. "The frogs bellowed in the marshes all night, we were plagued with insects, and to make matters worse, the stupid boatman simply let the mules out to graze, throwing the reins over a stone, and then falling asleep and snoring loudly. At dawn one of the passengers discovered we had been making no progress, leaped ashore, and gave the boatman a terrific beating."[3] It was a familiar story, perhaps as old as the Egyptians and Sumerians.

Greater works were undertaken by the later emperors. In A.D. 52 the mad Claudius constructed a drainage canal to carry off the waters of Lake Fucinus to the river Liris by boring a tunnel through the mountains. A similar drainage canal had been built to carry off the waters of the Alban Lake, but this was a small and comparatively unimportant venture in contrast with the draining of Lake Fucinus, nearly thirty miles in circumference. Thirty thousand workmen labored at the project for ten years. The tunnel was three miles long, seven feet wide by seven feet deep, surmounted by a stone archway, and partly cut through the living rock. No one knows why Claudius wanted it built. Suetonius suspected he hoped to make money out of it by renting the fertile, reclaimed land at

[2] The last traces of the canal vanished during an earthquake in A.D. 1538, which caused the disappearance of Lake Lucrinus and raised the level of the surrounding land.

[3] Horace, *Satires,* I, 5, 9.

the bottom of the lake, but it is just as likely that he wanted to show his superiority over Augustus, who had once been asked to reclaim the lake, and had refused.

For ten years the workmen labored uninterruptedly, and now at last with the tunnel completed Claudius decided to celebrate the occasion with a spectacular naval battle on the lake. He emptied the prisons, put nineteen thousand men into armor and placed them on specially built warships. People came from hundreds of miles to see the battle. To prevent the criminals from escaping he surrounded the lake with rafts, and brought in companies of the Praetorian Guard, who fired at the warships with catapults and ballistas. The emperor presided, wearing his scarlet military cloak, while the empress Agrippina sat beside him, wearing cloth of gold. The naval battle was fought vigorously, there was a good deal of satisfactory bloodshed, and at last the order came for letting the waters of the lake flow out through the drainage canal. Unfortunately, the work was unsatisfactory, and very little of the water escaped into the tunnel. Tacitus, who tells the story at considerable length and who hated Claudius, remains silent about the punishments inflicted on the incompetent engineers.

Some time later the excavations were deepened, and once again Claudius ordered a gladiatorial combat—this time the gladiators fought each other with swords and spears from rafts. There was a banquet set on tables near the mouth of the canal. Everything was arranged to the last detail. Narcissus, the chief engineer, was present, and so too were Agrippina and the emperor. Visitors from all parts of the empire were sitting down at the banquet, waiting for the moment when the lake waters would come roaring out of the mouth of the canal. But when the waters burst out of the mountains, with a roar like thunder, sweeping away many of the tables, and terrifying the emperor, a fantastic quarrel broke out. Agrippina screamed at Narcissus, accusing him of embezzling fabulous sums of money, and Narcissus shouted back at the empress, accusing her of attempting to dominate everyone with her extravagant ambitions. Agrippina was a vengeful woman, and when Claudius was dead and Nero had come to the throne, she threw Narcissus into prison even though the young engineer was a boon companion of the new emperor. He died in prison a few months later.

Historians and commentators have recorded the openings of great canals in detail throughout history, but there was never an opening like this. But the panic at the opening of the Lake Fucinus Canal was not typical of the Romans, who went about the business of digging canals with decorum and good sense, with armies of engineers, surveyors, inspectors, pipe masters, many of them recruited from the ranks of the public slaves. They were men with peculiarly practical minds. They built well, and calculated well. Frontinus in his *De Aquis Urbis Romae* (Concerning the Waters of the City of Rome) produced tables of stresses and described the nine aqueducts serving Rome at considerable length. Aqueducts are canals on stilts, and he went to great pains to discuss them in a manner fitting a practicing engineer. His book on strategy is filled with anecdotes, but there are no anecdotes in his book on waterworks. He writes dryly, succinctly, in a textbook manner, and his book is therefore all the more valuable. He says:

> I do not want to omit anything requisite for the comprehension of this subject, and so I shall discuss
> the names of the waters brought to the city,
> the persons responsible for bringing them and the dates,
> the sources of the aqueducts and their lengths,
> the underground channels, the masonry substructures, and the arches,
> the height of the aqueducts,
> the size and number of taps,
> the amount of water conveyed by each aqueduct,
> the delivery tanks and distribution of the waters within the city,
> the construction and maintenance of the aqueducts.[4]

He does precisely what he sets out to do; we learn that three of the major aqueducts were built by the famous Agrippa, or modernized by him. The Aqua Julia, coming from the cold springs

[4] Frontinus, *De Aquis Urbis Romae,* Introd. §3.

in the Alban Hills, was named after his wife, the daughter of Augustus. This aqueduct was fourteen miles long. The second was the old Aqua Tepula, which he remodeled, coming from the hot volcanic springs in the Alban Hills. The third was the Aqua Virgo from the springs in the valley of the Anio, said to have been discovered when some soldiers begged for water and were shown a small spring by a virgin. Cassiodorus, however, suggests that it was called Aqua Virgo because the water was so pure and unsullied. Most of the Aqua Virgo went underground. Altogether there were seven aqueducts in use in Rome during the reign of Augustus. Two more had been built by the time Frontinus became *Curator Aquarum,* and he was so proud of them that he declared: "With so many indispensable structures carrying so much water, we need fear no comparison with the idle pyramids of the Egyptians and the useless, though famous, works of the Greeks." [5]

No one ever built aqueducts so gracefully as the Romans, who built them all over their empire. There were four aqueducts in Lyons alone. An aqueduct at Metz crossed the Moselle on an arched bridge 3,600 feet long and over 100 feet high. The longest was at Fréjus (Forum Julii) on the south coast of France; it was twenty-five miles long. More than thirty cities in Gaul had Roman aqueducts. Aix-en-Provence had four, Marseilles and Vienne three each, Antibes two, and the most beautiful of all, the Pont du Gard, was built at Nîmes. The Emperor Julian, who loved Paris more than he loved any other city, gave her one, which was destroyed later by the Normans. Agrippa had done his work well: until the very end the tradition was maintained.

When the Romans discussed the making of aqueducts and canals, they dwelt on the hard facts of drainage, problems of subsoil, the best bricks to use, the ineluctable facts of engineering; and when the half-mad Claudius drove an enormous tunnel through a mountain to drain off the waters of Lake Fucinus, they acclaimed him, for he too possessed a mathematical mind and knew exactly what could be expected from his engineers, even though his pur-

[5] *Ibid.,* I, 16.

poses bordered on gigantomania. With the coming of Nero canal building enters the realm of fantasy. That strange, tormented emperor, the most gifted of the Claudian line and the one most determined upon his own destruction, possessed a fierce desire to write his name across the earth. *"Erat illi aeternitatis perpetuaque famae cupido sed inconsulta,"* says Suetonius tersely. "He possessed a longing for immortality and undying fame, though it was ill-considered." And how better to write one's name across the earth than by changing the courses of rivers, by lopping off the tops of mountains, or by digging vast canals?

Nero attempted all these, but very little came of them: it was Nero's fate that very little came of anything he set his hand to. He projected a canal from Ostia to Lake Avernus near Naples, to enable the journey to be made by ship yet not by sea. The length of the proposed canal was 160 Roman miles and its breadth sufficient to allow ships with five banks of oars to pass each other. When his engineers complained that there was insufficient manpower available for so great an operation, Nero decreed that all the prisoners of the empire, even those convicted of capital crimes, should immediately be transported to Italy, to serve out the punishment of their crimes in canal digging. Nero set his best engineers to work on the project. Severus and Celer, the engineers responsible for the rebuilding of Rome after the great fire, drew up the plans, and vast hordes of criminals were set to work, but with the death of Nero a few years later the project was abandoned. Nearly fifteen hundred years later, in 1507, some workmen draining the marshes on the north shores of Lake Avernus—that lake which Aeneas had descended in the company of the Sibyl in his progress to the underworld—came upon the ruins of an abandoned tunnel, all that remained of Nero's canal intended to link Rome and Naples with an inland waterway. The Romans feared the high seas, and these inland waterways with their safe harbors and covered passages were always in their minds.

In A.D. 66, accompanied by his entire court, Nero began his triumphal tour of the East. The empire was at peace. The eastern Mediterranean waited breathlessly to receive him who bore the proud title "Nero, Emperor and Victor, Crown of the Roman People and Possessor of the World." And so he wandered through Greece, desiring only to display himself, to demonstrate his power, his theatrical skill, his delight in receiving tribute. Potbellied and malodorous, with huge shoulders and thin little legs, his once handsome face wreathed in fat, gold dust sprinkled on his hair, Nero attended the games determined like the legendary Periodonicus to win all the prizes. He presented himself as musician, singer, tragic actor, and charioteer; and having won all the prizes by a faithful adherence to the rules and by giving large gifts to the judges, he decided to reward the Greeks with a still greater mark of his benevolence and his audacity. He would give them a canal through the Isthmus of Corinth.

In the past Agamemnon, Darius, and Xerxes had all contemplated the canal, and all had failed. From the earliest times of Greek history men had dreamed of this canal which would enable ships to pass between Corinth and the Piraeus without the long circuit round the peninsula. Periander, one of the seven sages of Greece, had dreamed of it when he was tyrant of Corinth in the sixth century B.C., and so too had Demetrius Poliorcetes, who for a brief while wore the mantle of Alexander. Julius Caesar had planned it in those last days when he was preparing to march against Persia, believing that by cutting the canal he would be able to check the Dacians who were pouring into Thrace and so safeguard his flank; but though the plans were drawn up his assassination put an end to them. Mad, pale Caligula, with his passion for lopping off the tops of mountains and building cities in the unreachable heights of the Alps, also turned his attention to the isthmus and even sent a chief centurion to measure the exact dimensions. Caligula was Nero's uncle, and it is possible that Nero was determined to succeed where his uncle had failed.

Nero was perfectly serious in his desire to build the canal. He appointed a commission of engineers and geologists, and examined the lay of the land with his own eyes. Convinced that the plan was feasible, he paid little attention to the rumors circulated by some

Egyptians that there was a difference in the levels of the water on either side of the canal. Seven years previously Apollonius of Tyana had made a mysterious prophecy. "The neck of the land shall be cut through," the philosopher pronounced, "or rather it shall not be cut." Nero seems to have been unimpressed by the implied warning from the lips of a philosopher reputed to be able to work miracles. Nothing daunted him, not even the cries of the people living on the isthmus who for centuries had transported small ships over the isthmus on wheeled sleds and who saw their source of livelihood imperiled if the canal was constructed. Once again Nero drew on his resources of convict labor. Ships sailed into Corinth loaded with prisoners from half the empire, among them six thousand vigorous Jews captured in the wars of Vespasian: for some reason Nero insisted that the heaviest work should be done by the Jews. The light work on the sandy beaches was entrusted to his own Praetorian Guard.

Nero planned everything to the last detail. The canal was to be four Roman miles long and from forty to fifty yards wide. Small mountains would have to be sliced, but such mountains had been sliced before, and he envisaged no unusual difficulties. Nero reserved for himself the honor of breaking the ground at a ceremony attended by representatives from all over Greece.

On the day of the ceremony, held in the town of Lechaeum near Corinth, Nero emerged from his tent singing an ode to Amphitrite and Neptune and other gods and goddesses of the sea. To the crowds who had gathered from all directions and were pressing around him, he announced his joy in being among them and prayed that the enterprise would turn out well for the emperor and the Roman people, significantly omitting any reference to the Roman Senate. The governor of Achaea presented him with a golden spade, and the emperor, pleased with himself, the cheers of the crowd ringing in his ears, immediately set about digging the first ceremonial spadeful of earth.

At this moment something happened which was so disconcerting that Nero paused, unable to decide whether a trick had been played on him or a threatened miracle was taking place. Exactly where Nero had been digging the earth was exuding a heavy red liquid like blood. Everyone was shouting at once. There were groans of anguish and screams of horror. People were jostling one another and shouting that the tutelary gods of the isthmus were showing their indignation at the sacrilege which was being committed by the emperor, who remained calm. He was an excessively superstitious man, but he was determined to go on with the ceremony; and if a trick was being played on him or if the tutelary gods were demanding vengeance, all this was a matter of indifference to him—the work must go on. A trumpet sounded. He dug the spade into the earth a second time, and then a third, and then he filled a hod with the earth and bore it away on his own shoulders after encouraging the workmen to continue digging. A few days later he abandoned his triumphal progress through the East and returned to Rome, to receive a hero's welcome. Once more there were triumphal marches and displays of imperial prowess, but Nero's days were numbered. For a few more months the work of canal digging went on, and soon political prisoners were being sent to join the labor force. One day the distinguished Stoic philosopher Musonius Rufus, banished to an island in the Cyclades for taking part in a conspiracy against Nero, was seen by another philosopher handling the spade and pickax. And now once again the men of science from Egypt were proclaiming that if the canal was completed, the waters of the Corinthian gulf, being higher than the Saronic, would submerge the island of Aegina. At last, a few months before he killed himself to avoid being assassinated by his own Praetorian Guard, Nero seems to have tired of the project and gave orders to abandon it. At the time of his death there was only half a mile of excavations to show for the labor of so many convicts. The prophecy of Apollonius of Tyana had come true, and for eighteen hundred more years men continued to dream of a canal through the Isthmus of Corinth. Then, in 1881, a French company prepared plans for cutting the present canal and after minutely examining four different routes they decided upon the one chosen by Nero.

Corinth Canal

Nero had hoped to complete the canal in a few years, but the French, with far better mechanical resources than the Romans ever possessed, labored on it for eleven long years. The mechanical difficulties were almost overwhelming. At one point the cutting was 285 feet deep, and the average cut was 190 feet, with a bottom width of 75 feet. So steep and deep were the rock faces that the French finally abandoned the project, as they abandoned Panama, and for some of the same reasons. A Greek company took control with a Hungarian engineer in charge, but the original plan was still carried through; and when the canal was finished, they discovered, as Nero's engineers had discovered long before, that the warnings of the Egyptian scientists could be disregarded: there was no danger of flooding Aegina, for the difference of sea levels at the outlets amounted to no more than a meter.

Seen from the air the Corinth Canal is an amazing spectacle, a heavy blue line, straight as an arrow, engraved on the earth. The traveler on shipboard, seeing the high walls of the canal above him, is confronted with a disturbing trick of perspective: he has the distinct impression that the ship is going uphill. But already this neatest of canals is almost an anachronism. The engineers did not allow for the increase in the size of ships, and today only ships up to ten thousand tons can use it, saving two hundred miles on the journey between Piraeus and the Adriatic. In 1944 the Germans blasted the canal, but not too effectively, for by 1948 it was reopened. Even today the canal, with its dangerously steep walls, is interrupted by landslips, and there is some belief among Corinthians that there is a curse on the canal, which cuts across the sanctuary of Poseidon and the site of the Isthmian games. Nero's memorial plaque can still be traced on the western end of the cut. He would have approved of the canal's indestructibility.

With the death of Nero the story of Roman canal building comes almost to an end. Here and there, particularly in North Africa, we find traces of vast canal projects, but no one knows whether they were ever completed—only the long ditches dug in the North African plains speak of a time when the canal diggers were reshaping the face of the earth. Airplane photographs taken recently in Algeria and Tunisia show the wavering lines of ancient diggings as clearly as the similar lines which are spread all over the sandy deserts of the Near East: but no trickle of water flows through the ditches. There are gaps in the history of Roman canals. We can only guess that the tradition once established survived through the years of the declining empire. Such vast projects can only be taken in hand at periods of relative peace, when the available labor force can be moved about at the whim of a dictator or a strong central government. And now for the Romans there remained only a few more years of peace.

Occasionally the great dreams returned, to haunt a weary emperor. Such a man was Probus, the Illyrian foot soldier, who assumed the purple in A.D. 276 when commander of the Roman armies in Syria. He came from Sirmium, the present Mitrovica in

Yugoslavia, and when, following the traditional custom of Roman emperors, he prepared to lead his legions against Persia, he decided to make his way through Illyria and to pause at Sirmium. He was in no particular hurry to confront the dreaded Persians, who only a few years before had captured a Roman emperor alive, killed him, stuffed him with straw and used him as a footstool. Probus had achieved great victories over the Germans and could afford to rest on his laurels. So he delayed through the long dry summer in his native town, and casting about for some means of occupying his soldiers, it occurred to him to drain the surrounding marshes and to plan a great canal with outlets flowing into the Sava, thus increasing the agricultural wealth of his own people. A calm and level-headed man, popular among his soldiers, he might have become another Hadrian, for he possessed all the instincts of an excellent emperor. His only failing was his affection for Sirmium. His soldiers asked why they should be turned into common laborers digging drainage ditches and shoring up the banks of a canal. They objected to the watchtowers where their officers, including the emperor himself, watched them at work. One day, when Probus was making a tour of inspection, the soldiers rebelled. The emperor ran to the safety of a watchtower, but the soldiers followed him and dispatched him. Afterward they were sorry, and built a vast mound over his grave. On the marble monument above the mound they engraved the words: "Here lies the Emperor Probus, a man of probity, conqueror of all the barbarian nations and victor over tyrants." They might have added that he was the last of the Roman emperors to dream of a great canal.

As the Roman Empire fell into decline the canal systems which drained the marshes south of Rome suffered from neglect. There, if anywhere, there was need to keep up the retaining walls of the canals, but there were not enough skilled engineers to work on them, and soon on either side of the Via Appia there was only malaria-stricken marshland. The canal between Forum Appii to the grove of Feronia, which Horace traveled, vanished without a trace, and nothing was left of the twenty-three cities which once stood on the

Pontine plain. By the time Attila sacked Rome, nearly all the Roman canals had crumbled away.

Throughout history the building of canals has been the prerogative of emperors, and in all the empires which arose on the ashes of the Roman Empire skilled engineers continued to build canals at the prompting of their masters. Canals represented wealth and power, speedy communication, increased revenues, immense profits in agriculture, a contented people. So in the Middle Ages the inheritors of Rome continued the long-established tradition. Charlemagne regarded canals and waterways as the links which bound his sprawling empire together, and planned to build a navigable canal between two small rivers which were tributary to the Main (which flows into the Rhine) and the Danube. But nothing came of his plans. Thousands of serfs and soldiers were ordered to build a canal a mile long and three hundred feet wide, and the emperor himself watched them at work, standing on the banks of the Altmühl River. The canal was hardly completed before the rains set in and washed it away, confirming the priests in their belief that God would punish those who changed the face of nature. Not until the time of the mad King Ludwig I of Bavaria was the canal completed.

No one knows what other canals were dug at the order of Charlemagne. No plans have survived, and there exist no accounts by contemporary chroniclers. Though we should like to know more about engineering in the Dark Ages, there is little likelihood that the documents will ever come to light.

But in the lands bordering on the eastern Mediterranean, in the vast areas which the Arabs took over from the Roman Empire, the building of canals continued, and the Arab chroniclers took pains to record the merit acquired by their rulers in constructing them. To the Arabs there was something almost holy in this gift of water; the emperor who provided a new waterway gave alms to all the people. "Those who possess the faith and accomplish good deeds shall enter gardens with running streams, and abide there for ever." So Muhammad had envisioned the heavenly paradise,

THIS BOOK IS THE PROPERTY OF
THE NATIONAL CITY PUBLIC LIBRARY

while the earthly rulers of the Arab Empire were content to create earthly gardens with as many canals and irrigation ditches as possible.

It happens that we possess the most minute and careful accounts of the canals built by the Omayyad caliphs, those luxury-loving inheritors of the stern creed of Islam, who settled in Damascus and astonished themselves with their own splendor. Within only a few years of Muhammad's death Damascus became the capital of the Islamic Empire, the power of the caliphate stretching out to Persia, Arabia, and North Africa. And how better could the caliphs celebrate their triumph than by decorating the city with the finest architecture and surrounding it with orchards?

From the earliest times there had existed an elaborate system of canals in Damascus, feeding off the waters of the Barada, known to the ancients as the Abana. That sparkling blue river flows along the north wall of Damascus, to vanish at last in the northern lakes. Swift, clear, and very deep, meandering among oleanders and poplars, this river possessed peculiar healing properties. It cured leprosy and blindness, and Naaman thought it better than all the waters of Israel, and therefore better than the Jordan. No river was ever so celebrated among the ancients. It seemed to bear the seeds of life, and everything it touched was turned to flowers and fruit. Accordingly the Omayyad caliphs vied with one another in carving canals out of the rocky plain and leading the waters into the city. The Caliph Yazid, the second of his dynasty and the murderer of Muhammad's grandson Husayn, dug the canal which is known today as the Nahr Yazid, tapping the river near the northern gate of the city. Other canals were dug by the Caliphs Sulayman and Hisham, who paid especial attention to regulating the flow of water in the canals. Altogether six canals were drawn off the Abana, and each of the canals entered the city at a different level, in tunnels excavated out of the rock; and sometimes one canal could be made to feed another, and there were places where they rose to the surface, the rushing waters forming pools and cascades. A place called "The Parting of the Streams," where the canals divided, was regarded as a local beauty spot. "To see the play of these waters," wrote an Arab chronicler, "is to know paradise. All cares are banished, and all sorrows are flown away."

Damascus never feared a drought. They stored their water deep in the rock, with the inevitable effect that the richest city of Syria suffered more than any of the others from malaria. The Arabs invented a complicated system by which the flow of water in the canals could be shut off from a central office in Damascus, but it never seems to have occurred to them that standing water was dangerous; and their ingenuity was repaid with epidemics of malaria. Malaria baffled them; the Damascenes died off like flies; and the Omayyad Caliphate failed to survive against the encroaching power of Persia partly because they were weakened by these epidemics. By the time the Abbasid Caliphate ruled over the Islamic Empire, hospitals were being built and simple remedies for malaria were being found.

The Abbasid Caliphate ruled from Baghdad, where the ancient irrigation systems were still in use. From immemorial times the lands between the Tigris and the Euphrates were honeycombed with canals, but with the coming of the Caliph al-Mansur, "The Victorious," to the throne, the making of canals assumed fantastic proportions. This unpitying soldier, who murdered his most capable general, was peculiarly aware of the importance of waterways, saying he had chosen to make his capital in Baghdad because it served as an admirable military camp and also because "the Tigris reaches out to lands as far away as China and brings me the produce of the sea and all the abundance of food from Mesopotamia, Armenia, and the surrounding countries, while the Euphrates brings me all the produce of Syria and the West." He went to work with a will, employing forced labor and putting his relatives in command. His first great canal was the Nahr Isa (the Jesus Canal), connecting Baghdad with the city of al-Anbar on the left bank of the Euphrates. Al-Anbar is today a ruined waste, but in those times it was a small and sumptuous city, embellished with the treasures of Damascus and all the cities of the conquered territories. For a few brief years al-Anbar had been the capital of the vast Abbasid Empire. There the Caliph al-Saffah, the elder brother of al-Mansur, had built his palace after destroying the power of the Omayyad caliphs, and there he had died of smallpox in his early thirties after bringing the greatest of the Islamic empires into existence. When the Caliph al-Mansur ordered his favorite nephew, Prince Isa, to build the canal, he had two things in mind: the canal was to be a symbol of affection and gratitude toward his dead brother and a symbol of the continuity of Abbasid rule. By putting his nephew in charge, the caliph was indicating the great trust he placed in him: Prince Isa was already being considered the successor to the throne. All through the history of the Abbasids we shall find these symbolic meanings attached to canals; and because great sums of money were poured into the making of them, and taxes on the use of these waterways brought in large revenues to the princes who controlled them, the canals inevitably became the subject of complicated court intrigues. In Baghdad, as elsewhere, canals represented wealth and power almost beyond men's dreams.

The Caliph al-Mansur made canals as he made war—pitilessly. Accounts of the vast revenues spent on them have survived, and the dazzling figures are only equaled by the vast numbers of men impressed into service. Hundreds of thousands of local farmers, and as many prisoners, were set to work. From the surviving accounts nearly everyone in Baghdad was in some way occupied with the building or financing of canals, or with provisioning the canal diggers, or with litigation over water rights. Branch canals proliferated. From the Nahr Isa came the great transverse canal called the Sarah, followed a little later by the Sarsar and the al-Malik, meaning the King's Canal. Another canal, the Dujayl, meaning the Little Tigris, had become silted up during the tenth century, and the name was given to a new loop canal which started from the Tigris and then rejoined it after throwing off a number of branches. Many of the Caliph al-Mansur's canals were simply rediggings of old Sasanian canals, which had become choked with blown sand, like the most famous of them all, the great Nahrawan Canal, which had once irrigated all the lands of the eastern bank of the Tigris from a hundred miles north of Baghdad to a hundred miles south; and this too was opened up again under the Abbasids. Each caliph burdened himself with the digging of at least one canal, and sometimes the court historians would credit them with entirely new canals when in fact the caliph might have only redug a canal already thousands of years old.

The Arabs were excellent mapmakers, but the task of making an accurate map of the canals in the neighborhood of Baghdad might be likened to mapping out the branches of a great oak tree, showing every bough and twig and leaf. There were, however, simpler ways of describing the canals. Here for example is ibn-Serapion, a geographer who came to the Abbasid court a hundred years after the Caliph al-Mansur, as he maps one of the larger canals meandering through Baghdad:

> The main canal passes on from Al-Khafka, and there skirts the Courtyard of the Oil Merchant, and at this place there branches from it the canal known as the Canal of the Fowl, and here it bends towards the Square of the Canal-diggers and then passes the Square of the Reed-weavers and the Road of the Pitch-workers, and finally it falls into the Tigris at the market-place of the sellers of cooked food. As for the main canal, it passes from the Courtyard of the Oil Merchant to the Asses' Mound, and turns off at this point into the Canal of the Dog, which passes to one side of Dogland Road, before finally falling into the Jesus Canal.[6]

So ibn-Serapion continues at great length his excursion on all the canals known to him, describing them minutely and accurately, and with little thought for the mapmakers who were to come after him. Arabic scholars recognize Al-Khafka, and they know, or think they know where Dogland Road could be found—the Caliph al-Mansur himself gave it this name after observing the wild dogs who haunted this desolate quarter of the city: but only the most learned scholar would attempt to trace the course of the canal on the evidence supplied by ibn-Serapion.

[6] Guy Le Strange, "Description of Mesopotamia and Baghdad, written about the year 900 A.D. by Ibn-Serapion," *Journal Royal Asiatic Society* (1895), pp. 287–288.

The caliph had a passion for giving unhappy names to places, and an unruly temper. A gaunt, sinister man, he resembled the great Sasanian Emperor Khosrau Parviz, the contemporary of the Prophet Muhammad, who when the Tigris and Euphrates both rose, spared neither men's lives nor money, "crucifying," according to the historian Biladhuri, "forty dikemen at a certain breach in one day, and yet was unable to master the water." And just as he put so much passion into building canals, so it sometimes happened that he put the same passion into destroying them. One day in A.D. 767 he received reports that his rebellious subjects in Egypt were threatening to use the ancient Pharaonic Canal, the forerunner of the modern Suez Canal, to launch an attack against his armies; and he immediately ordered the canal to be filled in, and so it remained, a barren and waterless waste, until De Lesseps carved it out again.

The caliph showed the same relentless character in his dealings with the young prince who built the Nahr Isa. Wearying of the prince, the caliph decided to murder him. Instructions were issued that the prince was to be given poison in his food. The prince swallowed the poison, fell ill, lost his hair and his beard, but recovered sufficiently to remind the caliph that he was still the successor to the throne, for had they not sworn to it on the Koran? The caliph thereupon enlisted the services of his vizier, Khalid, who produced thirty false witnesses to swear that the prince had solemnly revoked the agreement. The prince produced more witnesses to prove that the agreement had been made, and that both the caliph and the prince had sworn that it would never be broken. In despair the caliph decided upon extreme measures, ordered the prince to produce his young son at court, and then gave orders to his chamberlain to pretend to strangle the boy in the prince's presence. The prince protested no more. Taking his son with him, he lived out the rest of his life on his country estates as a millionaire recluse, for during the last act of the atrocious drama the caliph gave his nephew a fortune amounting to about $2,000,000. Prince Isa ibn-Musa

(Jesus, son of Moses) is nearly forgotten now, but the canal bearing his name still flows to the north of Baghdad.

In time the Abbasid caliphs, wearying of Baghdad and fearful for their own safety, decided to found a new capital. The Caliph Mu'tasim, the son of Harun al-Rashid by a Turkish slave, had good reason to fear his own subjects, for his Turkish guards who "galloped about and collided with everyone to right and left" were being murdered off by the Baghdadis who always vanished before the police could gather evidence of the attacks. Accompanied by his guards, the caliph made a leisurely tour up the Tigris in search of the new capital. Some sixty miles from Baghdad, he came upon a level plain, high up, shelving back from a cliff overlooking the river, and inhabited by only a handful of monks. The place was called Samarra, and the caliph was told that Samarra meant "Happy is he who sees it." In a surprisingly short space of time marble palaces were rising where previously there had been only the huts of the monks, and from all corners of the empire, from far away Latakia and Antioch in Syria and from the Christian churches of Egypt there came marble columns and pavements and rich carvings. Every day the caliph drove round the city, to urge the workmen to even greater feats of daring and to give costly presents to his engineers. Before he diea, he wanted to see Samarra completed, and he especially wanted to see the completion of the great mosque with its tower rising in the shape of a Babylonian ziggurat and its great hall, which was so vast that the floor space was almost three times that of St. Peter's in Rome.

The palace, rising above pebbly cliffs, looked down on orchards and flowering gardens with waterfalls. To the north lay a great artificial lake between grottoes and cisterns. There was no lack of water, for two branch canals fed off the Tigris in the neighborhood, and there were wells in plenty. But the Caliph Mu'tasim never lived to see the completion of Samarra, and when his successor the Caliph Mutawakkil came to the throne, still more palaces were built, more workmen were brought in, and more treasures from remote cities of the empire were floated up the Tigris to decorate the great mosque. Samarra had become a populous city, almost as crowded as Baghdad, but without the network of canals which allowed the Baghdadis to squander water as they pleased. And gradually in Samarra the supply of water failed, so that they were reduced to carrying it up the cliffside on the backs of donkeys or drawing it from wells. Mutawakkil was childishly proud of his great city with its palaces and mansions springing up at great pace. To survive, Samarra must have a constant water supply. He determined to build a gigantic canal to skirt Samarra on the east side. Once more a huge labor force was assembled, and the engineers were set to work. This new canal was one of the greatest engineering feats undertaken by the Abbasid caliphs and was said to have cost $8,000,000 in the currency of the time. Unfortunately the caliph placed too great reliance on the skill of his engineers, and on the day when the canal was opened he realized to his horror that the whole project had been in vain—only a trickle of water flowed into it from the Tigris.

For a few more years the caliphs remained at Samarra, surrounded by their loyal Turkish mercenaries, far from Baghdad, where the people were in a state of almost permanent rebellion. The caliphs rode in stately processions, but in fact the Turkish mercenaries were in command, holding the caliphs as their prisoners, murdering them at their leisure—Mutawakkil himself was stabbed to death shortly after he discovered that the great canal, excavated at the cost of so much labor and wealth, would never provide water for the city. It was as though these hard-riding mercenaries were punishing him for his failure to quench their thirst.

Today the visitor to the sandy plain of Samarra can see the ruins of the royal city, so well preserved that from the air one might guess it was still inhabited. Curving along the east of the city lie the high banks of the canal like a small mountain range—all that remains of Mutawakkil's greatest folly.

In A.D. 1258 Hulagu, brother of Kublai Khan, came roaring out of the east at the head of his Mongol armies and set fire to Baghdad until nothing remained except the charred stones and the crumbling brick. All the intricate calculations, the careful operation of sluice gates, the constant dredging and strengthening of the banks, all this came to an end; and now once again the sand drifted into the canals and smothered them. On these outlying frontiers of their empire the Mongols saw no need for a complex agricultural civilization and they amused themselves by riding along the canal banks and deliberately destroying them.

Thirteen hundred years before, Strabo had spoken about how dangerously easy it was to let these canals go to waste, even without deliberate destruction. "The soil is so soft, deep and yielding," he wrote, "that it is easily swept away by the streams, and then the plains are laid bare, and the canals are filled with earth."[7] He spoke at length of the good rulers who made it their business to prevent the streams from overflowing, remembering how Alexander the Great had paid careful attention to sluices and dams. But with the coming of Hulagu, the canals were choked and Baghdad became for a while a small and unimportant town on the frontiers of the Mongol Empire.

While the wild and murderous Hulagu amused himself by building towers of skulls and laying whole provinces to the sword, Kublai Khan was falling more and more under the influence of Chinese scholars, for whom the study of waterways was almost as important as the study of poetry. Every Chinese scholar who reached a position of power hoped to go down in local history as the creator of a canal. The idea of constructing a canal linking the Yellow River and the Yangtze was conceived and carried out in the Han Dynasty, and long stretches of this waterway remained in existence when Kublai Khan established his capital at Cambaluc near Peking. The problem then was to repair the dikes and establish the last remaining link between Cambaluc and the Yellow River—an eighty-mile stretch joining Cambaluc to the ancient system of artificial waterways completed hundreds and perhaps thou-

[7] *Geography,* XVI, i, 9.

sands of years before. As usual Kublai Khan was in a hurry. He appointed Kuo Chou-king, the most famous mathematician in the country, as the chief engineer of the project. Work was begun in 1289, and the first two years were spent in clearing the southern reaches of the old canal system. Finally, in the spring of 1292, work was begun on the new canal, and 20,261 workmen were kept busy until the autumn of 1293. Marco Polo left China just about the time the last stretch was being completed, but evidently the preliminary digging had been done and there was some kind of waterway already in existence, for he reported admiringly:

> You must understand that the Emperor has caused a water-communication to be made from Manji (South China) to Cambaluc in the shape of a wide and deep channel dug between stream and stream, between lake and lake, forming as it were a great river on which large vessels can ply. This magnificent work is deserving of admiration, and not so much from the manner in which it is conducted through the country, or its vast extent, as from the utility and benefit it produces to those cities which lie on its banks. On these banks there have been constructed strong and wide terraces, on which the traveler can walk at his convenience.[8]

In its heyday Kublai Khan's Grand Canal was 650 miles long, with another 100 miles of subsidiary canals, and stretched from Cambaluc in the north to Hangchow in the south, crossing the Yangtze at Chinkiang—Marco Polo's Chan-ghian-fu, where there were three Nestorian Christian churches. The canal was later improved by Yung Lo, the third emperor of the Ming Dynasty, who built the present city of Peking. All the early travelers in China commented on the great sweep of the canal and the large numbers of rice boats which crowded between the banks, so that sometimes the canal itself was hidden by ships. It seemed to them that all the ships in the world must be making their way to the capital.

Exact details of the Grand Canal have been handed down. We know how many workmen were employed, and how much they

[8] *Travels of Marco Polo,* lxxii.

were paid, and even how they spent their money. We know how the engineers made good use of the six lakes which lie between Hangchow and the Yellow River, and how they succeeded in carrying the canal across the Yellow River without the use of aqueducts. But when we go to earlier periods of Chinese history, canal making becomes inextricably confused with mythology. There was, for example, the Pien Canal, which formed the longest stretch of the Sui Grand Canal built in A.D. 609, during the reign of the Emperor Sui Yang Ti. This canal, which was carried out at great expense, linked Loyang on the Yellow River with the complex Yangtze Valley systems. A contemporary historian, in a work entitled "The Record of the Opening of the Canal," described how the canal came to be made:

> All men between the ages of 15 and 50 were ordered to assemble by royal edict. All who tried to hide were punished by decapitation. The laborers thus assembled numbered 3,600,000. Then each family was required to contribute a child or an old man or woman to prepare meals for the workers. Five thousand young and brave soldiers were ordered to be armed with sticks (to maintain discipline). Together with section chiefs and other administrators, the total number of people employed amounted to 5,430,000.
>
> At the beginning of the eighth month of the fifth year of the Emperor's reign, baskets and shovels were put to work. . . . When the work was done, the Emperor moved from Loyang to K'aifeng, and ordered the various prefectures on the Yangtse and Hwai areas to construct with the speed of fire 500 large boats (for imperial use), and those who refused to work on the boats were punished by flogging and neck weights.
>
> At last the dragon boats were completed and sent to K'aifeng, and were lined up one beside another, and when their silken sails passed, their perfume could be smelled for a thousand *li*.[9]

In such a way did the ancient emperors of China write their names across the map, and there is no reason to believe the figures entered so casually in the records of the court historians. The twenty thousand laborers who worked for Kublai Khan are more

[9] Chao-ting Chi, *Key Economic Areas in Chinese History* (London, George Allen and Unwin, Ltd., 1936), pp. 123–124.

credible than the five million who worked for Sui Yang Ti. It is the same with the earlier records of Chinese canal building—the figures sweep across the page, everything is accomplished "with the speed of fire," and murderous punishments lie in store for any workman who so much as dared to look away from the work in hand. Yet most of these canals were no more than slender ditches straddling the plains between the rivers and the lakes: in China the distinction between a ditch and a canal loses its significance over wide areas. For century upon century emperors and scholars ordered these canals to be built, so that in the neighborhood of the great rivers the landscape resembled the network of arteries and veins in the human body. But there was never any attempt to examine the principles of hydraulics or to calculate the flow of water or build dams. Sluice gates are mentioned in *The Book of Songs* and appear in the earliest records, but there were no locks until modern times.

A hundred years before Kublai Khan completed the longest and greatest canal in the world, a handful of engineers in the remote foothills of Lombardy were cutting a small and unimportant canal joining the river Ticino to the city of Milan, then in ruins. Out of their work was to come the next important advance in canal building and a vast impetus in engineering.

Sumeria and Egypt and Rome and the great Abbasid Empire had had their day, and for thousands of years the science of canal building had hardly progressed by more than a few inches. Now at last it was to move forward by leaps and bounds.

An experiment in Lombardy

The Lombards are a race apart, quick, cautious, and fine-boned, with a proud sense of independence which they derive from their Gallic and Etruscan ancestors. They are people of the plains and the mountains, the least Italian of Italians, intolerant of Rome, given to sudden explosive rages which die out as suddenly as they are aroused—it was, after all, in Lombardy that the body of Mussolini was trampled by a shrieking mob and hung up by the heels outside a gasoline station; nor was it the first time the Lombards had shown their detestation of dictators. They are a people with a passionate love of freedom, which comes perhaps from their closeness to the mountains, together with a genuine desire for order, which comes perhaps from cultivating their well-tilled fields. For centuries, from the time of Diocletian to the time of Attila the Hun, Milan in the heart of Lombardy was the capital of the Empire of the West; and the Milanese have never forgotten it.

Proud, rebellious, and always intolerant of foreigners, especially Germans, the people of Milan decided to resist when the Emperor Frederick Barbarossa attempted to assert the imperial power over the independent cities of Italy. In A.D. 1161 Frederick appeared outside the walls of Milan and demanded its surrender. The people refused, whereupon the emperor threatened the city with destruction. He would raze it to the ground, and leave no stone standing upon another. He called upon his army to surround the city and starve out the inhabitants, and when after the long siege the people at last surrendered he carried out all his threats, devastated the city and surrounding countryside, and went on to leave a trail of bloodshed and massacre throughout Lombardy, with the result that the spirit of revolt flared up in a hundred communes and five years later powerful guerrilla forces were striking at the imperial army. By A.D. 1167 Milan and the other important cities of northern Italy proclaimed their independence and formed the Lombard League for mutual protection. Less than ten years later their combined armies defeated the army of Frederick Barbarossa at Legnano: the free cities for the first time had overwhelmed a Holy Roman Emperor.

Milan stood at the head of the Lombard League, and to Milan men turned for a watchword and a sign. The threat of imperial vengeance remained. All the free cities could do was to put themselves in a state of readiness, and accumulate wealth and strength, to ward off the threatened invasion. There were few roads across the Lombardy plains; so they built roads. The cities on the plains possessed few natural defenses; so they built massive fortifications. Contemplating their ruined city, the Milanese decided to erect an impenetrable wall around it, and to surround the wall with a wide moat. With this moat, created in desperation, the modern era of canal building begins.

It began quietly, and no one watching the Milanese at work rebuilding their city would have guessed what influence that moat would have. It was not a particularly wide moat, perhaps twenty feet wide. The water came from local streams and was held in place by a sluice gate. Such moats had been constructed before, but no one had ever thought that a moat might be connected with a complicated irrigation system: that defense and agriculture and navigation and power for water mills might somehow be connected. But so it happened.

In A.D. 1177, the year after the battle of Legnano, the Milanese began to cut a canal joining the moat to the Ticino River, which flows southerly from Lake Maggiore to the Po, about sixteen miles to the southwest of Milan. Small canals already existed. In A.D. 1138 Cistercian monks from the neighboring monastery of Chiaravalle instituted irrigation canals over large areas and about the same time monks of the same order diverted a canal downstream from the Ticino. But no one had ever contemplated before in the twelfth century so stupendous an undertaking as a sixteen-mile canal. They built the whole canal in six years. According to Giovanni Battista Settala, who described this canal, known as the Ticinello, four hundred years later, the dimensions of the original canal were far beyond the dimensions of any canals constructed up to this time, except those of Egypt. The width of the canal at its mouth was 70 bracchia, or nearly 200 feet, diminishing to 25 bracchia, or nearly 70 feet, at Milan. The downstream or righthand bank was protected by blocks of stone laid dry to a height of ten feet, and then continued with a palisade of piles for nearly two miles. Elsewhere the banks 30 feet high and 30 feet wide were composed of earth dug during the excavations. There was almost no slope to the canal bottom. As a precaution against floods there were six water reliefs consisting of thick walls with wide doors through which excess water could be discharged into intersecting streams.

Almost at once the city fathers were confronted with the same problems which confront canal owners nearly everywhere. The main purpose of the canal was to supply water for the city moat. Soon short lengths were being run into the city, and branch canals were led off to irrigate the surrounding fields. Inevitably the level dropped, and stringent laws were put into operation to prevent unauthorized tapping. Many of the diverting dams were removed. Henceforth the water board made sure that the level of water in the canal remained high, and no one was allowed to forget that all this labor had come about in order to give the city a proper defense. The merchants protested, but they were not yet sufficiently powerful to take the law into their own hands.

There was, however, one member of the community who possessed sufficient authority to make himself heard above the voices of the soldiers and the captain-general. This was the Bishop of Milan, the successor of St. Ambrose; and when in A.D. 1385 Gian Galeazzo Visconti decided to celebrate his rise to power by building a cathedral which would put all the other cathedrals of Europe to shame, employing architects and master masons from all over Italy, Germany, and France, no one protested when the Church monopolized the canal with freight loads of stone which came from the Verbano quarries on the shores of Lake Maggiore, and so along the Ticino River and the Ticinello, then known as the Naviglio Grande. For years the stone was piled up on the wharves outside the city gates. At some time about A.D. 1400 it was decided to simplify the process by bringing the stone directly to the site of the cathedral. The interior canals were several feet lower than the Naviglio Grande. Accordingly, a crude lock was built. It consisted of a single gate which could be raised and lowered on pulleys. When the gate was shut, the water on both sides of the lock could be brought to the same level, and then the gate would be opened to allow free passage for the boats. It was a fairly dangerous operation, for any slight fall in the water level would produce floods; therefore strict orders were given that all withdrawals of water along the Naviglio Grande, for irrigation or for working water mills, would have to cease while the water was being dammed. It needed considerable skill and ingenuity to work the lock, but the Milanese were already showing a flair for mechanical knowledge. We hear of a labor-saving device, invented about A.D. 1407, for cutting marble blocks by machinery. Each machine was worked by a horse, which performed the work done formerly by four men.

Under the early Viscontis Milan enjoyed peace, and though the claims of defense and the Church were still being enforced, the merchants saw their opportunity. They demanded equal rights. They, too, would bring their produce straight to the market place, thus saving large sums of money spent in cartage and rehandling, and avoiding pilferage. Once the city council had been in the hands of the clergy and the soldiers, but now all over Italy power was falling into the hands of merchants; and soon they possessed the same rights as the Church. The result might have been expected. The Naviglio Grande was soon choked with traffic, and the farmers were complaining because they were not allowed to tap the canal while ships were moving up to the walls of Milan. Some better way had to be found, and so it came about that an unknown engineer solved the problem by designing the first double-gate canal lock. In a document in the archives of Milan, dated 1445, there is a reference to "a lower lock recently constructed," but there is some evidence to suggest that double-gate canal locks were in existence forty years previously. So it happened that because Gian Galeazzo Visconti murdered his uncle to become ruler of Milan and commanded the building of the largest cathedral in Christendom as an act of propitiation, and because the builders used stone from the quarries on Lake Maggiore and the Church insisted on floating the stone through the city walls and the merchants demanded the same privileges, the inventive genius of the Milanese was aroused. The modern canal lock came into existence as the result of a chain of fortuitous circumstances, and few of them had anything to do with engineering.

In A.D. 1446 Leon Battista Alberti, the illegitimate son of one of the most wealthy and powerful families in Florence, the close friend of Donatello, Ghiberti, Brunelleschi, and Luca della Robbia, temporarily abandoned his study of the arts and turned his mind to the sciences. The pope, Nicholas V, wanted advice on dredging up the sunken Roman galley in Lake Nemi. Alberti, who had recently completed an allegory on Greek mythology and a treatise on the nature of the family among many other works, threw himself into the work of raising the galley by means of a floating pontoon fitted with windlasses, and succeeded in raising part of the prow. The mathematics of the operation entranced him, and he set about applying his recently acquired knowledge to other problems. He invented a method for measuring the depth of the sea, and wrote a book called *Ludi matematici* (Mathematical Games), and shortly afterward gathered together in a single work all he knew about physics, hydraulics, mathematics, architecture, and surveying. He described the proper qualities of wood, sand, and stone for building purposes. He showed how foundations should be laid and how walls should be underpinned, and the proper manner of building bridges and sewers. He has chapters on fortifications, ancient classical architecture, and the making of cofferdams. It is a huge hodgepodge of information on ancient methods of construction and new techniques; and it is on this book, together with two important works on painting and sculpture, that his fame depends. The book was printed by Nicolo de Lorenzo Alamano in Florence in 1485, but manuscript copies were circulated as early as 1452. Alberti's *De re aedificatoria* (On Building) was the first printed book on construction ever to come from the presses. In it he described for the first time the making of the double-gate canal lock.

His discussion of the canal lock follows immediately after a description of a simple method of drawing a boat against a waterfall by means of a windlass—he was particularly impressed by windlasses and introduces them at every opportunity. He wrote:

> If you wish, you can make two gates cutting the river in two places at such a distance one from the other that a boat can lie for its full length between the two; and if the said boat desires to ascend when it arrives at the place, close the lower barrier and open the upper one, and conversely, when it is descending, close the upper and open the lower one. Thus the said boat shall have enough water to float it easily to the main canal, because the closing of the upper gate restrains the water from pushing it too violently, with fear of grounding.[1]

Alberti goes on to suggest a design for the gates, which would open horizontally, hinged on a vertical support, but with unequal arms, "so that a boy could open the barrier and then draw it back again quite easily." From his description the basin was only a little longer than the length of a single boat, and it is clear from the concluding sentence that one of the purposes he had in mind was to avoid the violent surge of water which accompanies the lifting of a

[1] W. B. Parsons, *Engineers and Engineering in the Renaissance* (The Williams & Wilkins Company, Baltimore, 1939), p. 375.

Lock with many gates, from Codice Laurenziano

single sluice gate even when the difference of the level on both sides is small. There is nothing in *De re aedificatoria* to suggest that he envisaged a series of locks with multiple gates.

Yet this next step was inevitable, and in the *Codice Laurenziano*, preserved in the Laurentian Library in Florence, the principle of the multiple lock is illustrated triumphantly by an unknown artist and accompanied by a text from an unknown author writing about A.D. 1465. No one knows the exact date of the manuscript, or for whom it was written, or how it passed into the hands of Leonardo da Vinci, who occasionally inserted notations in his characteristic handwriting on the pages. But here for the first time we are presented with a full-fledged design of four lock gates straddling the banks of a river, which pours through the gates of a small fortified town. All the mechanical details of the lock gates are clearly drawn. We see a boat ascending the river at the second gate, and the principle of the multiple lock, which can be employed on rivers as well as on canals, is stated briefly and succinctly and vividly for all to see. In the history of modern canal building the drawing in the *Codice Laurenziano* possesses a quite extraordinary importance. The drawing is accompanied by a text written in the elaborate handwriting of the fifteenth century:

> If we wish to conduct boats along a river, when the water-level is low and the slope is such that it might be impossible to navigate, then it is necessary to determine the fall. Let us suppose that the first part of the river has a drop of 30 *piede;* then construct at this point a high door in the manner of a portcullis with windlasses to raise it, and in this manner lay off the entire length of the river and all its falls with such doors. After the boat enters, and the door is closed, the boat will soon rise and be able to enter the second chamber, and so step by step you will be able to take the boat to wherever you wish. Should you desire to return, then by opening each door, the boat with the water will be led to the next door, and so from one to the other it will be possible to return to the sea. All boats should be made with flat bottoms, so that they will float on little water.[2]

The problem confronting the author of the text was not essentially concerned with canals. He was perturbed by the heavy drop of water level in Italian rivers, which occurs often in the late summer, when the Arno and sometimes even the Po become desolate little trickles flowing below their steep embankments. He was worried by the problem of how to maneuver ships upstream when

[2] *Ibid,* p. 373.

there is hardly enough water for them to float on, and so in the drawing he showed the steep and eroded banks and the boat almost lost beneath the high cliffs. But here at last was the multiple lock, and the application of the principle of the multiple lock to canal building could only be a matter of time. There is little doubt that multiple locks were employed by Bertola da Novate, the first and one of the greatest of Italian canal engineers.

One would like to know more about Bertola da Novate. In dusty documents hidden in the municipal archives of Milan and Pavia and twenty other cities of northern Italy, we come upon traces of his astonishing career as he journeyed from one city to the next, designing and constructing canals, bridges and locks, at the beck and call of princes and dukes, who quarreled over his services and always listened to his advice. No portrait of him has survived, but we can guess the quality of the man from his works. He was a citizen of Milan, and was always regarded as an engineer, never as an architect. The canal engineers who came later were nearly always men who regarded canal building as a minor accomplishment to be exercised in the midst of more elaborate works. Bertola da Novate seems to have possessed a one-track mind, dedicating all his skills to the building of canals. Francesco Sforza, the Duke of Milan, described him as "a man of fine intellect and skilled in these matters," and placed his entire confidence in him.

When Francesco Sforza rose to power in A.D. 1450, he immediately set about extending the commerce of Milan and envisaged a vast network of canals spreading over northern Italy, all under his own control. More than ever Milan depended upon trade and the control of trade routes. The matter was discussed at length, and it was decided that the first canal to be undertaken was one connecting Milan with Pavia, some twenty miles as the crow flies to the south. In the summer of 1452 Bertola da Novate was summoned to the ducal palace to receive his appointment as canal engineer in charge of the project.

Bertola da Novate was confronted with difficulties from the beginning. For topographical reasons a direct channel between the two cities was impracticable, however much the duke desired it. The Ticino River flowed past Pavia, and goods had been sent in the past along the Naviglio Grande and so into the Ticino and up to the walls of Pavia, but the Ticino was undependable and there were times when it was not navigable. The duke wanted a shorter route, and he also wanted the goods to go the whole way by canal. There existed an ancient irrigation ditch which ran parallel to the Ticino south of Abbiategrasso, deriving its waters from the Naviglio Grande, and it was decided to widen the ditch and extend it as far as Bereguardo, a small town some seven miles from Pavia and a mile from Pisarello, which lay on the Ticino. The obscure irrigation ditch, widened, dredged, and with its banks strengthened, became a highroad for the exchange of merchandise; but the problem of forming a direct channel between Milan and Pavia remained unsolved, for at Bereguardo goods were carried by portage to Pisarello and the last seven miles of the journey was made on small boats on the unpredictable Ticino. The Bereguardo Canal was nearly 12 miles long, with a fall of 82 feet. Italian engineers of the time regarded a fall of 15 feet in 12 miles as permissible. A fall of 82 feet implies the use of multiple locks, and there are good reasons for believing that Bertola da Novate was the first engineer to construct them. The canal is still in use, and the existing locks are probably on the site of the locks first put into place by Bertola da Novate, who appears to have completed the canal by 1457, for on this date the Duke of Milan appointed a commissioner with two deputies to assist the engineer in operating it.

Bertola da Novate did not spend his entire time superintending the construction of the canal, nor was he entirely at the service of the Duke of Milan, who paid him a retainer and had first call on his services, but allowed him to accept employment at the courts of other ruling princes. Bertola was in Mantua in May, 1453, for there survives an urgent letter written by the Duke of Milan to the Marquis of Mantua requesting the immediate return of the engineer to Milan. At the same time the duke wrote to Bertola, addressing him as "citizen and engineer" of Milan and begging him to make every effort to be in Milan in six days. Two years later, on July 23, 1455, Bertola was again at Mantua. On that day he wrote a long report to the Duke of Milan, saying that he had recently undertaken to advise the ruler of Parma on the construction of canals in his territory and intended to return there shortly "to put method and order into the work." A month later, on August 25th, he wrote another letter to the duke, to keep him in touch with affairs. It seems that the authorities in Parma wanted him to construct a canal without locks because no funds were available and because locks took a considerable time to build and put in place. Farm laborers could dig the canals at little expense to the state, and if there were protracted delays it would be cheaper to move goods by wagon. Bertola answered by suggesting that the authorities in Mantua were already preparing locks on *their* canal, and perhaps someone could be sent from Parma to Mantua to inspect them "so that every doubt they might have regarding locks might be removed." Bertola's letter breathes a sweet reasonableness, and the Duke of Milan evidently gave his engineer permission to stay in Parma, for on May 22, 1456, the elders of Parma wrote to the Duke of Milan, thanking him for sending Bertola, "with whose methods, orders, and designs they are well satisfied." Two years later the Parma Canal was built, but Bertola suffered endless trouble with the locks, which were not completed for another three years. Part of the trouble seems to have been that no one could understand Bertola's specifications and no one liked his chief assistant, an unpopular man with the extraordinary name of Ugolino delli Ughirosse.

Long before the Parma Canal was completed, Bertola received his most important assignment—the construction of a canal between Milan and the Adda River, which flows out of Lake Lecco, the southern branch of Lake Como. If this canal could be built successfully, Milan would have direct communication with the two northern lakes and two separate water routes to the Po Valley in the south: it would irrigate the fertile fields to the east and supply water power wherever it was wanted.

On June 1, 1457, Bertola received his commission from the duke and immediately set out to study the headwaters of the Adda. He had failed to push the Bereguardo Canal up to the walls of Pavia, and now once again he discovered that it was impossible to carry out his assignment. Between Lake Lecco and the little village of Trezzo on the banks of the Adda eighteen miles to the south, there was a fall of two hundred feet. Theoretically a multitude of locks would have solved the problem, but there were not enough skilled lock makers to build them and the expense would have been exorbitant. Bertola decided to make Trezzo his headquarters, and from there he would carve out a channel to Milan.

His first task was to build a diversion weir across the river, which slopes rapidly at this point, and by means of a dike separate the canal waters from the river. The dike was about one thousand feet long. Thereafter the water would flow along the bed of a canal excavated in the bank and cross the level plain which runs through Cassano, Gorgonzola, and Vimdrone to Milan. The total length of the canal was twenty-four miles with a fall of only sixty feet, which could be absorbed by two locks. Two rivers, the Molgora and the Lambro, meander across the plain, and Bertola solved the problem of carrying his canal past them by building a brick bridge with three spans over the Molgora and by laying the trough of the canal across the Lambro with the result that material carried in the suspension in the Lambro had to be washed out of the trough at frequent intervals. But there was no other solution: the Lambro was a fair-sized river and could not be disregarded. The canal joining Milan with Trezzo became known as the Naviglio della Martesana; and when it was completed about A.D. 1465, Bertola could point to the successful solution of a number of complex hydraulic problems. He had shown how canals could be carried across two small rivers and how to build a diverting dam. As far as we know, no one else had solved these problems before and no one else had built multiple locks.[3] With the building of the Martesana he disappears from history, for nothing is known about his subsequent life. But as the author of the Bereguardo and the Martesana he deserves a place among the great engineers of the early years of the Renaissance.

The Martesana was complete; boats brought merchandise to the gates of Milan and paid toll and went away again. The only unsolved problem was how to enable the boats to pass into the Naviglio Grande without danger of capsizing, for there was a difference between the levels of the two canals of five feet. This problem, together with many other problems connected with canals, was solved by Bertola's successor—Leonardo da Vinci.

Bertola thrust his foot in the door: Leonardo da Vinci threw the door wide open. Never before had there been a man so skilled in the understanding of the flow of water, and no one like him ever came afterward.

Leonardo was born in the little village of Castello da Vinci in 1452, the same year that Bertola received his commission as a ducal engineer from Francesco Sforza. According to Vasari, Leonardo showed an interest in hydraulics from childhood, and he was "a mere youth," perhaps thirteen or fourteen, when he first suggested a method for reducing the Arno from Pisa to Florence to a navigable stream. Many others, of course, had attempted to dominate that turbulent river. The Florentines planned a canal to the sea in 1347 and again in 1458, but nothing came of their plans. From ancient times the Lombards had constructed waterworks, and the main canals of Milan, laid out in the twelfth and thirteenth centuries, were constantly being improved and extended; but there was no comparable tradition in Tuscany. In Florence there were no incentives for studying hydraulics, and with the help of his father,

[3] There are no documents definitely assigning the credit for making the first multiple locks to Bertola da Novate. Joseph La Lande in his monumental *Traité de canaux de navigation* (1778) claimed that the first double-gate locks were invented by Dionisio and Pietro Domenico, two brothers from Viterbo, for a canal on the Brenta near Padua in 1481, but this is clearly too late a date. Here, and elsewhere, I have followed the remarkably precise investigations of General Parsons.

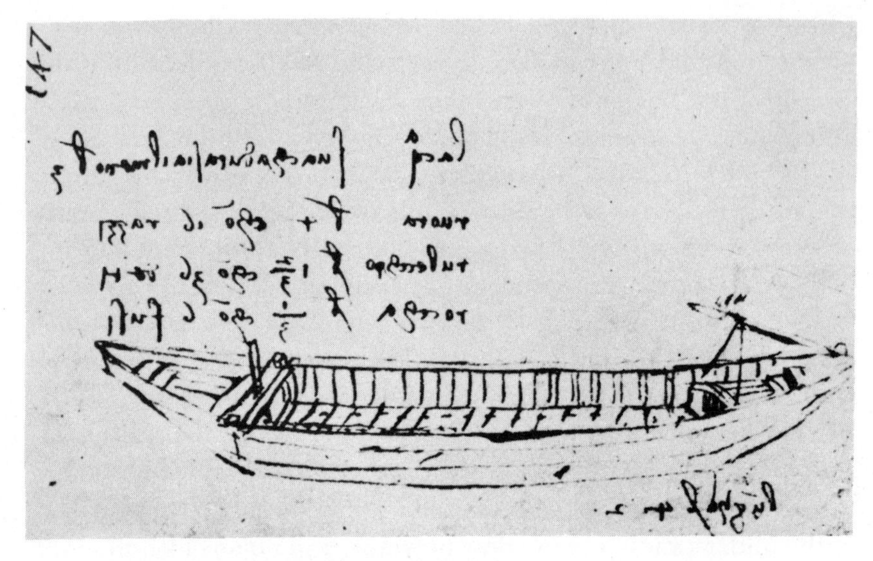

Leonardo's sketch for a canalboat, from Codex Atlanticus

Ser Piero Antonio da Vinci, Leonardo entered the workshop of Andrea Verrocchio, where he painted and sometimes studied music and demonstrated a profound interest in mathematics. In 1477, at the age of twenty-five, he opened his own studio. It was a time of turmoil. Lorenzo de' Medici was in power, spreading magnificent largesse among the painters and sculptors of Florence. But the year after Leonardo opened his studio, on an April morning, an attempt was made to assassinate Lorenzo and his handsome younger brother Giuliano during Mass in the Duomo. Giuliano perished beneath nineteen dagger wounds, and in revenge Lorenzo inaugurated a reign of terror, remaining quietly in his palace, while hired cut-throats murdered and threw into the Arno even the most distant relatives of the conspirators. It is possible that Leonardo had some remote connection with the conspirators. What is certain is that *Il Magnifico* showed no interest in the amazing talents of the young painter, and two years later, weary of Florence, weary of rebellions, and most of all weary of the Medicis, Leonardo offered his services to Ludovico Sforza, known as *Il Moro,* because he was dark-featured and resembled a Moor. A draft of the proud letter Leonardo wrote to the reigning Duke of Milan survives in his own handwriting. In this letter, filled with the fire of *terribiltà,* that outrageous and almost superhuman quality which Leonardo shared with Michelangelo, the twenty-eight-year-old artist asserted quite simply that there was no problem in the arts or in the sciences which he was not capable of solving. He said he could construct all manner of bridges and fortresses and engines of destruction, tunnels, mines, countermines, field pieces, mortars and machines for throwing fire. Almost casually in this famous letter he describes for the first time the armored tank—"covered wagons, secure and indestructible, which will enter with their artillery among the enemy and break up the largest body of armed men, with the infantry following unharmed and without any opposition." He concludes the letter with the assurance that he was equally capable of undertaking sculpture in bronze, marble, and terra cotta, and that he could paint as well as or better than any living painter. Above all he desired to construct a bronze horse "to the everlasting glory and eternal honor of My Lord your Father of blessed memory and the illustrious house of Sforza." Almost lost among the vast claims mentioned in the letter was the significant statement: "I can also conduct water from one place to another in canals."

Ludovico Sforza, though more cautious than Lorenzo de' Medici, was immediately attracted to the young Florentine painter, and it is possible that he was chiefly attracted by Leonardo's knowledge of canal building. Leonardo was summoned to Milan and offered an appointment as ducal engineer; and for the next twenty years Leonardo's fortunes were intimately associated with those of Ludovico. At first he seems to have been given comparatively minor tasks—among Leonardo's notebooks there is a drawing of a device for lowering the Sacred Nail in the Cathedral of Milan. Later, as *inzenarius ducalis,* he was responsible for the maintenance of public buildings and the upkeep of the canals, especially the Naviglio della Martesana, which increasingly occupied his attention. The Martesana had been built, but much remained to be done. There was still the gap between Trezzo and Lake Lecco. Though there was already in existence a lock at San Marco, near the Porta Nuova to the northeast of the city, where the Martesana flowed into the internal canal, there was need for a new and more efficient lock. The canal, with its shoals and unequal flow of water, resembled a series of fragments joined loosely together by the engineering skill of Bertola da Novate: the time had come to make it into a unified whole. Leonardo da Vinci threw himself into the task with such success that he was widely credited with being the builder of the canal, so that we find Raffaele du Fresne in a sketch of Leonardo's life which appeared in his edition of the *Trattato della Pittura,* published in Paris in 1651, saying that "the undertaking of the Martesana Canal was the occasion of his writing a book on the nature, weight, and motion of water, full of a great number of drawings of various wheels and engines for mills to regulate the flow of water and raise it to a height."

Leonardo did attempt such a work but, like nearly everything else which his wide-ranging mind attempted, he never finished it. Many chapters of the work survive in the Leicester Codex, and his notebooks are filled with an amazing flood of drawings and notations on subjects connected with canals. He designed sluice gates, locks, and weirs. He made sketches of excavating machines which would work on dry land and under water. He invented wheeled scrapers, special cranes, and special orifices for the passage of water. He drew up topographical maps showing the best routes to be followed in the making of half a dozen canals, and among the countless drawings he tossed off in moments of leisure he sketched an imaginary city on two levels, the upper level forming the highways and the lower level providing access to the canals. Nothing escaped him. He showed how a mattress of osiers should be made, for binding canal banks, and he designed small canalboats and set out their dimensions. He contemplated a book on how to conduct navigable canals over and beneath the rivers that intersect them and another on the soils which soak up the waters of canals and how to prevent seepage. He made careful studies of the formation of eddies

Leonardo's sketch for a canal below street level

around the piers of bridges and he was especially concerned to discover the varying rates of flow of water in the middle and on the sides of canals. For Leonardo the making of a canal was the demonstrable sign of man's power over nature. He would master the wild forces of water, if he could, and he could conceive of no better way of showing mastery over nature than by building networks of canals. Even at the very end of his life, when he was ill and paralyzed, a pensioner of the French King François I at Amboise, he was still contemplating the making of canals. His famous works on optics, physics, geography, the flight of birds, gunnery, painting, and sculpture form only a small part of his surviving writings. By far the greater part is concerned with the nature and the use of water, and therefore directly or indirectly concerned with canals.

We know too little about the early years of Leonardo's stay in Milan, and nearly all we know must be deduced from his notebooks. Quite early in his career in the service of the Duke of Milan, he seems to have been given the task of connecting the Naviglio della Martesana with the Naviglio Grande. To do so, it was necessary to redesign the lock at San Marco; and his drawing of the new lock, which appears among the vast array of papers assembled together in the *Codex Atlanticus*—it was felt that no other word but

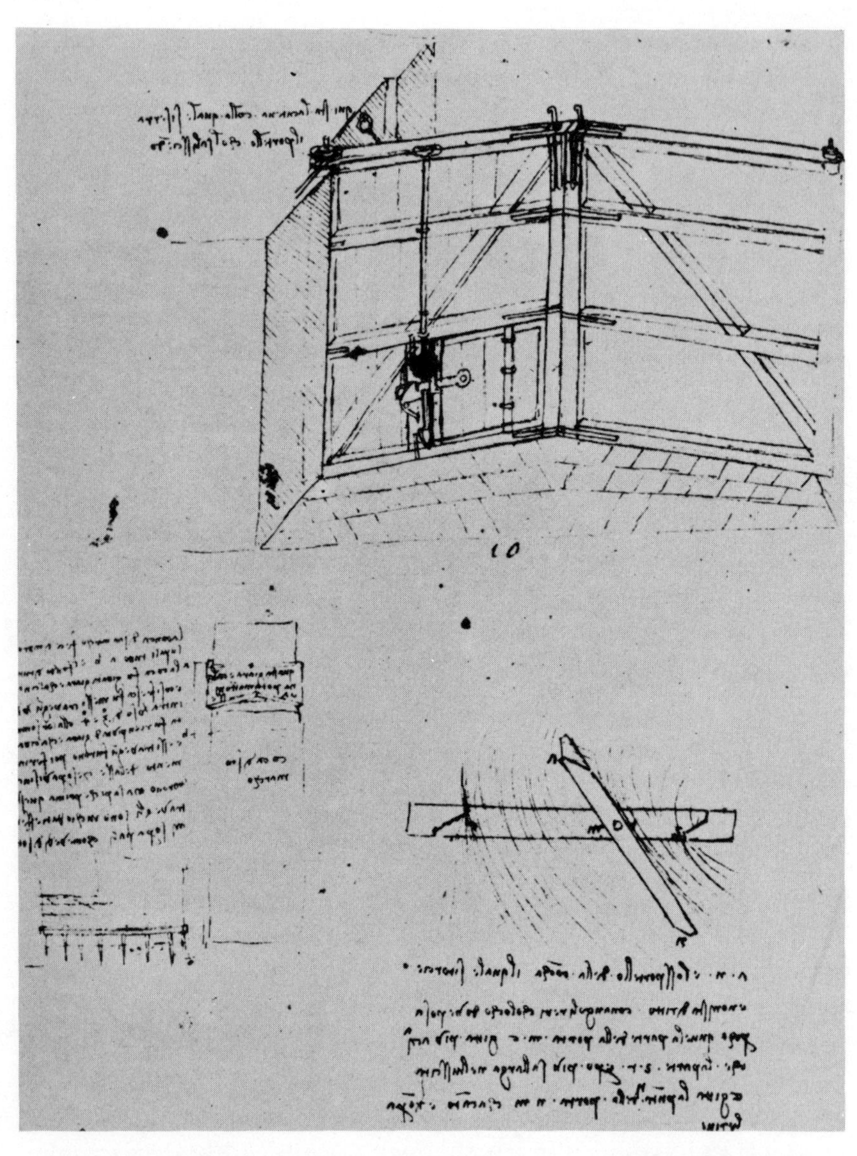

Leonardo's design for lock at San Marco, from Codex Atlanticus

"Atlantic" would convey the enormous sum of knowledge contained in it—shows him in full command of the problem. Here for the first time is the mitered gate and the wicket for letting water into the lock from the upper level. The drawing of the quadruple lock in the *Codice Laurenziano* with its portcullises and well-head method of raising the gates has a medieval air about it. Leonardo's design is such as a modern draftsman might make, complete to the last detail, without an unnecessary line on the page.

There is a sense in which this drawing stands at the end of the long history of canal building. For untold centuries men had dredged the earth and put up simple sluice gates and labored to irrigate their fields and divert floods and shore up the banks of canals, but it was to Leonardo's credit that he was the first to show the best form a water gate should take, and how another gate within the gate would serve to control the flow of water. Nearly all modern lock gates follow this principle, even the massive structures at Panama. And all over Europe and America, during the great period of canal building at the end of the eighteenth century and afterward, men have followed the principle first announced by Leonardo with such disarming simplicity.

Leonardo's design shows miter and quoin posts, the wooden planks arranged vertically, with horizontal and diagonal bracing, the joints sheathed with iron, the gates resting on a brick floor. Each gate folds back into a recess in the wall, and in a smaller, quickly sketched drawing underneath, Leonardo shows exactly how this is done. The hinged wicket gate, occupying about one-sixth of the gate area at the bottom of the lock gate, can be opened by means of a simple latch, which can be tripped by means of a wire or rope connected to a pulley on the canal bank. In another drawing immediately below the gate Leonardo shows how the wicket is hinged at a point about one-third of its length, so revolving less violently than if the hinge were placed at one end. On the side of the manuscript, in Leonardo's characteristic mirror writing, just above a sketch of timbers spiked together, he adds a brief note on the walls and foundations of the lock:

The lock of San Marco is of masonry on piles. The floor of the whole lock rests on a bed of gravel and lime, which, while still soft, was covered with crossbeams of green wood whose heads were buried in the same mortar. The other sides were laid close and spiked. In addition, the crossbeams were framed and nailed to the spikes.

But this was only the beginning, for he went on to make many more drawings of locks, among them at least two others connected with San Marco, one showing the metalwork on the lock gate, the clamps on the quoin post and the pintle turning in a metal cup bolted to the lock sill. He even shows exactly where he wants the bolts to be inserted. A third drawing shows a longitudinal section of the lock with all the measurements marked out clearly—the distance between the gates was nearly one hundred feet and the width of the lock was about twenty feet, and these dimensions correspond almost exactly to the present dimensions of the San Marco lock, which has been in use for nearly five hundred years. How it worked can be seen from the engraving in Vittorio Zonca's admirable *Novo Teatro di machine et edificii,* published in 1607. Zonca, who bore the title of "Architetto della Magnifica Communita di Padua," described and illustrated all the mechanical marvels of his age. He showed water wheels and printing presses in operation, and mechanical spits for roasting meat, and machines for pounding grain, but the best of the engravings shows a circular or oval-shaped brick basin with three small boats caught in the turbulence of the water as the miter gate opens, the boatmen straining at the oars to keep their boats from capsizing and the workmen straining at the windlasses; and around the walls the idle onlookers watch contentedly. The miter gate follows Leonardo's design, but for good measure Zonca shows a single-leaf gate as well. Leonardo made his two-dimensional sketch: Zonca provides a drawing in three dimensions, so vivid that we can almost hear the creaking of the timbers and the rush of water into the basin.

We do not know whether Leonardo spent his years in Milan entirely at the service of the duke. Like Bertola da Novate, he may have entered the service of other princes. He worked on the canal,

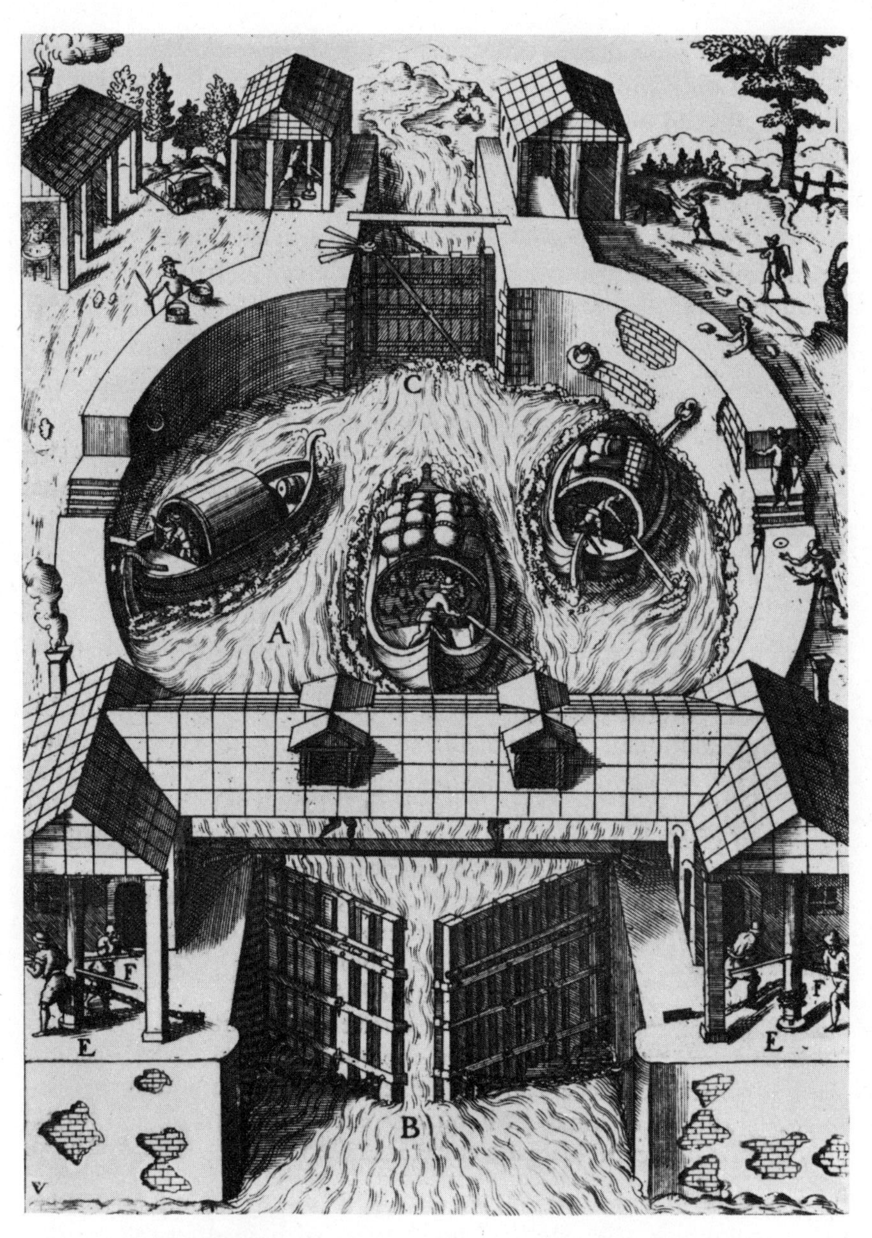

Canal gate opening, from Zonca's Novo Teatro, 1607

painted, erected a great equestrian statue in memory of Francesco Sforza, amused himself with toys which moved by clockwork, and pored endlessly over his notebooks. About this time he may have journeyed to Armenia, that country which he described so minutely in a series of letters addressed to an imaginary Lord of Soria, who may have been Ludovico Sforza in disguise: those letters which describe the Taurus Mountains disappearing beneath the Flood. As always he was haunted by the vast and terrifying power of water, and so he made drawings of great landscapes shuddering beneath the torrential rains, until at last they dissolved and vanished, and then there was nothing—only the roaring of the eternal waters, the earth given up to darkness again.

Long ago he had told himself that his mission was to civilize the waters, and when he heard in June, 1494, that the Arno had overflowed its banks and drowned the ripe cornfields above and below the city, he may have thought again of his youthful plans to regulate the river. According to Landucci, the knowledgeable old apothecary who kept a diary throughout these turbulent times, it was the worst flood in living memory, coming suddenly in the evening, when no one was prepared for it. But Florence had other troubles besides floods that year. In November, Charles VIII, King of France, entered the city at the head of his troops, who pillaged as they pleased and terrified the Florentines, who were not accustomed to having Frenchmen wandering through their streets at night. Piero de' Medici had fled; and when at last the king continued his march through Italy, the Florentines proclaimed a Republic, while Savonarola emerged from the Convent of San Marco to proclaim the Kingdom of God.

Now with the Medicis in flight and Florence ruled by the *Consiglio Maggiore,* the Greater Council formed of twenty elders of the city, Leonardo found it politic to return. The meeting place of the Council was the great hall on the first floor of the Signoria, the same hall from which the Medicis had ruled with insufferable pride, wearing their silks and jewels in a setting of the utmost luxury. The councilors wanted the hall refurnished and repainted, with all traces of the Medicis effaced. So Leonardo, Michelangelo, and other artists assembled to give advice on the best decoration suitable for a republican meeting place, and when the conference was over Leonardo was approached for his advice on how to meet the constant danger from the Arno. It seems to have been a casual request, for Leonardo was still in the service of the Duke of Milan and had no intention of remaining in Florence for any length of time. Apparently, Leonardo made no promise to the councilors. He returned to Milan, brooded over the problem, drew up maps and plans, and filled his notebooks with notations on the unruly behavior of the Arno and the best methods of mastering it.

From his notebooks we see his mind at work. First, he prepared a map of the whole watershed of the Arno, coiling like a snake among the foothills of the Apennines. He saw that the main problems were two: to produce a navigable stream and to control the floods. Because the Arno was so serpentine and difficult to navigate, he concluded that the only solution lay in digging a new channel. He drew up plans for building a reservoir in the Arezzo basin above Florence, which would gather the spring freshets from the melting snows: the water from the reservoirs would be released during the dry seasons. Then he mapped out the course of the new channel, running from Florence to Prato and so to Pistoia and Serravalle, forming a great arc which rejoined the Arno at Pisa. He made many variants of the map, but the principle of constructing a canal in a great arc can be seen on nearly all of them. After Pisa the river was to be deflected through the marsh of Stagno to Leghorn, thus avoiding the danger of silting up the mouth, and the greater danger of allowing the Pisans to control the mouth of the canal, for Pisa remained the inveterate enemy of Florence. And on some maps he shows the canal coming out at Vicopisano, just beyond the hills of Serravalle. He did not explain how he proposed to cross these hills. Surprisingly, he deliberately rejected the use of locks on the canal, saying that "locks are not everlasting and they always impose the cost of operation and maintenance." He suggested that the cost of building the canal should be met by the people who would benefit most from water power—the industrialists of the time.

Just as he described the most minute operations of the San Marco lock, so Leonardo described every detail of the new canal. It would be 40 feet wide at the bottom, 60 feet wide at the water surface, and 16 feet deep. He explained that this was far greater than needed for navigation, and he expected half of the water would be diverted for irrigation and power. He paid special attention to the cost of digging the canal, and devised drag lines and tripod cranes for moving the earth. As for the hills at Serravalle, he seems to have believed it would be possible to make a tunnel or a deep cut through them.

All this time Leonardo remained in Milan, working quietly on the painting of the Last Supper in the Church of Santa Maria delle Grazie, where it was observed that for long periods he was lost in meditation concerning things which had nothing to do with painting; and the monks complained that he was excessively dilatory and did not speak when he was spoken to. He completed the painting by 1498, and in the following year Louis XII, who claimed both the Duchy of Milan and the Kingdom of Naples, entered Milan, and Ludovico Sforza took to flight, to die at last in a French dungeon after scrawling on the walls of his cell the words, "I am unhappy."

Leonardo had lost his patron and protector in Milan, and had no intention of returning to Florence. Savonarola had been burned at the stake beneath the walls of the Signoria the year before, and the young Florentine Republic was shuddering under the edicts of the pope. Instead, Leonardo placed himself in the service of the Venetians. Turkish ships were sailing dangerously close to Venetian waters. Leonardo, as military adviser, offered to divert the coastal rivers and so drown the invading Turks in the floods, and prepared a sketch of a submarine armed with quick-firing guns to take the enemy vessels by surprise; but the Turkish threat subsided, and at long last Leonardo made his way back to Florence where he painted the *Virgin and Saint Anne* for the Church of the Annunciation. Then, wearying of the arts, he took service again under Cesare Borgia, the most disreputable of princes, but one who listened attentively to Leonardo's ideas for draining marshes and building canals. Among other plans, Leonardo submitted one for a canal between Cesena and the port of Cesenatico. Nothing came of the plan, which was pigeonholed by Cesare Borgia, to be discovered by engineers of a later day. Suddenly in 1503 Leonardo was summoned to Florence, then at war with Pisa. He was in good heart. As military adviser and expert on hydraulics, he showed how Pisa could be landlocked by altering the course of the Arno and channeling the water into the sea at Leghorn. He spent several months in the camp of the Florentine army above Pisa, supervising the Herculean task of digging two canals to carry the waters of the Arno to Leghorn, but the project was still unfinished when Pisa capitulated in the summer of 1509. It had been a desperate siege, with the people starved into surrender, and when it was over the people of Pisa filled in the partially dug ditches.

While the long siege of Pisa continued, Leonardo kept adding to his plans for dominating the river. Ideas suggested by the military project took root and proliferated. About this time he invented a leveling instrument, and more and more he found himself confronted by simple problems of topography. He abandoned for the moment any attempt to control the river by means of a canal; and the canal he envisaged was one which would cut the corners of the Arno, making it more navigable than the river. The new canal was planned to intersect the Bisenzio, a river between Florence and Prato; and when he saw that this was impracticable he devised an aqueduct built on a three-piered bridge with locks on each side. He drew an excellent sketch, showing exactly how the locks and aqueduct should be built—the bridge of stone, the lock gates mitered, houses for the windlasses, and steps leading up to the bridge from the shore—and below the sketch he added a careful note explaining that the arches of the bridge must be as high as possible to take care of the floods of the river passing below. It was the first time anyone had devised an aqueduct fitted with locks on each side. It was a hundred years before such a plan was put into operation, and then not by Italians but by French engineers on the Briare Canal joining the Loire to the Seine.

Leonardo's knowledge of canal engineering was the most comprehensive of his time, but sometimes he found himself facing problems which defied solution. He designed a tunnel through the hills between the valleys of the Stella and Nievole rivers, without apparently taking into account that the engineering knowledge of the time prohibited the carving of tunnels nearly a mile long. And increasingly Leonardo's notebooks are filled with notations on the economics of canal building. On one of the pages of the *Codex Atlanticus* he wrote:

> Since 180 shovelfuls represent 1 cubic bracchoi, it means that in 28²⁄₇ hours he will excavate 64 cubic bracchia, that is, a cubic canna in 2½ days. An ordinary shovelful of earth weighs ten libbre. A man throws five hundred shovelfuls per hour, or at 10 libbre the shovelful, 5000 libbre, representing 2½ quadretti. The square canna is equal to 65 quadretti, that is to say, 115,200 libbre, which the said workman lifts in 24⅗ hours, or two days of summer work. Let us see how many men a ditch 40 bracchia wide on top, 32 on the bottom and 16 deep will require?

So Leonardo goes on, never baffled by anything, and least of all by the problems of cost pricing, wages and man-hours. Such computations must have been commonplace in Renaissance times, but there is no previous record of an engineer working out the cost of digging a canal. Accustomed to making staggering demands upon himself, Leonardo seems to have made staggering demands on his workmen—a workman who could throw 500 shovelfuls of earth an hour for twelve consecutive hours was a paragon unlikely to be found everywhere. Leonardo set the day's wage as four sols, which may be equivalent to ten cents in our money, and he suggested that the best time for digging a canal was between the middle of March and the middle of June, when peasant labor was cheaper.

But all Leonardo's engineering plans in Florence were in vain. Day after day he made fruitless attempts to interest the councilors in building a canal, while the councilors were far more interested in the decorations of the council hall. These, too, Leonardo left unfinished. At last, on May 30, 1506, he sought from the Signoria permission to return to Milan. He posted a bond of fifty gold ducats against his failure to return to Florence and was permitted to leave.

The governor of Milan was Charles d'Amboise, who greeted Leonardo with enthusiasm and suggested that he attach himself to the French court. Leonardo was not yet prepared to leave Italy, and soon he was applying to the Signoria for an extension of his leave of absence. Permission was refused. "He has been drawing a goodly sum of money for a large work," they wrote, referring to the Anghiari mural, "and for this he has hardly even prepared a sketch, and has not acted with proper respect towards the Republic." They added that "in spite of the high estimation in which he is held by the government of Milan, they will find themselves protecting a criminal." When Louis XII arrived in Milan shortly afterward, the criminal was appointed "painter and engineer-in-ordinary" to the King; and then for a short while Leonardo was once again a military engineer, campaigning with the French against Venice, the city he had once helped defend against the Turks. At intervals he worked on the San Cristofano Canal, and there is a note in the *Codex Atlanticus* celebrating its completion: "Canal of San Cristofano of Milan, finished on the 3rd day of May, 1509." The king seems to have been especially pleased with the construction of the canal, and the water rights were ceded to Leonardo. For the rest of his life, until 1516, when he journeyed across the Alps to join the new King of France at Cloux near Amboise in Touraine, Leonardo seems to have lived on these rights, which were sufficiently important to be mentioned in his will. In his last days he was preparing plans for a canal connecting Tours, Amboise, and Lyon and sketches for a test channel from the Loire to Romorantin. He died quietly at Cloux, far from his Tuscan hills, in the spring of 1519, perhaps in the king's arms.

Then it was all over—the long years of pure dedication to all the arts and sciences, the incessant laboring over the notebooks, the endless sketches, the quick hand moving hurriedly across the page, growing quiet only when he wrote in his small, crabbed mirror-writing those careful notations on which his fame rests. In all his life he built few canals, but planned them endlessly; and in the forest of his notebooks it is difficult to know where one plan begins and another ends.

His successors in Italy and France were midgets, but at least they got the work done. Most of them possessed quirks of character which make them interesting, and some of them broke their heads against the massive problems which resulted from an inadequate knowledge of the strength of materials and the basic principles of hydraulics. Leonardo had solved most of the theoretical problems of hydraulics, but his notebooks were to remain hidden for years to come.

Perhaps it was at the instigation of Leonardo that François I decided to enlarge the Martesana. All we know for certain is that in 1516, three years before Leonardo's death, the king established an annuity of 10,000 gold ducats to pay for a continuing survey of the canal system north of Milan. Work on the Martesana went on, with the brilliant Benedetto da Missaglia following a plan originally outlined by Leonardo for a diversion canal branching off near the group of cliffs known as Tre Corni, re-entering the river at Rocchetta. The canal was to be a mile and a half long, with ten locks to overcome the fall of 90 feet, and it was thought that the cost of the canal would be 50,000 gold scudi. Work was begun in 1530, but when Charles V became Emperor of the Holy Roman Empire it was abruptly abandoned, to be revived again in 1567, when a new board of engineers was appointed. The canal waters were being tapped for irrigation, and the canal itself was no longer suitable for navigation. It was decided to raise the diversion dam at the mouth of the canal and to widen the entrance so that more water could pass through, but it was realized that these measures, though long overdue, were not enough. It was necessary to have an entirely new look at the canal.

At this point a young painter born in the parish of San Michele, Milan, the son of a public architect, enters the scene. Almost nothing about his obscure beginnings is known. We do not know why he gave up painting and threw himself headlong into canal building. His name was Giuseppe Meda, and he is rarely mentioned in Italian encyclopedias, but he ranks close to Leonardo and Bertola da Novate among the great engineers of his time. And in his designs there is the grace and daring which in later years came to be associated with Thomas Telford, who also arose from obscure beginnings.

Giuseppe Meda went straight to the heart of the problem: the difficult and steep slope of the river Adda in the neighborhood of the cliffs at Tre Corni. Benedetto da Missaglia had attempted a diversion canal with ten locks, but Meda proposed to solve the problem with as few locks as possible, but these of great height. He contemplated two locks instead of the original ten; and the 90-foot drop was to be taken up by locks of 60 and 30 feet. For their time these were staggering heights, and no one had ever built locks of such magnitude before.

Once he had settled the plan of the two immense locks, Meda worked out their details. He proposed to widen the canal to reduce the velocity of water and to build side weirs to release surplus water. Each lock basin was 140 feet long and 140 feet wide, built, according to a contemporary account, "with great blocks of natural stone, interlocked and laid in mortar." To reduce the shock of water falling with a sheer drop of 60 feet, he borrowed a device suggested by Leonardo and used by him at Vigevano by which the water in the regulating basin tumbled down a flight of steps, so that the shock of one great blow was distributed over many smaller ones. Realizing that the upper lock gates could not be made watertight, Meda suggested the use of a curtain gate just inside the lock with the bulkhead open at the bottom, so that water seeping through the main gate would be cushioned when it entered the lock. Such was the grandiose plan, which Meda proceeded to call his "Castello." And in 1580, after years of negotiations, a contract was drawn up between Meda and the city of Milan in a lengthy document printed by the royal printer. According to the contract Meda was to furnish designs for making the river navigable between Rocchetta and Lake Como, to provide "continuous and convenient towing paths," and pay all costs for making the canal above 4,000 gold scudi. He was to allow his plans to be inspected by experts from Milan and elsewhere. In exchange he was to receive two-thirds of the river tolls "for himself, his heirs and assigns in perpetuity." He was also allowed the privilege of building wharves and mills on the banks of the river wherever he pleased, and to use for his own account all materials left over from constructing the canal.

By this time Milan had fallen into the possession of the King of Spain, and it was ten years before the royal assent was received. Prices had gone up in the interval, and Meda insisted that the contract price should be raised to 6,000 gold scudi. At last, in 1591, work was begun, with Francesco Vallezzo, a contractor of Bergamo, assuming the responsibility for construction. There were last-minute changes in the plans, and soon Vallezzo was asking for additional funds. There were complicated financial intrigues, payments to the contractor were held up, and Meda fell ill through anxiety. Work was resumed in 1593, but in the following winter the ground froze with the result that the great walls of masonry were damaged, and though the contractor was bound by contract to repair the walls out of his own pocket, he refused. Meda was compelled to undertake the task himself.

During the next year the authorities in Milan, who had hoped to see the canal already completed, showed their impatience by ordering the construction of a towpath, so that some traffic could pass along the river. The towpath interfered with Meda's work, adding to the complications of the task. Meda protested, but to no avail, and shortly afterward the city brought suit against him for incompetence. This was bad enough, but when the workmen became insubordinate Meda went in fear of his life. He requested permission to carry arms, but the request was refused. All Milan began to believe the canal was a white elephant, and a drain on public moneys; and on the charge of incompetence Meda and Alessandro Bisnati, his chief engineer, were thrown into jail.

While Meda and his engineer languished in jail, an attempt was made to operate the half-finished canal, but when part of the embankment gave way all work on the canal was suspended. Meda offered to show how the canal could be completed cheaply, and was brought out of prison to face a board of water engineers; but since the board included a number of his private enemies he was simply thrown into prison again, and all hopes of completing the canal were set aside until 1599, when an independent expert, Francesco Romussi, the city engineer of Pavia, was called in to report on Meda's project. The report praised the whole design, including the giant locks, and gave complete approval to the work which had so far been accomplished. As a result of the report Meda was released from jail. He died in August, less than three months after the publication of the report, penniless and heartbroken; and with him the great period of canal building in Lombardy comes to an end.

The attempt to build the great locks at Tre Corni was only one of many plans undertaken by Meda. The Sforzas, and the Viscontis before them, had attempted to build a network of canals around Milan. In 1553 the plan to build a direct canal between Milan and Pavia was once more under consideration. The old canal which went by way of the portage at Pisarello had proved expensive to maintain and suffered from some unusual defects. That year the Ticino had flooded over, and the breakwater separating the mouth of the Naviglio Grande from the river had been destroyed. All traffic on the canal was suspended, and all the mills which derived their power from the waterways could no longer be used.

Meda attacked the problem at the source. He saw that the fault lay with the breakwater, which was built of stone and divided the river longitudinally. There was no dam across the river, no way to control the water and equalize the flow. He proposed the building of a dam which would regulate the flow of water and keep it at a constant level. Meda offered to let the magistrates have the full credit for the plan, if he was allowed to build it. There were the usual delays, with the magistrates haggling over details, but in the end Meda's plan was accepted on his own terms. The dam was built so successfully that for a few brief years Meda enjoyed the reputation of being the foremost hydraulic engineer in Italy, and when the magistrates of Milan remembered the plan to construct a direct Milan-Pavia canal the task was given to him.

Brilliant, wayward, and uncompromising, Meda showed himself to disadvantage when he solemnly presented the plans for the new canal to "the illustrious Presidents and Masters of the Extraordinary Ducal Revenues" on April 20, 1588. The plans were voluminous, fantastically detailed, and curiously lacking in directness. Meda did not seem to know exactly where he wanted to dig the canal, and he suggested variant channels, explaining at great length his reasons for each; and the magistrates seem to have been bewildered by the extent of his knowledge and the uncertainty of his intentions. For eight years the great document slumbered in the archives of the magistrates, and then at last Meda produced a stream-lined version. The first canal wandered in all directions: the new one was direct and simple, a straight line between Milan, Pavia, and the river Po, which runs just a little below Pavia. The new plan consisted simply of maps and specifications. He was no longer attempting to hide his own doubts and smother the magistrates under the massive weight of documentation. Like the plan for the Castello on the River Adda, it had the beauty of a simple exercise in logic. Between Milan and the Po there was a fall of 180 feet, and Meda calculated a little arbitrarily that the slope of the canal itself would absorb a fall of 36 feet, leaving 144 feet to be absorbed by two giant locks. Later he proposed four locks between Milan and Pavia, and four more between Pavia and the Po. Like Leonardo and Bertola da Novate, he proposed to carry the canal over the main streams by bridges, and he made ample provision for roads and underpasses. By careful calculation he had reduced the cost to manageable proportions. Previously, a direct line between Milan and the Po had been thought impossible. Meda showed how it could be done, but by the time his masterpiece had been presented to the magistrates he was already in disfavor; and when at last in 1598 the plan received the approval of the king, disaster had overtaken him. In the end the canal which Meda had planned so carefully was completed, but by that time he was dead. The glory had departed. Skill, intelligence, technical knowledge—all these remained, but in Italy there were to be no more great canal builders forging ahead through unknown territory with superb daring. The next great developments came from France.

In 1598, while Giuseppe Meda was in prison, King Henry IV addressed a letter to Cardinal de Joyeuse, Archbishop of Narbonne, concerning a canal which would join the Mediterranean with the Atlantic Ocean. The king had just signed the treaty of peace between the Huguenots and the Catholics, and he was in a mood for building a great construction which promised to assist commerce and unite his people.

There was nothing new in the plan, which had appealed to François I. Already in 1539 engineers had shown the desirability of a waterway from Narbonne to Carcassonne and so to Toulouse, where it would join the Garonne, and barges could either float down the Garonne to Bordeaux or along a canal dug beside the river. They proposed three locks between Toulouse and Bordeaux, one at each end and one midway, but said nothing about the locks between Narbonne and Toulouse. The plans were drawn up by two "expert levelers," Nicolas Bachelier and Arnaud Casanove, who showed a curious lack of knowledge of leveling. They estimated inaccurately that the Garonne had a fall of 80 feet per mile and believed that even with this steep fall the river could be made navigable to barges. François I approved of the plan, but nothing was done. The plan lay in the royal archives through the reigns of Henri II and Charles IX. Civil war broke out in France. Neither money nor labor was available. In the reign of Henri IV there was peace again under a king whose chief occupation was to increase the wealth of France.

Henri IV was a man of good will, erudite and gifted. He had an excellent knowledge of engineering, especially of fortifications, road building, and town planning, and the Cardinal de Joyeuse was one of his closest advisers. The cardinal's grandfather had exchanged the crozier for the marshal's baton, and the cardinal himself was a man of action. As soon as he received the king's letter he assembled a group of experts, and carefully examined the original plan, which provided for a canal some 6 feet deep and 48 feet wide. The experts suggested an even greater width of 60 feet, but otherwise they were prepared to accept the dimensions of Bachelier and Casanove. The cardinal drew up an estimate—400,000 écus for the excavation work, 200,000 écus for removing rocks, constructing locks, paying for land and diverting the river Aude—and he believed that with the help of 5,000 workmen the work could be completed in a year. He wrote to the king that the canal was eminently practicable, and would bring him fame and renown.

Henri IV failed to build the Languedoc Canal between the Mediterranean and the Atlantic because there were more canal projects closer to hand, in particular a canal linking the Rhone and the Seine and another linking the Seine and the Loire. Both of these projects came under the surveillance of the king's chief engineer, Maximilien de Béthune, Baron de Rosny, afterward Duc de Sully. Béthune was a mathematician and engineer-of-works with a specialized knowledge of fortifications. Though a Protestant, he became the close adviser of the king, and in 1598 he was placed in sole charge of the finances of the kingdom. One by one nearly all the posts of great authority in France were offered to him. He became Governor of Mantes, Captain-General and Governor of the Bastille, Governor of Poitou and Superintendant of Fortifications and Artillery. For a considerable period he occupied the post of *Grand Voyer de France,* in charge of all highways, waterways, and public works. It was as *Grand Voyer,* with complete power to build as many roads and canals as the state finances would permit, that Béthune decided against the Languedoc Canal. Instead, he made plans for canals nearer the capital, where they could be supervised more easily and where they would have greater effect on the internal economy. Above all he was a practical statesman, and he was determined to tackle simpler problems first. The canal linking the Rhone and the Seine was temporarily abandoned, while he concentrated on the short Briare Canal from the loop of the Loire to the river Loing, which flows into the Seine at Fontainebleau. Briare was a little village about forty-five miles above Orléans. The total contract price was estimated as 505,000 écus, of which about three-quarters was to be spent on excavation, while the rest of the cost would pay for forty-eight locks, five drawbridges, land rents, and river enlargements. The locks were to be simple wooden affairs braced with iron, and the total length of the Briare Canal was to be about thirty-four miles. There were pronounced differences between the level of the Loire, the Loing, and the Seine, and to overcome these differences Béthune proposed seventeen locks on the Loire side and thirty-one on the Loing side. In 1604 a contract for the construction of the canal was signed with Hugues Cosnier, and the work was begun.

Béthune kept tight control over the work from the beginning and made periodical inspections. To assist Cosnier, he assigned six thousand soldiers to provide the skilled labor. Soon, however, doubts began to assail him. The plan involved the canalization of the river Loing and the river Trézé, a small tributary. But the frequent floods on these rivers would inevitably affect the level and make the canals unmanageable. Béthune decided to take the matter in his own hands, appointed himself engineer-in-chief, and proceeded to prepare new plans for canals to be built alongside the rivers, digging them in the slopes of the hills. The simple wooden locks were abandoned, and masonry was substituted. By his orders the length of the lock basins was increased from 90 feet to 140 feet, so that they could accommodate the largest river boats. There were the inevitable delays, with the contractor requesting adjustments because the cost of the canal had vastly exceeded the original estimate. Béthune was perfectly fair. He appointed a "board of commissioners" consisting of exactly two people, one representing the king, the other the contractor, to decide on the matter. There were meetings of the board in December, 1606, and again in April, 1607. The board continued to meet frequently, and Béthune's relations with the contractor continued to be friendly. New estimates were submitted to the board in February, 1610, with Cosnier complaining that the excavation had already cost twice the amount originally set aside, and that everything—masonry, hauling, dredging, draining, foundations, machines, labor—all these had cost such stupendous amounts that he was in danger of being ruined. Floods had destroyed some embankments. Springs had suddenly risen out of the ground, where no one had expected them, with the result that a good deal of the work had to be done under water. They had had to build cofferdams to keep the water out of the excavations, and the lock gates, once installed, had to be redesigned for strength by workmen who had to be especially trained. The work was proceeding satisfactorily, but the contractor had no more heart for it.

As usual Béthune was the soul of sympathy. He called another meeting of the board, and Cosnier was summoned to appear. The arbitrators wrote out their findings—the document, which is still preserved in the Bibliothéque Nationale, consists of 104 sheets recording every detail of the work with meticulous care. They agreed that the original estimate should be revised upward and stated the new contractual price. In French money they offered 1,083,279 livres, 16 sols, 9 deniers, or roughly $400,000 of our money. The cost had been calculated down to the last farthing, and when the document was signed on April 25, 1610, Cosnier pronounced that he was eminently satisfied. Three-quarters of the work had already been done. Béthune began to believe that in a few more months he would have the pleasure of inviting the king to the ceremonial opening of the canal. He was at the height of his power. He had refused the office of High Constable of France only because he preferred to remain a Protestant, and against the king's wishes. But the king still regarded him as the ablest man in the kingdom.

All Béthune's hopes were crushed three weeks later, when Henri IV was assassinated by a madman. The new king, Louis

XIII, detested Béthune and all his works; and when some time during the following year a new board was convened to decide what should be done about the canal, it was decided to abandon it altogether on the grounds that even when it was finished the cost of upkeep would be prohibitive. Cosnier was ruined; Béthune faded into obscurity; the canal crumbled away for twenty-seven years. At last, in 1638, Cardinal de Richelieu decided to allow two promoters, Jacques Guyon and Guillaume Bonterone, to proceed with a modified plan. The idea of a great wide waterway was abandoned. The forty-eight locks were reduced to forty-one, and the width of the canal was fixed at fourteen feet. The promoters were granted a concession on condition that they put the canal in running order within four years. Cosnier and Béthune had done their work well, and the canal was opened for traffic three years later. A few months earlier, on a winter's day in 1641, at the age of eighty-two, Maximilien de Béthune, Baron de Rosny, Duc de Sully, died in complete obscurity. More than any other man he had prepared the way for Louis XIV, the Sun King, who came to the throne the following year.

Louis XIV followed in the footsteps of Henri IV. Scientists, engineers, and builders of forts attended his luxurious court. It was the time of Turenne and Condé, and a vast upsurge in the military power of France, with the baffled Dutch, Spanish, and Bavarians defeated by French armies. Money flowed into the capital, and the great Colbert was Controller-General of Finances.

In 1662 an obscure tax gatherer called Pierre-Paul Riquet wrote to Colbert, reminding him of the advantages of building the Languedoc Canal. Colbert had already studied the problem, but Riquet advanced new plans based on a careful survey and Colbert immediately recognized their importance. Riquet was no brilliant upstart. Born at Béziers in 1604, he was already past middle age, a man of some fortune and considerable repute. Interested in mathematics, he had taught himself surveying, using a rusty compass. He possessed a small property inland, and one day it had occurred to him that the value of the property would increase if it had access to the sea. Thereafter he had tramped the countryside, taking levels, working out the easiest direction for the canal, discussing the project with anyone who cared to listen. He hired a workman to make model canals in his garden: the models were so well constructed that visitors to his house two hundred years later found them still there.

On November 26, 1662, Riquet wrote his famous letter to Colbert, outlining his plans. It is a strangely formal letter, with an oddly ecclesiastical aroma:

Monseigneur,

I am writing from this village about a canal which could be constructed here in the Province of Languedoc, joining the two seas. You will be surprised to hear me speak of something of which apparently I know nothing—one does not expect tax gatherers to go about with leveling instruments. But you will excuse my daring when I explain that I am writing at the orders of Monseigneur the Archbishop of Toulouse. Some time ago the Archbishop did me the great honor of visiting me, and he asked how the canal could be constructed, for he had heard that I had made a particular study of the problem. I told him what I knew, and promised to meet him again on my return from Perpignan, and then I could show him the ground so that he could see exactly what the possibilities were; and I did this, and the Archbishop in the company of the Bishop of St. Papoul and various other dignitaries have all enquired about the matter. . . .

So he goes on in his formal seventeenth century style, explaining at length the advantages of by-passing Gibraltar and the delightful prospect of diminishing the revenues of the King of Spain. His preliminary report recommended a canal 50 feet wide at the surface, 9 feet deep, lock gates 18 feet high, and a total length of 144 miles from Toulouse to the Etang de Thau. This letter alone would have accomplished nothing, but another letter covering much the same ground was sent by Charles d'Anglure de Bourlemont, the very aristocratic Archbishop of Toulouse.

Colbert was so impressed with the letter that he brought it to the attention of the king, who immediately appointed a royal commission to examine the proposal. The commission reported favorably, though expressing some doubt about the means of supplying water to the canal at the highest point. Riquet offered to dig a "feeder" at his own expense to prove the soundness of his plan, and in a surprisingly short time this was done. Colbert was pleased, and Riquet was urged to proceed with the plan.

As usual there were money troubles. Riquet was a rich man, and he set out to build the canal lightheartedly: he had not calculated on the fact that the cost of building a canal always exceeds the original estimate, or on his own ill-health, or on the enemies he was to encounter at every turning of the way. It was agreed in Paris that part of the cost should be defrayed by the Royal Treasury, while the rest should be raised by taxes in Languedoc. When the representatives of the states refused to agree to raise money by taxation, Riquet suggested that in exchange for certain taxes already in existence, to be assigned to him for a period of six years, he would himself construct the portion of the canal lying between Toulouse and the river Aude, which curves inland from Narbonne. The amount of money involved corresponded to about $1,000,000. Riquet promised to complete the canal in eight years.

Colbert had complete confidence in Riquet's ability to complete the canal, and Riquet's offer was accepted. Through the years work on the canal went on slowly, but with increasing difficulty. The return from the taxes was less than Riquet had expected, and there were long intervals between the advances from the Royal Treasury. There was opposition from landlords who protested against having their estates bisected by the canal, and the two commissioners, one appointed by the king, the other by the States of Languedoc, caused endless trouble. These were difficulties familiar to all canal builders, but Riquet was a man of some experience in dealing with recalcitrant landlords and he devised an expedient for getting money out of them. Some of the landlords of Languedoc were also tenants of royal estates, who sometimes journeyed to Paris to discuss the renewal of their leases from the Controller-General of Finances. Riquet, as a tax gatherer, was usually excluded from these meetings. He suggested to Colbert that he might be allowed to enter the room and pretend to be on terms of closest friendship with the minister. Colbert delighted in the ruse, showed the utmost cordiality to Riquet in the presence of the landlords, and sometimes steered the discussion toward the canal. The landlords were impressed, and after the second meeting offered a loan of about $50,000. Riquet rejected the loan, saying it was too small for his needs, but after a third meeting he accepted a loan of $150,000. More loans came later, but he was continually in financial difficulties. His labor force consisted of several thousand workers, six hundred of whom were women, and all had to be paid regularly. There were other difficulties. Progress was slow; Riquet could rarely find sufficient bricks for his expensive locks, and the commissioners quarreled over the route the canal should take. When he proposed to carry the canal through a tunnel at Malpas, they told him it was impossible and ordered him to follow another course entirely. Riquet simply put their orders in his pocket, sent most of the workmen to another part of the canal, and set to work at the tunnel with a small group of picked men. The tunnel was completed within six days, and the commissioners were too startled to object.

The Languedoc Canal was a fantastic undertaking for its time. In its 144 miles it crosses rivers, passes through tunnels and runs through the middle of the Etang de Thau in a channel of its own. At its highest point, at Narouse, it is 620 feet above the level of the Mediterranean. In 3½ miles from the Garonne to Toulouse it rises 207 feet by means of 26 locks, and altogether there are 119 locks, most of them built of heavy masonry, with curved side walls and paved highway bridges. It was a fitting monument to the age of the Sun King. Far more substantial than most canals of its time, it is still in use.

Louis XIV opened the canal with great pomp and ceremony in 1681, but by this time Riquet was dead. The canal had taken fourteen years to build, and for half of those years Riquet had been a sick man. The canal had cost some $4,000,000, and he died heavily in debt, worn out by anxiety, with most of his shares in the work already sold. In time the canal changed its name and became the Canal du Midi, the pride of France. Riquet, too, changed his name. Ennobled by the king, he became Baron Riquet de Bonrepos after the obscure village where he was born. It was, after all, a strange name for a man who had known so little rest.

Years later, at the time of the First Empire, his descendants printed a memorial volume in his honor. Napoleon was on the throne, there was talk of more canals to be constructed to the glory of France, and the Riquets wanted to assure themselves of their ancestor's greatness. It is a pathetic little volume, full of special pleading, with all the letters exchanged between Riquet and Colbert printed at length, and bitter invectives against the commissioners who had done so much to make Riquet's work difficult. Riquet is shown as the hero of the hour, the man who fought against intolerable obstacles with firmness and integrity. And then quite suddenly we see Riquet as he was: proud, humble, often ill, weighed down by the burdens of responsibility, and perfectly capable of duplicity, for on July 29, 1671, we find him admitting to Colbert:

> I am following the plan I made at the beginning, which is the best possible route, and one I have never divulged to anyone for fear that my secret shall become known. I am keeping my secret, so that in the event of my death I will leave it as an inheritance to my children.

Colbert was amazed to discover that the plan of the fabulously expensive canal was locked up in the brain of the man who was always complaining so bitterly against the demands of the commissioners, but he kept his temper and seems not to have worried unduly. He liked Riquet, and understood the rages of this man from the South, who was so often ill that he had to be carried along the banks of the canal in a litter. "I share all your griefs and all your joys," Colbert wrote in one of his spirited letters to Riquet, and he evidently meant it. Vauban, the great builder of fortresses, showed unstinting admiration for the canal, which altogether cost 17,000,000 livres— 7,500,000 livres from the king, 6,000,000 livres from the provincial estates, and the rest—the very large rest—from Riquet himself. All the money he had set aside for his daughters' dowries went into the canal, and when he was asked why he did this, he answered simply: "The canal is my dearest child."

An engraving, based on a portrait by Richard de Lamarre, gives an astonishingly lifelike representation of the man—his pride, his humility, his determination to destroy all the obstacles in his path. There is something of D'Artagnan in this man with his dark curling wig, fine nose, firm chin and sensitive mouth, broken by bitterness. He had cause for bitterness, but he also had cause to rejoice.

Afterward there were to be skilled engineers and technicians without number, but Riquet belongs to the line of the great canal builders. There is a sense in which the great days were already over when Brindley and Telford, De Lesseps and Goethals carved their canals over England, Panama, and Suez.

The canals of England

Sometimes, looking at the map of Great Britain, we are struck by the improbability of the place. That strangely fashioned land with its curious prongs and protuberances, like a slender-waisted old woman soaring on piggyback over the continent of Europe, seems suddenly to acquire the air of an improvisation. There she flies, with her Irish wraith leading the way and her Scottish bonnet vanishing into the arctic mists, and no one would ever have guessed by looking at the map that this old woman would come to dominate the earth.

Centuries ago the Greek explorers who first penetrated southern England returned with reports of strange tribes who inhabited the marshes and the rain-drenched forests—a dank place, where the sunlight rarely filtered down through the thick leaves and the people lived out their lives in darkness and obscurity. When the Romans and Greeks thought of Britain, they remembered the tin mines of Cornwall, dark bluish pearls, the Druids uttering their spells, and the worship of the sacred mistletoe. It was a land of fens and marshes and lakes and smoking forests, and endless rains. Tacitus, writing about A.D. 100, speaks of the sky continually obscured by rains and cloud. "There is no place on earth," he says, "where the sea has a greater dominion, and the tides run in all directions, not merely ebbing and flowing by the shore, but penetrating far inland and working their way among the hills and mountains, as though the sea were in its own territory." Even in those ancient days England was bathed in water, and so she has remained through all her history.

The British, however, were not seamen: they were men of the rivers and marshes, building their towns nearly always inland, living for preference in places surrounded by forests, and reached only by water. Out of the fens of Norfolk Queen Boudicca led her armies of tribesmen against London, where they slaughtered 70,000 Romans and set fire to the city. Then she returned to the fens and the secret winding waterways until at last the Romans captured her, scourged her, and killed her children. Sometimes even today among the low-lying lands around the Wash, in Lincolnshire and Cambridgeshire and along the coasts of Norfolk, men come across the remains of the ancient coracles in which the ancient Britons navigated their rivers. The modern dike builders in the fens are the descendants of the ancient dike builders who shored up the earth and lived in hovels made of turf, brushwood, and stones in days before history began.

The history of England begins with the Romans. There is a sense in which it begins at that strange moment when Julius Caesar drew up his army along the south bank of the Thames and sent, of all things, an armored elephant across the river to frighten the enemy out of their wits. The British turned tail and fled, but not for long. For a hundred years they fought on doggedly, refusing to give up ground, using their knowledge of the rivers and waterways to escape from the traps which the Romans threw round them. Then, in the reign of Vespasian, two Roman governors were appointed to Britain—one was the brilliant and dashing Petillius Cerealis, who smashed the powerful tribe of the Brigantes in northern England, and the second was Julius Frontinus, who smashed the British strongholds in Wales. Frontinus was an engineer and the author of a treatise on military strategy, who later became *Curator Aquarum,* or chief water controller, at Rome: he was the one Roman who could be expected to have a full knowledge of British waterways and how they could be used to defeat the enemy. It was probably under his governorship that the Romans built a series of military canals to enable them to keep watch on the northern tribes and bring up reinforcements speedily. One canal, known as the Itchen Dike, ran across England from the river Trent to Winchester, so joining the North Sea to the Channel. Another called the Caer Dike ran forty miles from Peterborough to Lincoln along the edge of the southern Fenland. This canal was later continued for another ten miles from Lincoln to the river Trent near Torksey and called the Fosse Dike. The Caer Dike has vanished, but the Fosse Dike remains and is still in use. It was scoured out in the reign of Henry I, and deepened to allow larger vessels to use it, and deepened again in the reign of Elizabeth, and again in 1840, but through all these years it has followed the same path. In 1762 Smeaton and Grundy examined it and found the depth to be about two feet eight inches. For nearly two thousand years produce has been carried along this ancient waterway.

The Romans constructed a network of canals through England, and one might have expected the Normans to continue the tradition. But the art of canal digging had died, and we hear of no more through all the years of Norman England. There were no engineers, only skilled artisans, who dredged the rivers and shored their banks and kept them navigable. It was necessary to keep the rivers free from obstructions, and so we find a clause in the Magna Charta saying that "all kidels [fish weirs] from henceforth shall be utterly put down by Thames and Medway, and through all England, except only by the sea coast." Improvements in river navigation went on, and from 1215 onward innumerable charters were granted by the king to allow the improvements to be made, but the charters often only confused the issue. The millers, who wanted a head of water behind their weirs to drive their water wheels, fought doggedly against the farmers who wanted to channel off irrigation ditches and against the fishermen who still insisted on putting up their fish weirs and against the boatmen who wanted a clear, unobstructed stream. In time the management of rivers became so complex that no one knew for certain who possessed the right to use them, and the courts of those days are full of complaints and counterarguments and petitions—in so many ways did men's lives depend upon the rivers. Very probably there were the same interminable battles in the law courts of Sumer and Babylon.

About the time of Elizabeth, the old flash locks began to give way to the pound locks. Flash locks were simply wooden gates which could be thrown across the streams to hold back the water until it had acquired a sufficient head. The gates were then suddenly withdrawn, and the "flash" of water would carry the boats over the shallows below. It was a typically English invention, dangerous, exciting, and wasteful, for great quantities of water ran out whenever the gates were opened, and the boat might overturn in the sudden flash flood, and the surrounding fields were often inundated; yet it had the typically English advantage of being a compromise, enabling the boats to pass through and at the same time giving the millers a good head behind their weirs soon afterward. The pound lock was the familiar double-gate lock, which seems to have reached England about a hundred years after its invention in Italy.

The first canal built in England since the time of the Romans came about as the result of the exasperating quarrels between the citizens of Exeter and the descendants of Isabella de Fortibus, who built a weir across the river Exe in the reign of Henry III. By 1563 the citizens decided it was time to put an end to an obstruction which had lasted for three hundred years, and engaged John Trew of Glamorgan to build a canal to run from a point below Countess Weir to the city of Exeter. It was a very small affair, three feet deep and sixteen feet wide, but John Trew built locks on it with double top and single lower gates. They were the first locks known to have been built in England, and they are still in use. The English were feeling their way. There was no great period of expansion with locks and canals proliferating all over England. Here and there a small canal would be dug and pound locks would be set up. It was a time when men were giving serious attention to another kind of canal—the drinking-water canal, which possessed a brief history of its own.

There had been drinking-water canals, hardly larger than ditches, in the past. Such a canal was built between Tiverton and White Downs in Devon in 1240. It was five miles long, and perhaps two feet deep and three feet wide. There was another built in 1376 to convey drinking water from Hessle and Anlaby to Hull, and still another built by Sir Francis Drake in 1587 between the river Meavy and Plymouth. But the most famous of them all was the canal known as the New River or Myddleton's Glory, which brought the "sweet waters" of Hertfordshire to London.

In Elizabeth's time London's drinking water came from the Thames, from springs within the city walls, and from sixteen conduits which brought fresh water from places as far away as Highbury and Hampstead. Along the muddy streets the hard-swearing water carriers with heavy three-gallon tankards hanging from yokes round their necks shouted their wares, the noisiest of all the street sellers in London. The women water carriers were the equals of the men, screaming and fighting for their places at the outlets, using clubs and staves, and sometimes causing riots. Things reached such a state that a special proclamation was issued forbidding persons from resorting to the conduits with any weapons. There was need for a new and much larger conduit, drawing water from farther afield, with an outlet which could be controlled by the government. The need was fulfilled by Hugh Myddleton, the swashbuckling son of the governor of Denbigh Castle in North Wales.

The Myddletons were a distinguished Tudor family, and nearly all Hugh's brothers possessed the fiery Elizabethan temper. One of them was William Myddleton, who became a sea captain and a buccaneer, and was something of a classical scholar and a poet in his own right and an expert in Welsh prosody. Hugh was more civilized, less versatile, and rarely journeyed abroad. In his youth he was one of the young gallants who attended Elizabeth's court. A well-authenticated story gives him the credit for being the second man in England to "drink" tobacco, as he stood with Sir Walter Raleigh outside a booth in Basinghall Street puffing steadily on his pipe to the alarm of the Londoners who crowded from all parts of the city to see him. Hugh became a merchant and then a member of the Goldsmiths' Company, the bankers and money-changers of the time. Soon he was rich from financing expeditions to the Spanish Main, and in 1609, at the age of forty-nine, with the old queen dead and a new king on the throne, he looked about for some method of benefiting his countrymen. Some years before, the Corporation of the City of London had drawn up plans for channeling the springs of the Chadwell and Amwell in Hertfordshire to London. There were long discussions, but nothing came of them. Hugh Myddleton lost patience, and offered to bring the water to the city at his own expense, if he could retain the full profits of the enterprise. Stowe, the antiquarian, says: "The matter had been well mentioned though little minded—long debated though never concluded—till courage and resolution lovingly shook hands together in the Soule of this no-way-to-be-daunted, well-minded gentleman."

The well-minded gentleman threw himself into the work of digging a canal ten feet wide and four feet deep from Hertfordshire to Clerkenwell on the north of the city—a distance of about forty miles. He had the usual difficulties to contend with. In some places the ground was "oozy and very muddy," and in other places there were outcrops of rocks. But these were the least of his difficulties. There were times when half of England seemed to be engaged in lawsuits over rivers: now there was a multitude of threatened lawsuits against a canal which was not yet built. His opponents carried their complaints to the House of Commons. They said the canal would turn their meadows into quagmires, "their farms be mangled and the fields cut up into quillets and small pieces." They claimed that cattle were already falling into the cut, and when there were sudden rains the water would spill over from the canal and flood their fields. Priests objected to an unnatural use of the land which was evidently against the will of God. Myddleton was sufficiently powerful at court to disregard these taunts and threats; and his detractors were silenced by the spectacle of the sweet water flowing to the thirsty city. From ancient times the opening of a canal has been greeted with the wildest extravagances of rhetoric, and Stowe wrote about the canal as though he were talking about some newly discovered aspect of God's beneficence:

> For if those enemies of all good Endeavours: Difficulty, Impossibility, Distraction, Contempt, Scorn, Derision, yea and Desperate Despight could have prevailed by their accursed and malevolent interposition, either before at the beginning, in the very birth of the proceeding; or in the least stolen advantage of the whole prosecution, this work of so great worth had never been accomplished.

There is a good deal more about "this work of so great worth," but Hugh Myddleton's fortunes were being strained to the utmost to complete the canal. The last stages were the worst. There were aqueducts to be built at Enfield and Islington—the Enfield aqueduct was a quarter of a mile long and the stream had to be carried in a wooden trough lined with lead, fifty tons of it, which represented a vast fortune for those days. The cost kept mounting, and he was forced to apply to King James for help. The king, who had watched the progress of the canal from his palace at Theobald's just north of Enfield, recognized the importance of Myddleton's work and agreed to pay half the remaining costs in exchange for half the profits. A few months later the king had less reason to like the canal. There were hunting fields around Theobald's, and James liked hunting above all things. One winter's day he went out riding with Prince Charles and a few courtiers, and three miles from the palace the king's horse stumbled and threw James into the frozen canal water. The king disappeared under the ice with only his boots showing. One of the courtiers, Sir Richard Young, ran to his rescue and succeeded in dragging him out and laying him on the bank. "There came much water out of his mouth and body," says a contemporary chronicler. Finally the king came to life and mounted his horse and rode back to Theobald's, a warm bed and hot punch, and a violent cold. In a black rage he spoke about "Myddleton's Water," saying that it baffled him how a king should have to tolerate a canal flowing through his back yard.

In time the king relented, remembering perhaps the profits which would accrue to him. The work went on, with the canal flowing at last into a reservoir or cistern which was "artfully embellished" and came to be called the Ducking Pond. On September 29, 1613, after nearly five years of work, the waters of the Amwell and Chadwell springs entered the cistern for the first time to the accompaniment of speeches and parades, while workmen wearing green Monmouth caps and carrying spades, shovels, and pickaxes on their shoulders marched in front of the platform where the Mayor of London and all the aldermen and most of the city dignitaries greeted them. Sixty workmen represented the six hundred who had worked on the project. They were all there—overseers, clerks, mathematicians, measurers, bricklayers, engineers, borers, and paviers—so Anthony Munday describes the laborers who attended the ceremony in a poem written especially for the occasion. As Anthony Munday remembered it, transmuting common prose into rhyme and rhetoric, the speech at the cistern ascribed the successful completion of the work to the aid of Heaven and the king's most gracious love:

> Long have we laboured, long desir'd and pray'd
> For this great work's perfection; and by th' aid
> Of Heaven, and good men's wishes, 'tis at length
> Happily conquered by Cost, art and strength.
> And after five years' dear expense in dayes
> Travaile and paines, beside the infinite wayes
> Of Malice, Envie, false suggestions,
> Able to daunt the spirit of the mighty ones
> In wealth and Courage: this, a work so rare
> Only by one man's industry, cost and care,
> Is brought to blest effect, so much withstood.
> His only aim the Citie's general good,
> And where (before) many just complaints
> Enviously seated, caus'd oft restraints,
> Stops, and great crosses, to our Master's charge

> And the work's hindrance; favour now at large
> Spreads itself open to him and commends
> To admiration, both his pains and ends.
> (The King's most gracious love.) Perfection draws
> Favour from princes and (from all) applause.

The lame verse gathers to itself a little strength as the poet approaches the solemn moment when drums and trumpets sounded, and the sluice gates flew open:

> Now for the fruits then: Flow forth, precious spring,
> So long and dearly sought for, and now bring
> Comfort to all that love thee; loudly sing
> And with thy crystal murmurs strook together
> Bid all thy true well-wishers welcome hither.

Then—this is still according to Anthony Munday who rescued the words from Thomas Middleton, the dramatist—there were more drums and trumpets "sounding in triumphal manner," and "a brave peal of chambers gave a full issue to the intended entertainment." Hugh Myddleton descended from the platform, casks of ale were broached, and there were congratulations all round. It was a day when Hugh Myddleton had good reason to be pleased with himself and his family: on that same day his brother, Thomas Myddleton, merchant adventurer and member of the recently formed East India Company, was elected Lord Mayor of London.

Hugh Myddleton was now at the height of his fame. At great expense he had dug a forty-mile canal, and he could look forward to a baronetcy and the quiet enjoyment of his profits. Unfortunately there was little profit in the enterprise, and it was some years before James gave him the baronetcy. Worse still, nobody seemed to want the water from the cistern, which was too far away from the center of London. The water carriers complained bitterly of their trade being taken away, and spoke darkly about the waters being poisoned. In time the water was distributed through the city by means of wooden pipes—elms were planted beside the canal to supply wood for them—and most of these pipes were still in existence up to the nineteenth century, when they were replaced with iron ones. And the descendants of the Londoners who had complained about the poisoned water at Clerkenwell complained just as bitterly against the iron pipes. It was thought that drinking water pouring through iron pipes led to cancer.

Nine years later Hugh Myddleton received the baronetcy he wanted above all other things; and in granting it to him James drew up a brief list of Hugh's qualifications for the honor. He had dug the New River Canal against all opposition; he had reclaimed land from the sea at Brading in the Isle of Wight; and he had found and opened silver mines near his father's castle at Denbigh, and offered the silver to the Crown. So exemplary a life showed a profound impatience with unworldly things, and for the rest of his life he attempted to put the world in order, with one impracticable scheme after another. Toward the end he seems to have lost hope, and he died alone and nearly forgotten at the age of seventy-six in his house at Enfield. In his will he left small legacies to the poor, and remembered his young Welsh assistant, Hywel Jones, leaving him thirty pounds "to the end that he might continue his care of the New River Waterworks."

Myddleton's Glory remains, and it is still used to bring drinking water to Londoners, though much of the stream has been culverted, and by skillful engineering the forty miles have been reduced to twenty-seven. In June, 1780, when Lord George Gordon and the "No Popery" rioters put half of London to the flames, they also thought of cutting off London's water supply, so that the flames would not be put out too easily. They attacked the canal, hoping to sever it, but were fought off by the police and soldiers. During World War II the canal came into prominence again at the height of the Blitz, when three huge water mains were broken by a single bomb. These water mains by-passed a length of the canal. With the city threatened by a water shortage and once more in desperate need of water for fighting fires, it was decided to open up Myddleton's old "loop" at Enfield. Soon over a thousand soldiers and firemen were hurriedly excavating the part of the old canal which had been filled in; and within twenty-four hours the flow of water was restored. Myddleton's Glory had once more justified itself.

Today at Chadwell Springs a monument to Myddleton is still standing. With a slight change of words, it might be the translation of an inscription carved by one of the Sumerian kings. It reads:

> Sacred to the memory of Sir Hugh Myddleton, Baronet, whose successful care, assisted by the patronage of his King, conveyed this stream to London: an immortal work, since man cannot more nearly imitate the Deity than in bestowing health.

There was nothing particularly new in equating the canal builder with God. It had been done in ancient times, and no doubt it will continue into the future.

Myddleton's Glory was important at the time, but it solved no difficult engineering problems and added nothing new to the history of canals. The New River hardly differed from similar canals dug in ancient times in the Near East. The mathematicians, measurers, and bricklayers who constructed it had not advanced beyond the knowledge of the workmen who diverted the Nile at Memphis in the fourth millennium before Christ. Two hundred and fifty years were to pass before the canal builders took another step forward. It was a giant step, and they surpassed themselves. With the new canals they made possible the Industrial Revolution, and changed the face of England and the world.

The Industrial Revolution began in Manchester, England, and the very moment of its birth was probably the day in 1759 when a young and foppish duke encountered a gnarled, middle-aged millwright called James Brindley. The duke immediately took to the millwright and engaged him to survey the land between his coal mines at Worsley and the river Irwell, and to plan the route of a canal.

James Brindley was the son of a crofter of the High Peak of Derbyshire, too poor for any schooling. His childhood was miserable, and the farmhouse where he was born was left to rot when the family moved away. He took odd jobs while a boy, and when he was seventeen, in 1733, he was apprenticed to a wheelwright near Macclesfield, and after a few weeks' trial he was bound for seven years. In those days a wheelwright's trade covered many crafts, and Brindley was sometimes sent to Macclesfield to build and repair the mill machinery. He was a born mechanic, and liked to make wooden models of any machines he saw. He was almost excessively conscientious and careful in carrying out repairs, and sometimes his master complained: "Doan't tha knaw as firmness o' wark's t'ruin o' trade?" Once when Brindley had difficulty in putting up a piece of machinery, he walked twenty-five miles on Saturday to see another like it, spent all Sunday examining it, and walked back on Sunday evening and then spent the whole night working on the job. Yet it was not his responsibility to prepare plans and working diagrams and discover how the machinery should be put together: this responsibility belonged to his master. All through his life he liked to get to the heart of a problem, whatever the cost in time and labor, and in his own way. He liked to prepare his own material. If timber was required, he would find his own tree, cut it down, and haul it himself to his workshop. A heavy-set man, with full cheeks, thick lips and large innocent eyes, he walked with the slow, deliberate gait of a farmer to the end. He never made much money and never learned how to spell, yet he ranks with the great innovators—with Amenemhet III and Bertola da Novate and Leonardo da Vinci. He was among those who helped most to change the face of the earth.

There was nothing in the least auspicious in the first meeting between the third Duke of Bridgewater and the obscure workman: no sense of great things to come. The duke was twenty-three, pale, sickly, and foolish. His father was dead, his mother had made another brilliant marriage, and he was left to his own resources with large estates and a comfortable fortune. He had made the Grand Tour in the company of his tutor Robert Wood, the author of a well-known work on Troy, Baalbek, and Palmyra. He had a taste for travel and a taste for pretty girls, but an unhappy love affair with one of the prettiest debutants of the season had soured him. He owned coal pits at Worsley, near Manchester; and remembering his father's plan for a waterway to carry coal from the Worsley collieries to Manchester, he obtained an Act of Parliament to enable him to build a canal from Worsley to join the river Irwell at Barton. There would be a steep flight of locks at Barton to allow the coal boats to navigate the river to Manchester.

The duke threw himself into plans for the canal and made his own survey in the company of his land agent, John Gilbert. It was John Gilbert who suggested the employment of James Brindley, then working on his own as a wheelwright at Leek in Staffordshire and as a consultant to the Corporation of Liverpool and Earl Gower, the duke's brother-in-law, who were promoting a canal to connect the rivers Trent and Mersey. Brindley was sent to survey the territory—he called it an "ochilor servey or a ricconitoring"—and returned with the recommendation that the junction with the river Irwell and the flight of locks should be abandoned. He disliked locks, and avoided them wherever possible. "Water is a giant," he said once; "therefore lay him down on his back." He meant: "Whatever else you do, keep the canal flat." The duke had proposed a series of locks down one side of a valley and another series of locks up the other side. Instead, Brindley suggested a viaduct two hundred yards long and twelve yards wide, raised on arches, with the piers of masonry and the canal lined with puddled clay, which was simply well-tempered clay and sand kneaded with water.

Across Stretford meadows the canal was raised on an embankment more than half a mile long and nearly forty yards wide at the base: here again Brindley avoided the use of a lock. He liked things to go directly to their source, and so he arranged that at the Worsley end the canal should go straight into the coal mine by means of a tunnel bored into the side of a steep hill. Brindley had the same directness when it came to making plans for the canal outlet in Manchester. Originally it was intended to unload the barges at the foot of Castle Hill, and the coal would then be carried up the hillside. Brindley suggested it would be altogether simpler to sink a shaft from the top of the hill which would meet a tunnel bored into its side. In this way, for the whole length of the journey between Worsley and Manchester, the giant water was laid on its back.

Brindley's plans were approved by the duke, but there were many who disapproved. Submitted to another engineer, who may have been John Smeaton, they were regarded as hopelessly impractical. "I have often heard of castles in the air," the engineer said, "but never before have I seen where any of them were to be erected." The duke was not discouraged. He had great faith in Brindley's ability to carry out the plan. Brindley himself grew nervous toward the end, worrying whether there had been defects of design or workmanship which had escaped his notice. On the day when the water was let into the canal he dared not be present. He went to the Wheatsheaf Hotel at Stretford and took to his bed, refusing to come out until he learned that the canal was operating successfully.

He was always going to bed—to rest, to think out problems, to forget his worries. The poet Robert Southey described him well: "Brindley was a singular character, a man of real genius for this particular employment, who thought of nothing but locks and levels, perforating hills, and floating barges on aqueduct bridges over unmanageable streams. When he had a plan to form, he usually went to bed, and lay there working it out in his head till the design was completed. Being asked before the Houses of Parliament for what he supposed rivers were created, he answered after a pause—'to feed navigable canals.'"

Brindley got on well with the duke, who was highhanded and strangely remote, the perfect type of the young aristocrat disenchanted with the ways of the world. In time the duke's magnificence became widely known, and many years later it was remembered by Mark Twain in Hannibal, Missouri, when he came to write *Huckleberry Finn.* When the duke in the story thought of some name which would be appropriate to his own grandeur, the name

Duke of Bridgewater and Brindley's aqueduct in background

that came to his lips was "Bridgewater." But Brindley did not get on so well with John Gilbert, the land agent. They quarreled fiercely over one of Brindley's mares which was attacked by one of Gilbert's stallions. At last Brindley broke off all contact with the land agent. Years later there were found in Brindley's notebooks the revealing words: "A meshender [messenger] from Mr. G. I retorned the anser No more sosiety."

But Brindley's fame was now assured, and from all over the country people flocked to admire the canal, with the basin at Worsley built at the foot of the sandstone cliffs and the two-hundred-yard-long aqueduct across the river Irwell. The young duke had himself painted in a three-cornered hat and an elegant velveteen coat, pointing languidly toward the aqueduct, with ships sailing beneath the arches, while the coal barges are hauled over it. The duke looks a little like a Chinese mandarin who has mysteriously conjured roads in the air from his silken cuffs. It is worth pausing for a moment over this portrait, for there, if anywhere, we see the beginning of the Industrial Revolution, and for a little while longer the workers will be no more than specks on the landscape, with the feudal aristocracy filling the foreground. Soon, very soon, the picture would change. The French Revolution was still thirty years away, and the full tide of the Industrial Revolution was yet to come.

The canal made Manchester, for with the price of coal now reduced from 7d. to 3½d. a hundredweight and the supply coming regularly, not irregularly as in the past, the town was able to forge ahead with its industries. There was no cheaper coal anywhere in England. Four years after the canal was opened in 1761, Watt made the improvements on the steam engine, and by the end of the century Manchester had become the hub of industrial England.

With the Worsley-Manchester Canal completed, Brindley surveyed the land from Manchester to Liverpool, which was now a growing port, with more than a thousand ships entering the Mersey every year, though hardly more than a hundred came in 1701. Once again in making his plans Brindley followed the lay of the land as closely as possible. Seen from the air, the canal would have resembled a wriggling snake: southwest from Manchester, then west from Altrincham, then running beside the Mersey until at Preston in Cheshire it turns again northward to join the Mersey. At one point it crossed the Mersey by a seventy-foot bridge. It crossed Sale Moor, which was bogland, on a framework of timbers, and in order to provide against a burst embankment Brindley had gates fixed in the canal bed which automatically cut off a section where a break occurred if the water flowed too swiftly. Brindley had his own blacksmith's, carpenter's and mason's shops on the canal, so that they could be floated into place wherever they were required. He superintended every operation. He was tireless in inventing tricks to save money, though the cost of building the canal was almost prohibitive and in the end, in order to borrow the money, the duke had to give a mortgage on all his estates. But the canal, as originally planned, was never completed. Lord Gower had obtained an Act of Parliament authorizing the construction of a canal from the Mersey to the Trent. It was known as the Grand Trunk Canal, and was built largely at the instigation of Josiah Wedgwood to supply the potteries. Brindley constructed both canals and arranged that they should meet at Runcorn Gap, where for the first time he permitted himself the luxury of locks.

Once again, as in the time of Hugh Myddleton, there was opposition. The landowners were afraid that the new waterway would drown their water meadows and that their birds would be shot out of the sky by bargemen unfamiliar with the game laws. The owners of riverboats objected to the heavy losses they would face if trade moved along canals. There were large vested interests bent upon keeping trade to the rivers and the portages, but at last they were overcome, and on July 26, 1776, there occurred at Burslem in Staffordshire the ceremonial cutting of the sod. The people of Burslem took the day off to celebrate. Everyone put on his best clothes. Lord Gower, Lord Anson, and Lord Gray were present, to give tone and encouragement to the proceedings. Speeches were made. Josiah Wedgwood was praised for "his indefatigable services in this good

Mr. JAMES BRINDLEY.

cause," and he was allowed to cut the first sod, while Brindley, the engineer of the canal, was allowed to wheel it away in a barrow. Afterward there was a luncheon at the Leopard Inn for the more privileged members who had attended the ceremony. A sheep was roasted whole for the benefit of the poor potters, and at sunset there were bonfires all over Burslem, while *feux de joie* were fired in front of Mr. Wedgwood's house. At the time it was thought the canal might be completed in three or four years, but it was eleven years before they met to celebrate the opening, and by that time Brindley had died of overwork.

Brindley was everywhere, taking to his bed on occasion to work out problems, but nearly always on the move, living in inns, drawing up plans by candlelight, seeing that suitable clay was found for the local brickworks and that the right stone was brought from the quarries. At Harecastle he planned a tunnel 2,880 yards long through a small mountain. He employed miners for the work, who set their charges of gunpowder by the light of candles and were sometimes drowned; millions of gallons of water had to be pumped away through another small tunnel. Shafts were sunk from above to provide ventilation. There were many shafts, and in some of them fires were lit, and so there would be down-drafts in some shafts and up-drafts in others. The workmen who dug these inland navigations were called navigators, but this soon became transformed to "navvies," and the name has stuck. Brindley was working on half a dozen big schemes. His health began to fail. He had married a young wife and bought a house at Tunstall near the Harecastle Tunnel, and sometimes he would go down to London to attend parliamentary committees inquiring into the building of canals, and once he attended a performance of *Richard III* with David Garrick playing the leading role, and was so shocked and terrified by what he saw on the stage that he took to his bed again and remained there for two days. He was surveying a reach of canal near Leek in Staffordshire, where he had once kept a wheelwright's shop, when he got soaking wet and caught pneumonia. He was on his deathbed when some canal engineers came to him for advice. They explained their difficulty—they could not make the canal hold water. "Then puddle it," Brindley said. They told him they had already done so. "Then puddle it again—and again," he said, and died soon afterward. He died on September 27, 1771, at the age of fifty-five.

Perhaps the best thing ever said about him was spoken by Josiah Wedgwood, the man most responsible for getting the canal built. He did not mention Brindley's name when he described the locks at Runcorn, but Brindley's presence was implied. Wedgwood said:

> I was astonish'd at the vastness of the plan and the greatness of stile in the execution. The Walls of the Locks are truly admirable, both for strength and beauty of workmanship. The front Lock next the sea (for such it seems when the Tide is in) in particular, whose walls are compos'd of vast stones from 1 to 12 Tons weight, yet by the excellent machinery made use of, some of which is still left standing, they had as perfect command of these huge masses of Rock as a common brick-layer of the brick in his hand. In short, to behold Ten of these Locks all at a view, with their Gates, Aqueducts, Cisterns, Sluices, bridges, &c. &c., the whole seems to be the work of the Titans, rather than the production of our Pigmy race of beings. . . .

In England the canal builders who came afterward accepted Wedgwood's verdict: Brindley was a Titan among them, the greatest of them all.

In the end England was to be crisscrossed with a web of canals: canals feeding on rivers, and branching off from canals, and these branches in turn branching off again, until there was almost no place in England more than fifteen miles from a canal or a river. From the Grand Trunk was built the Staffordshire and Worcester, which linked the Trent and the Mersey with the Severn at Stourport, and the Oxford and Coventry, which joined the same rivers with the Thames at Oxford—both these canals were designed by Brindley, who did not live to see them completed. The Oxford and Coventry was ninety miles long, and took twenty years to build. There was nothing unusual in this: the Leeds and Liverpool canal was built over a period of forty-six years, and there were others that required even longer.

Canals had come to stay, at least for a little while, and by 1790 there was almost a mania for canal building, with every municipality attempting to raise bonds and put an Act through Parliament. Trade flourished along the canalways. It could hardly be otherwise, since canals reduced the cost of transport sometimes by four-fifths. The cost of shipping goods from Liverpool to the potteries in Staffordshire, for example, had been about £2.10s. a ton, which the canal reduced to 13 shillings. Formerly a horse could carry only one sack of wheat, but a horse pulling a barge along a canal bank could pull forty tons, or more. There was not only more trade, but more traveling and more contact between the towns and the villages. Twenty years after the first canal was opened, John Wesley wrote: "How is the whole face of this country changed in about twenty years! Since the potteries were introduced, inhabitants have continually flowed in from every side. Hence the wilderness is literally become a fruitful field: houses, villages, towns, have sprung up; and the country is not more improved than the people." John Wesley had good reason to know what was happening, for more than any other man of his time he was traveling up and down the country.

Inevitably the canals produced troubles of their own. When John Wesley spoke about the improvement of the people, he was referring to a general improvement in morals, not to the particular morals of the navvies, who were recruited among farm laborers and workers from the fen districts and ne'er-do-wells. They lived in shacks built beside the canals, and got their women from the neighboring villages, and drank lustily, and sometimes their quarrels led to murder. The newspapers of those days are filled with accounts of the drunken bouts of the navvies and the murders they committed; and sometimes the navvies were murdered by villagers who had grown weary of seeing their women wandering away into the navvy camps. It was a phenomenon which accompanied canal

Thomas Telford, by Raeburn (Lady Lever Collection, Port Sunlight)

building everywhere, and we shall see the same in America when some sixty years later the first American canals were pushed through.

The canal engineers, however, were a race apart: quiet men, slow-speaking and methodical, and some of them had a touch of genius. They were skilled mechanics who had to know a good deal about the strength of materials, hydraulics and geology, and how to take correct levels, and how to manage men. Many of them, like James Brindley, were born in poverty. There was Thomas Telford, born in a remote valley near the little town of Langholm in Eskdale, Dumfriesshire. He became a working stonemason, first in Langholm, then in Edinburgh and finally in London, where he worked under Sir William Chambers on Somerset House. In 1784, at the age of twenty-seven, he was sent to work on the new Commissioner's House at Portsmouth Dockyard. By this time he had attracted the notice of a patron, William Pulteney, said to be the wealthiest commoner in England, and through Pulteney he secured the post of Surveyor of Shropshire, which made him responsible for all the public works undertaken in that county. He built a new jail at Shrewsbury and designed churches for Bridgnorth and Madeley; but it was bridge building which attracted him most, and through bridge building he came to build his first canals.

Telford was a man of all trades, civilized, intelligent, with a gift for leadership and an infallible knack for finding the right man for the job. Brindley possessed a mystical sense of the earth's rightness: Telford delighted in soaring arches, delicately proportioned bridges, thrust and counterthrust, the play of metals. Brindley was of the earth, earthy; Telford belonged to the air and the sunlight and the flow of waters. He came at the beginning of the engineering age, and no one ever built more gracefully.

He was an unrivaled master in the use of iron, and delighted in building suspension bridges. When most of the bridges of Shropshire were swept away by abnormal floods, he set to work to build bridges which no floods would ever sweep away; and in five years he built forty bridges, some of stone, others of cast iron, and all of them beautiful. He was building a bridge at Buildwas when he came into association with the great Shropshire ironmaster Abraham Darby, and it was through Darby's influence that he was appointed agent, engineer, and architect to the Ellesmere Canal Company, which after a succession of false starts, had obtained an Act of Parliament enabling it to join the three rivers Severn, Dee, and Mersey by a canal from Ellesmere Port on the Mersey across the Wirral Peninsula to Chester, and so through Chirk, Ellesmere, and Preston to Shrewsbury on the Severn. As originally planned, the Ellesmere Canal was never completed, chiefly because the upper Severn provided unmanageable problems of navigation. The line ended at Weston, where there were lime kilns, and so barges moving down the canal with coal were able to return fully loaded with lime.

Telford's first task was to cut the canal across the Wirral Peninsula. This canal, which began to pay its way shortly after it was opened in 1795, presented few difficult engineering problems. Then it was decided to cut the intermediate branch line between Llangollen and Weston, and here at once Telford found himself confronted with extraordinary problems and extraordinary opportunities. To carry the Ellesmere Canal over the valley of the Dee, he designed and built the aqueduct at Pont-Cysyllte, over 1,000 feet long and 127 feet high. Astonishingly graceful, with its nineteen arches spanning the vale of Llangollen, it represented a completely new form of aqueduct. The heavy aqueducts of the Romans march across Italy and southern France like legionnaires in full armor: Telford built an aqueduct which suggests the lightness of young dancers. Where Brindley lined his aqueducts with puddled clay, Telford solved the problem with a cast-iron trough, so reducing the weight on the slender stone piers. Unlike the solid rubble-filled piers of the past, these were no more than hollow walls strengthened by internal bracing. It was a method he employed in all his subsequent bridge building. The first stone for the aqueduct at Pont-Cysyllte was laid in June, 1795, and the canal was opened for traffic ten years later. By an odd coincidence the first stone was laid by Richard Myddleton of Chirk, a member of Parliament and lineal descendant of the Hugh Myddleton who had brought the New River Canal to London nearly two hundred years earlier.

Telford was now at the height of his fame. The beauty of the Pont-Cysyllte aqueduct showed that engineering need not be divorced from art: it was a time when men looked forward eagerly to a marriage between the sciences and the arts. Telford became the apostle of lighter and more adventurous structures; and when in 1800 he was sent by the Lords Commissioners of His Majesty's Treasury to report on the construction of a canal across the Great Glen of Scotland, it was expected that he would find easy and graceful ways of circumventing a host of problems. There were excellent

The Pont-Cysyllte aqueduct

reasons for building such a canal. Scotland had not yet recovered from the outbreak of Forty-five, and the government, fearing wholesale emigration, was planning a network of good roads through the Highlands to bolster the decaying economy. It was the time of the Napoleonic wars, and there were strategic advantages in digging a canal which would allow ships to sail from one side of Great Britain to the other, undetected by Napoleon's privateers. Yet it was realized that the cost would be high, and perhaps prohibitive. Telford had worked on the Crinan Canal, a short nine-mile stretch from Ardrishaig on Loch Fyne to Crinan, providing a sheltered passage from the Clyde ports to the islands of the west, shortening the journey by nearly eighty-five miles. He had worked well, taking with him the men who had built the Ellesmere Canal, and he was obviously the man to report on the canal through the Great Glen.

He reported in 1802 that the canal was eminently practicable, would take seven years to build and would cost £350,000. He favored a canal which would take large merchantmen and warships up to the size of a thirty-two gun frigate. It would be formed of four sections connecting Loch Linnhe, Loch Lochy, Loch Oich, and Loch Ness, where the Loch Ness monster was even then slumbering. He declared hopefully that the canal should be twenty feet deep, but this depth was rarely attained—the present minimum depth is fourteen feet. He planned twenty-nine locks, and these were built exactly as he had planned them, with the water level maintained by gravity from Loch Oich at the summit level. He estimated that the canal would need to be cut for only twenty-two miles, the rest of the waterway being provided by the lochs.

The Caledonian Canal was unlucky from the beginning. Like Brindley, Telford was overworked. He was always being consulted about canal problems in other parts of Britain, and he was continually building bridges and roads and fighting for more appropriations. The original estimate was increased to £474,000, but by the time the canal was completed in 1822 it had cost the government over a million pounds, and even then it could not take the bigger ships which were expected to boost Scottish trade. The only ships that could pass through the canal in the weeks after it was opened were fishing vessels. The *Inverness Courier* reported the grand opening at length—the proud passage of the vessels carrying the commissioners and other notables from Inverness to Fort William, where there were the usual bonfires and an unusual number of toasts greeted "with genuine Highland spirit." Soon everything was going wrong. Too late, it was realized that Telford had forgotten to design towing paths, and the Great Glen itself could become a funnel of wind, holding up ships for days, so that it was sometimes simpler to take boats around the tip of Scotland than to leave them to the mercies of the Caledonian Canal.

In time, however, the canal vindicated itself. Built too late to be of use in the Napoleonic war, it was used successfully during World War I, when mines and sinkers from America were landed at the western end of the canal, loaded into lighters and shipped to Inverness, where they were assembled and strung together to form the great Northern Barrage, the minefield stretching from the Orkneys to the coast of Norway. It was used again for similar purposes during World War II. Today only about a hundred vessels a month pass through the canal, mostly coasting craft and small tankers up to five hundred tons, with a sprinkling of fishing vessels and barges. In the summer MacBrayne's steamers coast slowly up the canal for the benefit of summer tourists in search of the Loch Ness monster. They called it Telford's white elephant, and so it has remained, a monument to the errors of a great man who was sometimes impatient with details.

Telford did better when he went to Sweden and supervised the cutting of the Göta Canal from the North Sea to the Baltic. The Swedes were excellent canal builders—they had built a canal with locks between Eskilstuna and Lake Mälaren as early as 1606—but they bowed before Telford's greater experience and knowledge. He brought his own men with him; among them were engineers and craftsmen who had worked with him for twenty years. The same men returned with him to Wales and helped him to build the great suspension bridges across the Menai and the Conway. These, with the Pont-Cysyllte aqueduct, were to remain the enduring monuments of his fame.

His last canal was the Birmingham and Liverpool Junction Canal, which marked the end of a period. The previous canal joining Birmingham to Liverpool had ninety-nine locks in 114 miles. Telford proposed a plan for reducing the distance by twenty miles and the number of locks by thirty. The plan was accepted, and he immediately went to work on it, but the canal was still being built after his death in 1834 at the age of seventy-seven.

Brindley was the innovator, but Telford was the man of daring. Robert Southey called him "the Colossus of the Roads," and Sir Walter Scott described the Pont-Cysyllte aqueduct as the most impressive work of art he had ever seen. Toward the end of Telford's life superlatives crowded around him, and people remembered the number of canals he had brought into being—there were over thirty—and the number of honors he had received from foreign governments and scientific societies, and how he had become the father of modern engineering, and how he spoke on equal terms with the greatest in the land. He seemed to be shrewd, clear-cut, practical, but in fact there was much of the dreamer in him. "I am a queer creature," he wrote once, "and not ashamed to be thought singular." He gave the impression of a man who never brooded, but he brooded endlessly, wrote yards of poetry, studied Greek—he said once that among ancient writers he thought Thucydides most resembled an Englishman, meaning perhaps that Thucydides most resembled himself—and when Tom Paine published *The Rights of Man* Telford was swept off his feet. He never married, and only one record exists that he ever took the slightest notice of women. He died in 1834, loaded with honors, a thin white-haired shrunken man with a peculiarly sweet smile, and to the very end he possessed the gift of getting down to the heart of a problem.

The Birmingham and Liverpool Junction Canal shows the measure of the man. It marches in a straight line with deep cuttings and high embankments, as straight and beautiful as the Menai Bridge, with no nonsense about following the contours of the land. Brindley's canals were always narrow and winding, and seemed to follow the paths which rivers would have taken if they had been so minded. Telford came at the beginning of a new age.

When the great ironmaster Abraham Darby learned to smelt iron with coke, the iron age began, and Telford was among the first to master the use of iron in constructions. As far back as 1800, he foresaw that the railways would put the canals out of business. "In countries whose surfaces are rugged, or where it is difficult to obtain water for lockage, where the weight of the articles of produce is great in comparison with their bulk, and when they are mostly to be conveyed from a higher to a lower level—in these cases iron railways are in general preferable to canal navigation." [1] When he died, the Birmingham and Liverpool Railway had already been operating for four years, and the great days of canals were nearly over.

The English canals were a long time dying, and they are not dead yet. The worst blow they faced was the depression of 1825, which cut off financial assistance at a time when they might have been able to reorganize and place themselves in a better economic position to offset the encroachment of railways. The first railways were canal feeders. There was Richard Trevithick's railroad to a canal feeder in South Wales, and George Stephenson's steam engine drew coals from the Killingworth Colliery to the Tyne. But once the Stockton to Darlington line was opened in 1825—it was the first public railroad ever built, and though steam locomotives were used from the start, most of the work was still done by horses—the vast and intricate canal system was doomed for the reasons which Telford had explained many years before. Lockage was always presenting difficulties which could be surmounted only at great expense. Sending freight by canal was relatively inexpensive, but it was always slow, and with perishable goods it was especially uneconomical.

Ironically, canals themselves helped to introduce the railways, for the canals brought more coal, and more coal brought more iron, and more iron brought the railways. Soon the canal companies were seeking authorization to build railways along the banks of canals. The first canal company to go over to the enemy was the Manchester, Bolton and Bury Canal Company, which obtained in 1831 an Act of Parliament authorizing it to change its name to the Company of Proprietors of the Manchester, Bolton and Bury Canal Navigation and Railway. The new railway was opened in 1838.

[1] *General View of the Agriculture of Shropshire,* J. Plymley, 1813. Article by Thomas Telford dated 1800. Quoted in Charles Hadfield, *British Canals* (Readers Union, London, 1952), p. 99.

Sketch map of English Canal System

Thereafter every year saw the surrender of more canal companies to the railways. Seventeen canal companies sold themselves to the railways in the year 1846 alone.

The face of England was changing again. During the fifty years of the canal age hundreds of miles of waterway and hundreds of bridges and aqueducts were built. In the three decades between 1830 and 1860 the railway age produced more than 25,000 bridges, a greater number than all the bridges which previously existed in the country. There was no stopping the railways. They bought and leased canals, and sometimes the canals acquired by the railways were only a source of embarrassment to them—better routes could have been obtained by other means. And those who hoped to see a healthy rivalry between the canals and railways were also disappointed. The truth was that for heavy goods railways were cheaper and more efficient. The cost of laying a railroad could be calculated exactly, whereas there were nearly always unexpected costs to be met in building canals, as De Lesseps was to discover when he built the Suez Canal and went on to attempt a canal across the Isthmus of Panama. With the Birmingham and Liverpool Junction Canal, Telford had hoped to show that an improved canal could compete with the railways, but he too had been faced with unexpected expenses, and for some time people doubted whether it would ever be opened.

If railways had come a few years later, it might have been possible to reorganize the waterways, amalgamate them and place them under regional control. But they were never given a breathing space, and the railways deliberately bought up canals until they owned about one-third of all the canals in the country. Throughout the nineteenth century the canals were at the mercy of the railroads. They perished and dried up and were filled in, and there is hardly a county in England where a wanderer will not come across the sunken course of a canal which once carried gaily colored barges from river to river, and from city to city. It seemed that all the waterways were doomed, and nothing at all would remain of the great spider-web system of canals which was the glory of England.

But the waterways were not allowed to perish completely. Toward the end of the century a number of far-seeing men realized that under special circumstances there was a place for modernized canals, larger and more efficient than the slender thread-like canals of an earlier age. Manchester had suffered a depression as the result of the American Civil War. A Manchester engineer, Daniel Adamson, thought it might be possible to dig a ship canal directly to the sea, thirty-five miles away. In May, 1882, he published a pamphlet called *Facts and Figures in Favour of a Tidal Navigation to Manchester,* which immediately went into several editions. During the next month he called a meeting at his house, attended by sixty-eight prominent businessmen. All approved his plan enthusiastically. In a sense what he wanted to build was far more than a canal: it was in fact an elongated harbor thirty-five miles long, very deep, giving Manchester access to the open sea.

There were difficulties in the way. Liverpool objected, as it had objected many times before whenever the idea of the Manchester Ship Canal was raised. As far back as 1825, the *Liverpool Mercury* laughed at the plan:

Sweet squires of the shuttle,
As ye guzzle and guttle,
Have some bowels for poor Liverpool!
Your great Ship Canal
Will produce a cabal,
Then stick to the jenny and mule.

Your sea scheme abandon
For rail-roads the land on:
And to save us from utter perdition,
Cut your throats if you like
But don't cut the dyke,
And this is our humble petition.

But in the interval between 1825 and 1882 Manchester had grown wealthy and powerful, determined to do things its own way. Meetings were held, money was subscribed, a bill was hurried through Parliament, and Lord Egerton, a kinsman of the Duke of Bridgewater, became chairman of the enterprise. It was estimated that the canal would cost £7,000,000, and some six years were spent in raising the money, preparing plans, and assembling the necessary equipment.

The new canal was by far the most expensive and most complex undertaken in Britain. From the beginning everything went wrong. The railways objected to the canal, and so all goods that came by railway for use in the canal construction were slow in arriving. The contractor died, and there was trouble with his executors. Torrential rains and floods hindered the work. In January, 1890, the Mersey and Irwell overflowed, and the work of months was destroyed in a single night. In November of the same year a great storm flooded six miles of the workings, with water pouring along the ditch in a wave ten feet high. In some places the water was forty feet deep, and three thousand men were thrown out of employment. The bad luck continued through the following year. The canal crossed over a maze of rivers and railways. It lay beneath the old Bridgewater Canal, and so Brindley's famous aqueduct, which had been in service since 1761, had to be pulled down, to make way for a new aqueduct which would permit the passage of large ships. The new aqueduct was formed in the shape of a swing bridge which, when big ships came down the Manchester Ship Canal, swung parallel to the direction of the canal, with the water in the swing bridge sealed at both ends. The astonishing conception worked well, and no one seemed particularly surprised at this new invention which gave one canal the power to spin in the air above another. Queen Victoria herself presided over the opening of the canal on May 21, 1894. There were speeches and parades, and Manchester rejoiced, while some of the financiers wondered whether they would ever get their money back, for the canal had cost nearly £15,000,000—more than twice the original estimate.

From the beginning the Manchester Ship Canal was a success. It filled a need. Revenue poured in. In 1900 revenue amounted to about £300,000, but it increased steadily with the years, and by 1950 it amounted to over £2,000,000. The Manchester Ship Canal proved conclusively that under certain circumstances a canal could perform services the railways were incapable of performing as efficiently. Efficiency became the watchword. The old privately owned canals, gently following the contours of the valleys, became an anachronism, and in 1929 it was decided to place most of the canals in central England under a single authority. Canal companies which had been in existence for more than a hundred years were amalgamated into a single company under the name of the Grand Union Canal. The new canal comprised the Grand Junction Canal (formed in 1793), the Leicestershire and Northamptonshire Union Canal (1793), the Warwick and Birmingham Canal (1793), the Warwick and Napton Canal (1794), the Grand Union Canal (1810), the Regent's Canal (1812), the Hertford Union Canal (1824), and the Birmingham and Warwick Junction Canal (1840). So it came about that a man could take a canal boat at Wapping and make his way to Birmingham on a single canal, where previously it had been necessary to go from one to another. Standardization came in, with all its advantages and its attendant horrors. Once there were some 12,000 miles of canals threading their way across England, Scotland, and Wales; now there are only 2,800 miles in active use, and soon there will be less.

Once long ago the old Duke of Bridgewater, grown so paunchy with age that he could stand upright only with difficulty, had stood on the banks of the Bridgewater Canal and watched the canal boats as they passed out of sight, laden with coal from the Worsley mines. He said nothing for a while, then took a pinch of snuff and said, "Well, they will last my time, but I see mischief in those damned tramroads."

There had been more mischief in the "damned tramroads" than he ever knew or guessed.

America pushes back the frontiers

From the time when white men first set foot on the shores of America they must have thought about canals. The eastern coast of America, so deeply indented, with so many rivers flowing into the Atlantic, with so many capes jutting out into the ocean, cried out for canals. No one knows any longer the name of the first American canal. Probably it was the canal cut across Long Island from Mecox Bay to Peconic Bay by Mongotucksee, the chief of the Montauk Indians, long before the white settlement of the country.

Mongotucksee means "Long Knife"; there were to be many long knives later, busily scraping at the earth to let the sea or the rivers in. As early as 1623 Myles Standish, the "little Pint Pot" who was placed in charge of the defenses of New Plymouth, dreamed of cutting a canal through the Isthmus of Cape Cod, so allowing the English shallops to meet the Dutch for trading at the head of Buzzards Bay. According to Johnson's *History of Cecil County, Maryland,* "as early as 1680, one Augustus Hermen, Lord of Bohemia Manor, contemplated the construction of a canal to connect Delaware and Chesapeake Bays." Men dreamed, but little came of their dreams; they made plans, but the plans were pigeonholed. In 1724 Cadwallader Colden, Surveyor of the Province of New York, realized that a canal could be dug between the Hudson River at Albany and Lake Erie at Buffalo, but the plan slumbered for nearly a hundred years. When at last it was carried out, it changed the face of New

York State, temporarily ruined Pennsylvania, and altered the course of history. More than anything else that 360-mile ditch contributed toward making New York the Empire State. But with the British in control there was little incentive for digging canals. The canal era came in with the Revolution, and then quite suddenly everyone seemed to be talking about a vast network of canals which would bring goods to the seaports from the frontier lands of the West. Franklin yearned for them, had indeed yearned for them almost since he could open his eyes. "Rivers are ungovernable things, especially in Hilly Countries," he wrote to the mayor of Philadelphia in 1772. "Canals are quiet and very manageable." Then he proceeded to outline a complicated canal system of his own, which would bring wealth to Philadelphia from all the wheatfields and coal mines around, and he was particularly in favor of a Susquehanna-Schuylkill canal. The next year Washington was discussing the feasibility of a canal joining the Potomac and Ohio rivers. Then the Revolutionary War came, and sometimes during the fighting Washington would find himself poring over maps and dreaming of peaceful canals, where now there was the tread of marching armies.

Washington was haunted by canals, as other men are haunted by dreams. Even before peace was declared he rushed off to make a long, dangerous tour of the Mohawk Valley, examining the portages and marking on his maps the places where canals might be built. He wrote to Chevalier de Castellux at Princeton on October 12, 1783:

> Prompted by these actual observations, I could not help taking a more extensive view of the vast inland navigation of these United States and could not but be struck by the immense extent and importance of it, and with the goodness of that Providence, which has dealt its favors to us with so profuse a hand. Would to God we had wisdom enough to improve them. I shall not rest contented until I have explored the western country, and traversed those lines, or great part of them, which have given bounds to a new empire.

A year later he carried out his plan of western exploration, and once again his journals are full of lengthy discussions about portages and canals. After a journey of 680 miles, most of it on horseback, he wrote to Jacob Read, the delegate from South Carolina to the Continental Congress, a long letter on the advantages of canals for binding the hinterland to the coastal regions:

> Extend the inland navigation of the eastern waters, communicate them as near as possible (by excellent roads) with those which run to the westward. Open these to the Ohio and such others as extend from Ohio towards Lake Erie, and we shall not only draw the produce of the western settlers, but the fur and peltry trades of the lakes also, to our ports (being the nearest and easiest of transportation) to the amazing increase of our exports, while we bind these people to a chain which can never be broken.

The letter was dated November 3, 1784, and by that time work was already beginning on the small seven-mile canal around the falls of the James River in Virginia. That was the year when Christopher Colles made a survey of the Mohawk Valley and submitted plans to the New York State Legislature for a canal joining the Hudson River and Lake Ontario. He was awarded the profits of the scheme if he would carry it out, but was unable to raise the necessary capital. He had used up all his money, and the legislature appropriated $125 to enable him to complete the survey, but nothing came of it. Money lay at the heart of the problem—the vast sums of money which would be necessary to bring a great canal to completion.

The first true canal in the country cost over a million dollars. This was the Santee Canal built in South Carolina to connect the Santee River with the headwaters of Cooper River, which falls into Charleston Harbor. The engineer in charge was a Swede, Christian Senf, who had come to America with Burgoyne's Hessian troops and fallen into American hands with the surrender at Saratoga; during the later years of the war he served as engineer with the South Carolina militia. He was a master craftsman of great energy and vast pride, who insisted on doing things his own way. The location he selected ran along a high dry ridge instead of along one of the Santee tributary streams, with the result that the canal when finished sometimes became unworkable in summer because it was impossible to provide sufficient water at the summit level. Also, he chose to run the canal through virgin forests. Nevertheless in 1793 he won the approval of the directors and started work on the canal.

Other men might have quailed before so difficult an undertaking, but Senf was in his element. With a huge labor force which sometimes amounted to a thousand Negro slaves, he supervised the whole project himself. There was trouble with the slaves, who were sometimes needed on the plantations, and the white workmen died off like flies in the feverish summers, but at length in 1800 the canal was completed, twenty-two miles long and thirty-five feet wide, with twelve locks and eight aqueducts carrying the canal on masonry bridges across the streams and swamps. It was the greatest engineering feat of its time.

It was a good time for building canals. The Little Falls Canal on the Mohawk River was begun in the same year that saw the beginning of the Santee Canal, but there was no Christian Senf to assume the role of taskmaster. It began slowly, with a force of three hundred men, who gave up after a few months because there were not sufficient funds to pay them. They began to work again at the end of the year. The canal took two years to build, half of it cut through solid rock, with five locks to carry the boats through a fall of forty feet. When it was opened on November 17, 1795, nine boats passed through toll free, and during the next thirty days "eight large boats, and one hundred and two small boats passed the Little Falls on the Mohawk and paid toll to the aggregate of £80. 10s." A greater achievement, rivaling the Santee, was the Middlesex Canal in Massachusetts. Begun in 1790 and completed fourteen years later, it was 27¼ miles long, with 7 aqueducts, 50 bridges and 20 locks. It cost $630,000, and in its time it was the largest canal built in America.

Men were dreaming of great canals cutting in straight lines across the continent. Washington had journeyed across the Allegheny Mountains and placed his stamp of approval on vast canal projects. Father Marquette, portaging through the swamps of Illinois, foresaw a canal between Lake Michigan and the Illinois River.

Thomas Jefferson had traced a canal route between Lake Erie's Cuyahoga River and the Big Beaver Creek which flows into the Upper Ohio. Everyone conjectured, drew up plans, debated, approved and saw visions, but there was no driving force, no one determined to push the project through to a conclusion.

Years later Gouverneur Morris remembered that he had celebrated the virtues of a canal joining the Hudson and the Great Lakes as early as 1777, but it was not until October, 1795, when he paid a visit to Scotland that he saw the vision in all its splendor. The Scotch canals fascinated him. "When I see this," he declared, "my mind opens to a view of wealth for the interior of America, which hitherto I had rather conjectured than seen." When the proud and fiery DeWitt Clinton became Mayor of New York, Gouverneur Morris interested him in the scheme. Clinton had become mayor at the youthful age of thirty-five. He put all his strength into the project, cut through obstacles, proclaimed that he would die rather than let the good people of New York suffer from the lack of a direct waterway to the Great Lakes.

There were endless delays, endless obstacles. Not until April 15, 1817, was an Act passed through the New York State Legislature permitting the construction of the canal, and it was two months later before the first contracts were signed. All through the summer of 1817 men worked in the dense forests and swamps, driving rows of stakes into the earth, from Albany to the west. The outer rows of stakes were sixty feet apart, indicating the land which had to be grubbed. There was an inner row of stakes forty feet apart, indicating the exact dimensions of the canal. Then came the borers who bored to a depth of twelve feet to learn the nature of the soil, so that the profiles could be made by the engineers. After the borers came the levelers. An army of workmen was digging, scraping, hauling, and cementing in forests where no pioneers had ever penetrated before, carving a sixty-foot swath across the land. Men died like flies when the canal line approached the swampy valley of the Seneca. They worked with primitive bulldozers and machines for hauling stumps, tree breakers and plows for cutting roots. In the

DeWitt Clinton, by Samuel F. B. Morse (Metropolitan Museum of Art)

summer of 1822 no one knew exactly where the canal would break on the shores of Lake Erie. Then there was a meeting in Benjamin Rathbun's tavern on Main Street, Buffalo, between the canal commissioners and the citizens of Buffalo and the neighboring town of Black Rock. DeWitt Clinton summed up the evidence and pronounced in favor of Buffalo. The next summer the canal was open from Rochester to Schenectady, and two years later the canal was completed. It had 82 locks for a drop of 571 feet, and everyone was saying it was the greatest engineering feat ever performed.

In the past trade with New York had been confined to the

valleys of the Hudson, Connecticut, and Raritan. Now all the wide basin of the Great Lakes was made tributary to New York.

On October 26, 1825, all of New York State celebrated the opening of the canal. A fine swift packet boat, built of Lake Erie red cedar, the *Seneca Chief,* set out from Lake Erie to New York. There was no telegraph in those days, and so cannon were placed at intervals along the route to carry the news to Albany, and along the Hudson to New York City. At ten o'clock the first signal gun was fired. At eleven o'clock the Albany gun rang out, and twenty-one minutes later New York heard that the canal had been officially opened. From Buffalo four ships began the long journey, headed by the *Seneca Chief* with DeWitt Clinton on board. There were two large brightly colored paintings hanging on the ship, one with a picture of Buffalo and the canal, the other showing DeWitt Clinton as Hercules, dressed in Roman costume, and resting from his labors. Behind the *Seneca Chief* came *The Young Lion of the West,* which was as good as a circus parade, for it carried a pair of eagles, a pair of wolves, a fox, a fawn, and four raccoons. For some reason there was a great desire to carry animals in the triumphal procession, and soon the *Seneca Chief* was joined by the *Noah's Ark,* another packet boat, which carried a restless black bear, two eagles, two fawns, several fish, and two Indian boys. When half the journey was accomplished a challenge rang out across the water:

"Who goes there?"

"Your brothers from the West, on the waters of the Great Lakes," came the answer.

"By what means have they been diverted so far from their natural course?"

"By the channel of the Grand Erie."

"By whose authority, and by whom, was the work of such magnitude accomplished?"

"By the authority and by the enterprise of the patriotic people of the State of New York."

So the procession passed along the canal with the signal guns booming, bands playing, church bells ringing day and night, and great feasts whenever the boats paused on their journey. DeWitt Clinton was the hero of the hour. President Jefferson had dismissed the project as a mad scheme, but the people of New York State knew better, and they had made DeWitt Clinton governor as a reward for risking his career. Now he stood on the bow of the *Seneca Chief,* a tall man with a grave dignity about him, and the light of triumph in his eyes. It was a hero's welcome, and no one who saw that bridal party of canalboats ever forgot it.

There were moments, however, when it was a little less than a triumph. They reached Little Falls at night, to see great bonfires roaring out of tar barrels along the edges of the cliff above the locks. At Rome they had employed tar barrels in a different way, pouring the tar into the canal as a mark of their annoyance because the canal was built half a mile south of the town. But Fort Plain outdid itself. At Wagner's Hotel a sumptuous dinner was spread across the entire length of the ballroom. There were thirty-two toasts, and the local schoolmaster jumped on the table after delivering a lengthy speech, and the whole table promptly collapsed. At Schenectady there was gloom, for everyone knew that the town, once the port of entry for goods going west, was at the mercy of the canal. The Union College cadets came to the canal bank, fired a welcoming salute, and then returned to the college. There were no toasts, no speeches. "The distinguished guests were received respectfully, but without enthusiasm, and conducted to a hotel where dinner was eaten in a sober manner." But there was little sobriety when they reached Albany. There were parades to the Capitol, congratulatory addresses, grand illuminations. Tables were set up on the gaily decorated Columbia Street Bridge for six hundred guests. DeWitt Clinton thanked everyone, smiled, bowed to the ladies, and enjoyed the fireworks. Then the procession moved on to New York, where people went mad with excitement. The fleet of canal barges sailed out to a point near Sandy Hook, formed a circle and celebrated "the wedding of the waters." On board the *Seneca Chief* were two brass-bound kegs of Lake Erie water, amounting to about five gallons, together with bottles of water from the Nile, the Ganges, the Indus, the Thames, the Seine, the Rhine, the Elbe, the Orinoco, the Columbia, the Río de la Plata, and four other rivers. The governor emptied the kegs and bottles into the salt waters of the Atlantic. It was a solemn moment, and he was profoundly aware of its solemnity as he intoned: "May the God of the Heavens and the earth smile propitiously on this work and render it subservient to the best interests of the human race." Everyone cheered, cannon boomed, and soon the *Seneca Chief* was turning her course back to Buffalo with a cask of salt water to pour into Lake Erie.

But before the second "wedding of the waters," New York was allowed to greet its governor. A procession five miles long marched down Broadway to the Battery to welcome him. The tall, handsome governor was greeted as though he were a miracle worker, as though he alone with his bare hands had carved the canal. In the processions people were chanting:

> 'Tis done! 'Tis done! The mighty chain
> Which joins bright Erie to the Main,
> For ages shall perpetuate
> The glory of our native state!

Better songs about the canal were to come later, but everyone was too delirious with joy to care. City Hall was ablaze with twenty-three hundred candles and lamps. There was a great ball, and during supper the guests were invited to see a miniature canalboat, made entirely of maple sugar, floating on genuine Erie water. DeWitt Clinton made speeches, and listened to so many that he fell asleep, and soon it was time to make the return journey.

The New Yorkers knew they had scored a victory. They knew that the Grand Canal would change their way of life. The canal spawned the new states in the Ohio Valley and the Northwest Territory, and forced Philadelphia to yield to New York as the first port in the nation. It bound the West to the East, forging a bond of common interest between the states on both sides of the Appalachian barrier. Once the legislators of New York had called the canal a "gutter," but now they spoke reverently of "Clinton's ditch." For years they had fumbled, argued, fought delaying actions. They had described the scheme as a ruse of the Clintonians to capture the state, and said he must be mad to think of digging a ditch nearly four hundred miles long. Now at last they bowed to the inevitable and joined the bandwagon.

The New Yorkers had good cause for their jubilation. That enormous ditch, 363 miles long, 40 feet wide and 4 feet deep, more than half of it cut through forest and swamp, paid back its original cost of $7,000,000 within twelve years. The project had been a New York State venture from the beginning, with money raised partly from a lottery and partly from a $1 tax on all persons who traveled a hundred miles or more by steamboat. Soon it was earning so much money for the state that sober-minded legislators were suggesting that the income from the canal was sufficient to supplant all real-estate taxes. Within ten years it had to be widened. Until the railways came, it was the highroad to the West, the great blood vessel pouring nourishment and wealth into New York. It was successful beyond men's dreams, with branch canals proliferating from it, and soon Buffalo, which had been no more than a village twenty-five years earlier, and Rochester, which had been a mere clearing with a single log cabin, became vast cities.

Now for the first time there was an all-water route to the Western prairies. Freight rates dropped fantastically—from $32 a ton for a hundred miles by wagon to $1 a ton by canal steamer. By 1836 there were three thousand canalboats plying the canal, leaving Albany at all hours of the day and night, jammed with immigrants making their way to the prairies where they were to become the founding fathers of new cities, new commonwealths. From Buffalo the immigrant ships sailed across the blue Lake Erie to Detroit. In May, 1836, ninety steamboats arrived in Detroit, one of them, the *United States,* bringing seven hundred new settlers. Everyone benefited, and the owners of the lake steamers earned nearly the whole cost of their vessels in a single year.

With the Erie Canal showing a profit even before it was finished, the race for building bigger and better canals began.

Ohio was the great grain center, a vast sprawling frontier land, ambitious to send its wheat to New York and to all the states on the Eastern seaboard and overseas. In 1823, when the Erie Canal was nearing completion, the Governor of Ohio summoned James Geddes, who had been DeWitt Clinton's surveyor, and sent him out to survey the lands between the lake and the Ohio River. Geddes settled upon five possible routes, and in a burst of confidence the Ohio State Legislature decided to dig ditches along two of the traces he had marked out on the map. The Ohio and Erie Canal linked Cleveland with Portsmouth by way of the Cuyahoga, Tuscarawas, Licking, and Scioto rivers, to the dismay of the people of Marietta who, belonging to the senior colony in Ohio, thought they had a prior claim for an Erie-Marietta Canal. Another route marked out by Geddes joined Cincinnati and Toledo by way of the Great Miami, Auglaize, and Maumee rivers—this became the Miami and Erie Canal. Both projects were audacious undertakings, and one might have expected them to be cut one at a time. The Ohio State Legislature decided to cut them simultaneously, or nearly simultaneously.

The opening celebrations were planned for July 4, 1825, Ohio's twenty-first birthday. At Licking Summit, three miles from Newark, Governor DeWitt Clinton and Governor Jeremiah Morrow stood before a crowd of ten thousand people and each solemnly lifted a shovelful of earth, while other dignitaries contended for the honor of digging the third. Thomas Ewing, the orator of the day, proclaimed the greatness of the hour and the greatness of the infant state, which had dared to accept the vast wealth which would surely flow to it from the abundance of the canal. Such speeches, of course, had fallen from the lips of Assyrian kings, Egyptian Pharaohs and Roman emperors, but Thomas Ewing almost outdid them. He said:

> See what my country has done in her juvenile state! And if she has achieved this gigantic enterprise in infancy, what will she not effect in

the maturity of her strength, when her population becomes exuberant and her whole territory in full cultivation. And your sister states, and the civilized world, will be astonished. It will be a spectacle, unprecedented and amazing. An infant wielding the club of Hercules, and managing the lever of Archimedes with irresistible power. When the eagle, in its first flight from the aerie soars to the heavens, looks at the sun with an unfailing eye, and bears in its talons the thunderbolts of Jove, who will not admire this sublime sight?[1]

Then bands played, and troops stood at attention, and soon the Irish laborers were spitting on their hands, seizing mattocks and shovels and digging deep in the earth, and mule teams strained at scoop buckets. And there was no end to the celebrations. The two governors went off to Dayton and Cincinnati to preside over the celebrations for the digging of the Miami and Erie Canal. On July 21st they were at Middletown, but they were only warming up for their triumphal tour, which led them amidst the ringing of bells and firing of cannon through Chillicothe, Circleville, Lancaster, Zanesville, Cambridge, and a score of other towns.

It was a time when everyone believed that canal building was a panacea for all the ills of society, and a guerdon for the future. Even before the canals were opened, when there were only a few short cuts later to be linked together, Ohio was dizzy with success. Ohio farmers and their sons, with gangs of Irish and German laborers, worked through the sweltering summers for a pay of thirty cents a day, plus board and a few jiggers of whisky, until they were struck down by malaria. They followed the general plan of the Erie Canal, cutting a swath sixty feet wide, for a canal which would be forty feet wide at the waterline, twenty-six feet wide at the bottom and four feet deep. The dimensions had become standard, and no one guessed that in a few years all the canals would have to be widened, and that in a few more years competition with the railways would produce insuperable problems.

In those days only a sixth of Ohio had been cleared and cultivated: the paths of the canals stretched sometimes through un-

[1] R. Carlyle Buley, *The Old Northwest: Pioneer Period, 1815–1840* (Indiana Historical Society, Indianapolis, 1950). I, 495.

mapped wilderness. Some excavations were in rock, some under water. The Erie Canal provided few serious engineering difficulties, but the Ohio and Erie Canal challenged the skill of the engineers, who had to carry their canal over rivers and secure an adequate water supply at higher levels by means of reservoirs and feeders, and all this without concrete or structural steel, with earth, wood, stone, rubble, and clay alone. The canal crossed the Tuscarawas by a dam and recrossed it by an aqueduct. The work went on through the snows of the winter of 1826–1827, and though it slowed up during the pestilential summer of the following year, Governor Trimble was able to leave Portage Summit in the brightly painted *State of Ohio* for Cleveland thirty-eight miles away on July 3, 1827. To celebrate the completion of this link in the canal chain, the people of Cleveland came out on the streets, there were prayers and processions and public feasts, and once again the orators spoke of the infant Hercules with his club, now a giant and in the full strength of his manhood.

When the canal reached Chillicothe in October, 1831, eight thousand people lined the banks of the canal, crowded the doors and windows, and covered the roofs of the houses to watch the procession of beflagged ships with more than five hundred ladies and gentlemen on board. The Chillicothe band played, guns roared, everyone yelled and waved flags. The Rose Bowl parades of our own time may be more magnificent, but "John Buckeye" was consumed with admiration for the feat which brought towns and villages deep into the interior close to the sea lanes of the world; and he had a right to rejoice.

Sometimes there was no rejoicing; sometimes there were threats of war.

The dispute between Ohio and Michigan over the northern Ohio boundary nearly led to war in 1835. The militia was called out, generals consulted their maps and debated future campaigns. Both Ohio and Michigan coveted the strategic corner of Lake Erie and the lake port at the Maumee mouth. Michigan had 2,400 troops under arms, ready to pounce on the Ohio forces preparing to infiltrate the territory. There followed a war of wits, words, fists, and some inaccurate gunfire. A man called Two Stickney resisted arrest with a penknife and was reported to have been "mortally wounded." An Ohio flag was torn down and tied to horses' tails, and the Governor of Michigan promised "hospitable graves" to anyone who ventured out of Ohio over the disputed border. But in the end the war was won by Ohio with the loss of one dead horse, and then the surveyors came in to draw the line of the canal to Toledo.

Canals made strange bedfellows. The hard-drinking and easy-spending Irish and German laborers, reinforced by a sprinkling of Norwegians, found themselves working with the pietistic Christian communists who called themselves Zoarites. The Zoarites of Tuscarawas County believed that the Holy Ghost spoke through the mouth of a former Württemberg schoolteacher, Joseph Michael Bimmeler. Their communist society was incorporated under the laws of the State of Ohio. Their elder brethren lived in the Garden of the New Jerusalem, with twelve paths representing the twelve tribes of Israel radiating from the Tree of Life. They were good farmers and good ditchdiggers, and they earned $20,000 cutting a ditch across their fields, and made further profits by selling supplies to contractors. With the money they built a tannery, a brickyard, and an ore furnace, and soon their leather, bricks, and ironware were carried down on the canal barges to market.

The Zoarites, always singing hymns, were the most peaceful canal diggers, the Irish the most quarrelsome. Ulstermen fought with the men of Cork; the "Corkians" and the "Fardowns" kept up a fierce guerrilla warfare, intermittent during the week, exploding on payday. For months the battles raged murderously, with an intensity which frightened the big gentle Norskies. Bodies vanished in the great heaps of earth lining the canal bank, never to be seen again. The war cries of the Irish were more terrifying than the war cries of the Indians. Even without these wars, mortality was high. Men died from malaria and cholera, from powder blasts, from the kicks of the heavy mules hauling the scoops and dredges. They calculated that one man died for every six miles of canal.

The work went on, with canals entering more and more into the life of the country. Canals were intended to bring remote country districts close to the ocean, but their main effect at the beginning was to bring about intercourse between the big cities and the interior. Canals introduced a new way of life, warm, exotic, audacious, and uncomfortable. Showboats tied up at the wharves, and soon the songs of New York were being sung on the remote plains of Ohio, Indiana, and Michigan. Canal barges crowded with merchandise became huge floating emporiums, laden with the latest dresses, whalebone corsets, jimcrack jewelry, and agricultural implements. Captains of barges saluted each other with musical blasts from their horns, while their wives hung out washing on clotheslines and looked after the pigs and chickens on board.

The first canalboats were simple keelboats with pointed bows and sterns, but change came quickly. Soon they were blunt-nosed, wide-beamed, with cabin walls rising six feet above the hull, and the passenger boats were garishly decorated, following the tradition of the Conestoga wagons and stagecoaches. Usually in the bows there was a small cabin for the crew, then came the ladies' dressing room and in the middle and rear were the saloon, which served as cabin for the men, dining room, sleeping parlor, promenade, and card room. Men slept in narrow bunks, three in a tier, and sometimes eighty were crowded in berths meant for forty. People slept on the floors, and coughed and choked during the long night. There was little ventilation, and in summer the mosquitoes found wonderful breeding grounds on the still waters of canals.

Most of the canal boats traveled slowly. Those on the Erie Canal traveled at the exact speed a team of horses would make, so that a trip from New York to Buffalo took about five days. The luxuriously fitted packet boats traveled only a little faster, averaging perhaps a mile an hour more speed. The regular line boats, overcrowded, unventilated, packed with immigrants, who brought their own food and bedding, were miserable conveyances. Men could die of boredom on them, for there was none of the excitement of steamboats. The young bloods sometimes jumped ashore at bridge crossings or locks, to wander along the towpaths for a space, but the even tenor of the slow progress was rarely broken. Horace Greeley remembered the miseries of the line boats. "I say nothing about the good old times," he said, "but if anyone would recall the good old line boats, I object."

The Erie Canal had burst a passage through to the Great Lakes, but in all the states south of New York the frenzy of canal building went on. There was a Chesapeake and Delaware Canal, which had a long history, going back to the day in 1786 when Benjamin Franklin, James Madison, and Benjamin Rush met in Wilmington to consider canal plans. There was no short route from Philadelphia, only the long journey by stagecoach or a four-hundred-mile sea voyage around Cape Charles. They saw clearly the need for a canal cutting across the isthmus of the peninsula from the Delaware River to Chesapeake Bay, but nothing came of their plans until 1799, when Maryland chartered the Chesapeake and Delaware Canal Company with a capital stock of $500,000. Surveys were made, but work did not start for another twenty-five years. It might never have started if it had not been for lotteries and financial grants from Maryland, Pennsylvania, and the Federal Government.

The northern tip of Chesapeake Bay curls eastward in the direction of Delaware Bay to a point where there are only twenty miles of flat and marshy land separating the two inland waterways. From the map it looks as though nothing could be easier than cutting a canal through land as flat as a table top. The work, done entirely by pick and shovel, proved to be costly and difficult. For some distance the route followed St. Georges Creek and its marshes. The engineers constructed a bank along the side of the channel to hold the water and to serve as a towpath for the mules and their drivers, but the effect of the bank was to flood the lowlands to the north, with the result that there was an epidemic of malaria, hundreds of Irish immigrant workers died, and all the neighboring counties were affected. There was trouble, too, with litigation over the right of the original surveyor to retain his job. Fired for neglect and incompetence, he fought back through the courts and was eventually awarded damages of a quarter of a million dollars.

The canal was completed and officially opened on October 17, 1829. It had cost $2,000,000, but its prosperity seemed assured. Tolls two years later ran to $2,600 a week. Soon the people of Delaware City, at the eastern terminus of the canal, were beginning to think they would rival Philadelphia as a port. They saw the coal barges coming down the Susquehanna River, entering the Chesapeake and Delaware Canal, and tying up at Delaware City, before being towed by steam tugs to Philadelphia, and other cities of the East, as a source of their fortunes; but it never quite happened as they had hoped. Philadelphia retained its pre-eminence, and Delaware City failed to rival it.

The Delaware and Chesapeake Canal is still in use. After the canal had remained a privately owned toll-collecting waterway for ninety years, the government decided to purchase it. President Theodore Roosevelt, delighted with his success in Panama, appointed a commission to report on the route with the thought of making it a free and open waterway. Nothing happened until 1919, when the Federal Government purchased the entire property for $2,514,000, which was only a little more than it cost to build. Now only a few coal barges move between those quiet shores: mostly the traffic is in tankers.

The fever to dig longer and better canals led to some strange adventures, notably in Pennsylvania, where a canal was built which went uphill, with the help of a portage railway. From the beginning the Pennsylvania Canal was a monstrosity. Four mountain rivers flow across the state—the Susquehanna, the Juniata, the Conemaugh, and the Kiskiminetas, and an attempt was made to canalize all these rivers; but while the Erie Canal had to surmount an altitude of some 500 feet by means of locks in a distance of 360 miles, the Pennsylvania Canal would have to surmount an altitude of 2,300 feet in a distance of some 400 miles. The people of Pennsylvania were determined to have a canal, whatever the cost, and on February 25, 1826, Governor John Shulze signed "an Act to provide for the Commencement of a Canal, to be constructed at the expense of the state, and to be styled the Pennsylvania Canal."

From that moment there was no turning back. The problem was to connect Philadelphia with Pittsburgh, and it was solved by introducing every mode of travel known at that time—horsedrawn railroad, two long stretches of canal and ten inclined planes, with the traveler changing cars at every plane. When it was completed, the Pennsylvania Canal was something of a triumph, for it offered a trip of 394 miles in four days over some of the wildest mountains in the state. The passenger stepped into a canalboat, or rather a section of a canalboat, at Third and Walnut streets, Philadelphia, and he stepped out of a canalboat in Pittsburgh after crossing the Alleghenies. It was safe, and it was astonishing, but it was only with the greatest license that the passenger could say he had made the journey by canal.

The first stretch of the Pennsylvania Canal was made by horse-drawn boat over a railway ninety miles long from Philadelphia to Columbia, a town on the Susquehanna River. Near Philadelphia there was a hill: the boat was carried over the hill by means of a cable over an inclined plane 2,805 feet long. The cable was operated by a stationary steam engine. Thereafter the horses took charge until the boat arrived at Columbia, where it traveled for the next 172 miles to Hollidaysburg. The canal was 4 feet deep, 40 feet wide at the top and 28 feet wide at the bottom, and there were 108 locks —a lock almost every mile and a half. The next step was the most audacious, for between Hollidaysburg and Johnstown at the summit of the Alleghenies the mountains rose 2,300 feet above sea level along precipitous broken slopes, and the promoters were faced with the task of carrying the boats up 1,400 feet and then dropping them some 1,170 feet. The boats were lifted up the inclined planes with the help of two 35-horsepower steam engines, five inclined planes going up and five going down. The rest of the journey from Johnstown to Pittsburgh was performed on a canal even more cluttered with locks than the canal between Columbia and Hollidaysburg—there were 66 locks over a distance of 104 miles.

In 1842 Charles Dickens made the journey over the Portage Railroad and reported that it was entirely enjoyable. He wrote in his *American Notes:*

> On Sunday morning we arrived at the foot of the mountain, which is crossed by rail road. There are ten inclined planes, five *as*cending and five *de*scending; the carriages are dragged up the former and let slowly down the latter by stationary engines; the comparatively level spaces between being traversed sometimes by horse and sometimes by engine power, as the case demands. Occasionally the rails are laid upon the extreme verge of a giddy precipice; and looking from the carriage window the traveller gazes sheer down without a stone or scrap of fence between, into the mountain depths below. The journey is very carefully made, however, only two carriages travelling together; and while proper precautions are taken is not to be dreaded for its dangers.

It is said that there were never any serious accidents along the thirty-six-mile Portage Railroad.

The Pennsylvanians were wildly jubilant when the first boat leaped over the Alleghenies fifty years to the month since Washington had issued his great call for a Virginia waterway. Soon they were building more waterways, so that by 1840 there were nearly a thousand miles of canals in the possession of the state. Unfortunately, the cost of running the Pennsylvania Canal was prohibitive, and when the railways came in more than half of the Pennsylvania Canal system fell into disuse.

The Pennsylvania Canal was begun in 1826 and completed eight years later. The Chesapeake and Ohio Canal was begun in 1828 and never completed—the waterway gave up the ghost when it came within sight of the Allegheny Mountains. It took thirty-two years to span the distance of 184 miles from tidewater to Cumberland, Maryland, and it cost $14,000,000. From the beginning it was a white elephant, and of all the canals built in America it suffered the most miserable fate.

Perhaps it was the fault of Washington, who was consumed with the desire to see a canal system connecting the Potomac with the Great Lakes. Also, he wanted a ship canal to make the Potomac navigable to Cumberland. Accordingly, in 1784 he became president of the Potomac Canal Company, and ordered surveys to be made. Nothing came of the surveys, and at the time of his death active interest in the canal fell off, only to be revived around 1816, when the mania for canal digging was at its height. At last, in 1824, the Chesapeake and Ohio Canal Company was incorporated, and capitalized at $6,000,000. Two years later it was decided that the time had come to start digging the canal which Washington had envisioned as the road to westward expansion.

On July 4, 1828, President John Quincy Adams was invited to perform the opening ceremony. Accompanied by a guard of honor, his cabinet, and some survivors of the Revolutionary War, he sailed on the steamboat *Surprise* to the Great Falls of the Potomac near Georgetown, and then disembarked near the remnants of the old unfinished canal begun by Washington's Potomac Canal Company. There were the usual interminable speeches. Someone remarked incautiously that "the canal would remain when all other vestiges of glory have disappeared from the earth." Then it was the President's turn to speak. He smiled, took a spade from the hands of Mr. Mercer, the president of the Chesapeake and Ohio Canal Company, and began a long oration on the purpose of the canal, and the benefits which would surely arise. "To subdue the earth," he declared, "is pre-eminently the purpose of this undertaking, to the accomplishment of which the first stroke of this spade is now to be struck. That it should be struck by this hand, I invite you now to witness."

When Nero struck his golden spade into the earth near Corinth, blood spurted. When John Quincy Adams struck his iron spade into the earth near the Great Falls something far worse happened —he struck a root. Undeterred, he tried again. He struck three or four more roots, then threw down the spade, removed his hat and coat, picked up the spade, and made another vigorous thrust into the ground. This time he was more successful, and there was a burst of cheering. That night the President wrote up his diary. He remembered that it had been an uncommonly cold day, he had felt strangely nervous and he had made a completely unremarkable speech which did him no credit. He was glad he had taken off his coat. He thought the incident had "struck the fancy of the spectators more than all the flowers of rhetoric in my speech, and diverted their attention from the stammering and hesitation of a deficient memory."

Soon everyone was wishing the canal had never been begun. By the summer of 1831 only twenty miles of the canal were completed. The company was in financial difficulties, and the government was preparing to withdraw from the project. In the following year the Federal Government withdrew completely from the project, leaving Maryland to assume the whole responsibility. By 1837 construction had been finished to one hundred miles west of Georgetown, but since that was the year of a depression progress became increasingly slow. At last, on October 10, 1850, the canal was opened to through traffic. It had reached Cumberland, and there it stopped. It was 184 miles long, 68 feet wide, 6 feet deep, and it climbed an elevation of 609 feet with the help of 73 locks. For some years it was used for transporting coal from the Cumberland mines to Washington, but it never paid its way. Today only a few traces of the canal remain—some rickety footbridges, and here and there pools of stagnant water, and banks choked with sedges. Never was $14,000,000 so cavalierly thrown down the drain.

But if the Chesapeake and Ohio Canal was a failure, there were great successes to be recorded in other parts of America. Great cities arose as the offspring of canals. Among them was Chicago.

In 1778 only one man lived at Checaugaux (Chicago), a French fur trader called Jean Baptiste Point de Saible. A fort was built there in 1803, but the settlement that sprang up around it was destroyed in the Indian massacre of 1812. Rebuilding proceeded slowly, and in 1825 Chicago was still an unimportant village with only fourteen taxpayers on the tax rolls. But in 1822 the Illinois Legislature passed a canal bill and set up a commission of five members to survey the route for a canal between the Illinois River and Lake Michigan. No one was very excited by the canal, and in

March, 1833, the canal commission was quietly abolished. It was generally believed that there was no need for a canal, and very little need for a town at Chicago. Then in 1834 Joseph Duncan, who had worked for the Illinois and Michigan Canal while in Congress, became governor, and immediately announced that in his view Chicago offered great advantages for canal building, and that a canal was preferable to railroads, which "are kept in repair at very heavy expense and will last but about fifteen years." In his campaign for the canal he was actively assisted by a young Whig representative in the State Assembly—Abraham Lincoln. Duncan marshaled his forces, and on Independence Day, 1836, the obscure little town of Chicago with a population of perhaps four thousand men celebrated noisily the first spade of earth turned for the new Illinois and Michigan Canal.

From miles around people had gathered to watch the spectacle. Cannons boomed and horse pistols were fired, while the townspeople crowded into three boats which moved up the river to where the South Fork joins the South Branch, where today Archer Avenue crosses Ashland Avenue. It was not far from the place where Father Marquette passed his first terrible winter. It was the year when the total exports of Chicago amounted to exactly $1,000.64. The engineers were saying that it would cost $8,000,000 to dig the canal and clear the Chicago River, but in the impoverished little town no one seemed to care.

Almost from the moment when the first spade was thrust into the earth, Chicago's wealth and population began to increase by leaps and bounds. Long ago men had foreseen that the Chicago Portage was one of the keys of the continent, necessary to connect the Great Lakes with the Gulf of Mexico. Workmen came from Canada and New England; they stepped off the immigrant ships from Ireland and were sent to work on the canal. By the end of 1838 there were over 2,000 men at work, and soon there were so many applicants for work that instead of paying $40 a month per man and $80 per yoke of oxen, wages dropped to $16 per man and $45 per yoke of oxen. The work was backbreaking, and in the long hot summers there were days when almost no work was done—most of the labor force was suffering from malaria and the unknown diseases which spread out of the miasma of the bottom lands.

Already the engineers of the Erie Canal were regretting they had made it forty feet wide. Nearly all the canals begun in the thirties were sixty feet wide, and the Illinois and Michigan Canal was no exception. It was six feet deep and thirty-six feet wide at the bottom, and took twelve years to complete. By this time the population of Chicago had increased fivefold to twenty thousand people.

On April 10, 1848, the canal was ceremonially opened, and a few days later the *General Thornton,* loaded with sugar from New Orleans, having climbed up the Mississippi and Illinois rivers, made its way along the whole length of the canal from La Salle to Chicago, and went on to Buffalo. Nothing like this had ever happened before. Only the previous December President James K. Polk had declared that he looked forward to a waterway joining the Pacific and the Atlantic. "Rend America asunder and unite the binding sea!" he cried. But though the oceans remained unjoined, there was now a canal which bound the Gulf of Mexico to Lake Michigan.

The new canal was a financial success from the beginning. In 1848 Chicago's exports jumped to $10,700,000. Chicago grew rich on the wealth that flowed in by canalboat. By 1871 the canal was beginning to outlive its usefulness, and the city fathers ordered that the overflow of Chicago's sewerage should be poured into it: pumps were installed to empty "black water" into the canal. By the 1890's the canal was slowly giving up its life. It had served its purpose, and brought vast wealth to the city, and was ready to die. Of all the canals which have left their mark on history, it had the shortest life. It died, and in the mysterious way of canals came to life again many years afterward, when the State of Michigan decided to re-open it. Some time later it was taken over by the Federal Government, which completed the present nine-foot canalized waterway in 1933. Today it is a major link in the Lakes to Gulf Waterway system, and one of the most heavily used routes in the country.

Traffic had increased from 1.7 million tons in 1914 to 23.4 million tons in 1956, and a duplicate set of locks is being recommended to handle the traffic.

Little is now left of the great canals which caused so much excitement in the thirties and forties of the last century. The Ohio and Erie took eight years to build, and the Miami and Erie twenty years, but within forty years of being built both these canals were being abandoned. Floods and storms tore them apart. The deluge of 1913 washed away the aqueducts: soon the canal lands were being rented out to farmers. Here and there some trace of them remains, and a stretch at Massillon still bears traffic. At Dayton and Cincinnati nearly all traces of the canal have gone, but the Ohio and Erie Canal still wanders through the heart of Akron. Here and there, too, small strips of the canal have been preserved for boating and fishing, and some of the old stone locks survive as memorials to an age before the coming of the railways. The old Erie Canal did better than most. Down to 1882, when toll charges were abolished, it had cost $78,862,153 to maintain, but the total receipts during this period amounted to $121,461,871—a clear profit to the state. Today nothing remains of the original Erie Canal except a bare fifteen miles of scattered ditches, stagnant and covered with green slime, running through cornfields. Between 1903 and 1918 a new canal was dug, largely parallel to the Erie Canal, and called the New York State Barge Canal. It was wider and deeper and could carry heavier ships, but there were many who regretted the passing of the old canal, which had been so much a part of history.

At their peak in the early 1850's there were 4,500 miles of canals in use in the United States. By 1880 over 2,000 miles had been abandoned. Gradually all over the land the canals dried up, caved in, and filled with weeds. By 1908 there were barely 2,000 miles of canal in existence, for the railroads were successfully drying up all water-borne commerce. Gradually the importance of canal building to provide the cheapest available form of transportation became recognized, and a staggering revival took place in the thirties. Old canals were reopened; new ones were dug, and all kinds of modern improvements were added to make them more efficient, with the result that traffic on the American waterways had grown from 8.6 billion ton miles in 1929 to 109.3 billion ton miles in 1956. Today there are over 22,000 miles of canals in America:

Under 6 feet in depth. These are largely natural river channels kept open to relatively shallow depths by minor maintenance operations, but include some older canalized waterways with locks and dams. Of little commercial importance but used by recreational craft.	6,700 miles
6 feet to 9 feet in depth. Canals and natural rivers. Generally feeders to major waterways.	3,500 miles
9 feet to 14 feet in depth. This is the active inland and intracoastal canal and waterway system which carries the great bulk of commercial tonnage. It includes the canalized Ohio and Illinois rivers and the Mississippi.	9,800 miles
Over 14 feet. These are largely the coastal rivers and channels, such as the Mississippi below Baton Rouge and the Houston Ship Channel, which carry ocean-going shipping.	2,100 miles

The canal has changed its nature. Now that men have mastered the power of the sun, we may expect to see the great rivers tamed and converted into canals, flowing at a rate which men can control. The ancient emperors hoped to change the face of nature, and did no more than scratch their names in sand. Already in embryo we can see the shape of things to come—the Rhine, the Danube, the Yangtze, and the Yellow rivers, the Indus and the Ganges, the Mississippi and the Colorado, all refashioned into canals and placed at the service of man. On the St. Lawrence Seaway and on the Volga we see already, on the mirroring waters, the strange stark features of the formidable future.

Panama: the sea and the jungle

About the time that Ponce de León was searching for the Fountain of Youth in Florida, a thickset young man from Jerez de los Caballeros was leading an expedition across the Isthmus of Darien, searching for the fabled lands of the East. He was very tall and well built, with reddish-gold hair and beard, and he walked with sinewy grace of movement. He had been a fencing master, and some obscure quarrel with swords had led him to America. Like Columbus, and twenty other explorers, he believed that once he reached America he would find China and India with all their treasures of gold and silk and jewels lying almost within reach.

One day toward the end of 1512 he encountered near Antigua del Darien a small principality ruled by a chieftain named Comogre. The chieftain welcomed him to his palace, a vast building supported on pillars and surrounded by a stone wall. Inside the palace were granaries and storerooms and great chambers where the desiccated bodies of former rulers, wrapped in finely woven cotton and adorned with gold and pearls, hung from the rafters. Comogre was friendly. His eldest son Panquiaco was even more friendly. When the young explorer spoke of treasure, Panquiaco pointed south and suggested that if the Spaniards would only go beyond the mountains they would come upon another sea: on the borders of this sea men used gold vessels for drinking and eating, and built ships only a little smaller than Spanish ships. Panquiaco asked where the swords and armor of the Spaniards came from, and was told they came from the province of Biscay. "You will find that those people of the other sea," said Panquiaco, "have more gold than all of the iron in Biscay."

So on September 1, 1513, an expedition set out to discover the land of gold. They sailed from Antigua in a brigantine and nine large canoes, with 190 Spaniards and 800 Indians, and a pack of bloodhounds trained to attack any enemies who crossed their path. At Puerto Carreta, sixty miles northward along the coast, they landed and turned westward to cross the Cordilleras. It was rough territory, progress was slow, and there were frequent skirmishes with Indians. Surprisingly, some of the Indians wore breastplates of gold. For three weeks the Spaniards plodded on, sometimes going naked through the swamps, holding their clothes on shields above their heads, losing so many men from wounds and sickness that only sixty-seven remained when, at about ten o'clock on the morning of September 25th, they saw the blue waters of the Pacific. As they stood there on the hills, weary and bloodstained, they knew they were the first men from Europe to set eyes on *la mar del sud.* The leader of the expedition was Vasco Núñez de Balboa, and beside him stood Francisco Pizarro, the future conqueror of Peru. At Balboa's feet was the famous bloodhound Leoncico, the "little lion," which drew a captain's pay and accompanied him on all his journeys.

After they had turned their faces to the south and knelt and prayed, Balboa said to his companions: "You see now that the words of Panquiaco are true concerning the great riches of the lands to the south."

Four days later they reached the shores of the ocean, and Balboa solemnly took possession of the Pacific and all the islands in it and the lands surrounding it in the name of King Ferdinand of Spain and his daughter Juana, carving the letters *F* and *J* on all the trees around the cross which marked the place where he had first looked down on the ocean. Balboa believed he had reached the waters of Cipango and Cathay, and somewhere close by there must be the Straits of Panama, already marked in the early maps—the straits are shown on the Mappemonde of Martin Waldseemüller in 1507, the John Ruysch map in 1508, the Hunt-Lenox globe, engraved by an anonymous artist about 1510, and Johannes Schöner's map in 1515. At that moment China seemed to be only a day's journey away.

The discovery of the Pacific was greeted in Spain with jubilation. Balboa was given the title of Adelantado of the Coast of the South Sea, and honors were heaped upon him. Five years later, as the result of court intrigues, he was executed in the miserable little town of Acla, once an Indian battlefield, not far from Puerto Carreta, the starting point of his journey across the isthmus. His last words were: "I always desired to serve the king and enlarge his dominions with all my power and strength."

Balboa had shown the way, and it remained for his successor, the treacherous Pedrarias Dávila, the governor of the province of Castilla de Oro, to make use of the discovery. Pedrarias was a middle-aged infantry officer, who had served with distinction in the Moorish wars in Spain and Africa, and was known for his ferocious temper. He was responsible for the execution of Balboa and was determined to show himself at least the equal of that intrepid adventurer. Some months after the execution of Balboa he crossed the isthmus and sailed up the coast until he came to a deep and shelving bay, where he cast anchor, attracted by the rolling country lying between the coast and the blue summits of the Cordilleras. Here he found a small fishing village beside a stream, and when he asked the Indians the name of the place he was told it was Panama, meaning "abounding in fish." He was under orders from the king to found a settlement on the Pacific coast. Two years later the small settlement, consisting of only a few huts on the plain, was made a city by royal decree of Charles V. The conquest of the Pacific had begun.

Panama grew slowly. This small frontier settlement, clinging to the isthmus, might have vanished from the map if Pizarro had not conquered Peru: then through Panama came the great cavalcades bearing gold and jewels from the mines of the Incas. A road was built from Panama to Nombre de Dios on the Atlantic coast, cutting through the jungle, roughly paved, with guard posts along the way, for sometimes the Indians came out of the forests and attacked the heavy lumbering carts laden with spoil from the Incas. And still the search went on for a waterway through the isthmus, to avoid the dangerous and expensive portage. In 1534 Charles V directed a survey to be made along the valley of the Chagres in the hope that his engineers would be able to map a short cut across the isthmus, but nothing came of it. The Spanish historian Francisco Lopez de Gómara, writing his history of the Indians in 1551, declared that there were at least four places where a canal could be built, and named Darién, Panama, Nicaragua, and Tehuantepec. "There are mountains," he wrote proudly, "but there are also hands. If determination is not lacking, means will not fail. The Indians themselves will provide the means; and the King of Spain, seeking the wealth of Indian commerce, will find everything which is possible is also easy."

Charles V was a man of iron, but Philip II lacked his inflexible temper. He ordered a survey of the isthmus in 1556, and when he saw the difficulties of building a canal, he observed, "God has shown His will by creating a continual isthmus." For nearly three hundred years the Spanish waged war across the length and breadth of South America, while the dreams of a canal gathered dust in the archives in Madrid.

The English, too, had their eyes on the isthmus. The Earl of Warwick, responsible for settlements in Massachusetts and Connecticut, dispatched the *Seaflower* under charter from Charles I to colonize the Caribbean islands of Providence and St. Andrew, and with luck to take over portions of Central America. Ninety Puritans, all men, sailed from England in 1630 and settled in the islands which lay across the route of the Spanish treasure ships from Porto Bello. For eleven years they held on to these small toeholds in the Atlantic, until the Spanish pushed them into the sea. The Puritans, however, had shown the way to Sir Henry Morgan and the Buccaneers who dreamed of setting up their Buccaneer commonwealth on them; and from the islands Morgan launched his attack on Panama, entering the city behind a wall of priests and women, and putting it to the flames.

The Buccaneers found allies among the Indians of the Mosquito Coast on the Atlantic shore of Nicaragua. These Indians had fifty-foot canoes, and could descry a sail at sea farther than any white man. They were invaluable as cutthroats and guides along forest trails, and it was rare to find a Buccaneer vessel without a group of Mosquito Indians on board. These Indians thirsted for spoil and took quickly to the Buccaneers, and learned English with amazing rapidity. They had no love for the French and hated the Spaniards mortally, and eventually came to regard themselves as subjects of the King of England. William Dampier, who knew them well, described them admiringly: "Well-made, raw-boned, lusty, strong and nimble of foot; long-visaged, with lank black hair, a stern look and rough-hewn features, with skins of a dark copper color." In the course of time the English established a virtual protectorate over the Mosquitos, and soon Englishmen were dreaming of crossing from the Atlantic to the Pacific by sailing up the San Juan River to Lake Nicaragua and so by canal to the sea.

"By seizing the Isthmus of Darien you will wrest the keys of the world from Spain," Sir Walter Raleigh told Queen Elizabeth, but the power of the Spaniards was still increasing along the isthmus and the English were safe only in Nicaragua. One last determined effort to wrest the isthmus from Spain was made in 1694 by a Scot, William Paterson, who founded "the Company of Scotland Trading to Africa and the Indies." With a thousand settlers he sailed from Leith and established a colony at Puerto Escoces, or Scotch Port, under the noses of the Spaniards. Scotch Port was only a few miles from Acla, where Balboa was executed. It was a feat of fantastic daring, buoyed up by dreams of empire. Paterson spoke in the authentic tones of Raleigh when he declared:

> This door of the seas and key of the universe will enable its possessors to become the legislators of both worlds and the arbitrators of commerce. The settlers of Darien will acquire a nobler empire than Alexander or Caesar, without fatigue, expense or danger, as well as without incurring the guilt and bloodshed of conquerors.

So he wrote and set out on the journey and planted the towns of New Edinburgh and New St. Andrews on the inhospitable coast, where the climate was intolerable and the Spaniards and Indians were a constant menace. When the rains came, they took to drink and quarreling among themselves, and soon more than half of them were dying of fever. In the summer of 1699, after a year of intense suffering, the survivors set sail for New York. Of the original colonists 744 had died, some were stranded in Jamaica, and only a handful reached New York. The expedition was a disaster.

With the Spaniards still in control of the isthmus, the English next turned their attention to Nicaragua. In 1780 a twenty-one-year-old post captain, Horatio Nelson, sailed up the San Juan River. "I intend to possess the Lake of Nicaragua," he wrote. "As it commands the only waterpass between the two oceans, by our possession of it Spanish America is divided in two." Fever ruined Nelson's plans, and after a battle on the river he was forced to return home. Until the Panama Canal was built the British continued to believe that the Nicaragua Canal offered the best hopes for the future.

In 1800 Spanish power in South America was coming to an end: the whole empire was in revolt. In 1814 the Spanish Cortes in a last desperate gesture to retain power over its crumbling colonies gave orders for the construction of a canal through the isthmus, but it was already too late. By 1823 the Spanish Empire had completely disintegrated, and soon power over the isthmus was being wielded by the untried revolutionaries who created the Federal Republic of the United Provinces of Central America. If the canal was ever to be built, permission would have to come from them; and at the time no one knew which way they would turn.

All over Europe and along the eastern seaboard of North America and especially in England, canals were being built with new engineering techniques unknown in the days when the Spaniards were ruling their vast empire. Canals were bringing the Industrial Revolution into existence. They were pushing back the undeveloped frontiers of the American West, and converting England into a lacy network of waterways; and along these waterways power—the industrial power of the nineteenth century—moved silently and efficiently. Once the great Spanish treasure ships had traced the routes of power upon the waters. Now the visible power lay in iron mills and smelters, in coal barges and ironclad ships and the wide-ranging canal systems which allowed trade to function smoothly. The earth was entering a new age; and the day of the conquistadors was over.

It was a time when men dreamed of international trade as the cement which would weld nations together in friendship and brotherhood. When Alexander von Humboldt visited Central and South America in the early years of the nineteenth century, he interrupted his researches on botany and geology to examine the possibility of carving a channel across the isthmus. It was widely believed there was a difference of level between the waters of the Pacific and the Atlantic, but Humboldt showed there was no difference. He was a little afraid that if the canal were cut, it would affect the temperature of the British Isles by diverting the Gulf Stream. But a drop in the temperature at London was a small price to pay for the advantages in international trade arising from the construction of the canal. He declared that any government which undertook the project would immortalize itself by bringing untold benefits to humanity. The world would become one. Out of Chinese ports there would flow an endless stream of goods for the markets of America and Europe. From New York goods would flow speedily to the Ganges. It was a delightful vision, and he wrote about it at length in his *Political Essay on New Spain,* which was widely publicized. He showed how simple it was—all that was necessary was to dig a ditch, and then almost by magic Asia and America and Europe would be linked together in a perpetual marriage.

Humboldt's essay fell into the hands of Goethe, who devoured it at a gulp and shortly afterward discussed the book with Eckermann. Goethe was himself the embodiment of the new age—he had shown in *Faust* that he regarded the greatest heroes as those who reclaimed land from the sea and placed their mechanical knowledge at the service of mankind. He had Leonardo's gift of prophecy. His discussion on the Panama Canal should be quoted at some length, because here at last, after the years of conquest and torment, can be heard the authentic voice of the new age. Humboldt had suggested altogether nine possible routes for the canal, including Tehuantepec, Nicaragua, Panama, and Darién, and Goethe commented:

I see that Humboldt with his great practical knowledge has suggested a number of places where, by using the rivers flowing into the Gulf of Mexico, the canal could be built more advantageously than at Panama. Well, all this is reserved for posterity, and for some great creative spirit. But this much I know: if a project of this kind succeeds in enabling ships of all sizes and lading to go through a canal from the Gulf of Mexico to the Pacific Ocean, incalculable benefits will accrue to the whole of civilised and uncivilised humanity.

It would surprise me, however, if the United States allowed such an opportunity to slip from their hands. We may expect this youthful power, which already possesses a tendency to move westward, to occupy and settle the vast areas of land beyond the Rocky Mountains in thirty or forty years. Further, we may expect that along the whole length of the Pacific Coast, where nature has already provided them with the largest and safest harbors, there will soon arise commercial cities of the utmost importance, with trade flowing out from the United States to China and the East Indies. And if this happens, then it becomes desirable and almost necessary that merchantmen and warships should have a rapid passage between the east and west coasts of North America—much easier than the wearisome, disagreeable and expensive journey round the Cape.

I repeat, then: it is absolutely indispensable for the United States to effect a passage from the Gulf of Mexico to the Pacific Ocean, and I am certain they will do it. They will do it one day, but I shall not live to see it. Also, I would like to see a connection established between the Danube and the Rhine, but this is so vast an undertaking that I doubt whether it will be done, especially when I consider our German way of doing things. Finally, I would like to see the English in possession of a Suez Canal. I would like to live long enough to see these three great things, and for their sake it would be almost worth while to hold out for another fifty years.[1]

Goethe, however, was only one of many who saw the Panama Canal in the light of an eternal benevolence. The Comte Henri de

[1] *Conversations with Eckermann,* Feb. 21, 1827.

Saint-Simon had made an effort to interest the Mexican viceroy in the project of cutting the canal. It became a commonplace of social conversation. No one doubted any longer that the canal was highly desirable and would produce untold benefits to civilization, but no one knew exactly how it would be carried out.

Occasionally the European governments threw out feelers, but little came of them. In 1829 the King of Holland was granted a canal concession by the Nicaraguan Government, but the enterprise came to an end with the revolutionary outbreak in Holland and Belgium. Six years previously President Monroe had pronounced the "Monroe Doctrine," by which the American continents were "henceforth not to be considered as subjects for future colonization by any European power." But the European powers were not particularly impressed by the doctrine, and the European adventurers and soldiers of fortune who flocked to the isthmus remained undisturbed by American power. In the fifty years between 1820 and 1870 an army of eccentrics descended upon the isthmus, many of them from the French aristocracy. In 1834 the Baron Charles de Thierry formed a syndicate at Panama to build an interoceanic canal—he seems to have thought that the canal would improve trade with New Zealand, where he had vast holdings and some pretensions to the Maori crown. The Congress of New Granada granted him a concession on condition that the canal be built in three years. The baron seems to have been entirely mad. He suggested that New Granada could quite easily build a railroad across the isthmus, preferably of gold, which could be obtained locally, thus obviating the necessity for importing foreign steel, though he noted that some misguided individuals might tear up the rails and run off with them. A few years later the Marquis Claude Drigon de Magny proposed that canals should be dug at Suez and Panama under Vatican auspices, with the surrounding territories placed under the temporal and religious supervision of the French religious order of Saint-Pie, to which he belonged. Prince Louis Napoleon, later Napoleon III, was another addict. After his escape from the fortress-prison of Ham in northern France, he took refuge in England and amused himself by publishing a pamphlet extolling the virtues of a canal which would pass through the Nicaraguan town of León, perhaps because he was friendly with Francisco Castellón, Central American Minister to France and native of that obscure town. It is a strange pamphlet, and some of it should be quoted as an example of the greater lunacy which hovers over canals:

> As Constantinople is the center of the ancient world, occupying the key position between Europe, Asia and Africa, so she became the entrepôt of all the commerce of these countries and maintained her power over them; for in politics, as in strategy, the center commands the circumference. So might Constantinople have been, but it so happened that she failed in her purpose, for, as Montesquieu observed, "God permitted the Turks to exist on earth, as a people most fitted to possess uselessly a great empire."
>
> But there exists in the New World a state as admirably situated as Constantinople, and just as uselessly ordered. We allude to the State of Nicaragua. For as Constantinople is the center of the ancient world, so is the city of León the center of the new, and if the tongue of land which separates its two lakes from the Pacific Ocean were cut through, she would command by virtue of her central position the entire coast of North and South America. The State of Nicaragua can become greater than Constantinople. . . .

There is nothing particularly remarkable in Napoleon's claims. Such claims were being made every day in the revolutionary literature of the states which had broken away from Spain. What is remarkable is that Napoleon ever became emperor. An air of opera-bouffe lingers over those Central American states during the time when they were still uncertain of their position in the world.

Stark tragedy came in with the discovery of gold in California. In the first years of the gold rush fleets of dilapidated schooners, barges, sailing ships, harbor tugs, and flat-bottomed river steamers sailed through the Caribbean and disgorged their passengers along the coast at Chagres, to stream across the isthmus and catch other ships to San Francisco. Many prospectors died or were killed during the journey through the jungle, and more died while waiting for a berth in fever-stricken Panama. Soon a railway was being built across the isthmus. Early in June, 1850, forty laborers were at work clearing the marshes of Manzanillo Island. There were no ceremonies of inauguration. Two American workmen leaped ashore from a canoe, accompanied by half a dozen Indians who set about clearing the pathways with machetes. It was the rainy season, with mosquitoes swarming out of the underbrush, and at night they all crowded in the suffocating heat of an ancient brig. Two years later the railway extended to Barbacoas, halfway across the isthmus. By May, 1854, it reached Gorgona, so eliminating the canoe trip up the Chagres and leaving only eighteen miles of the old transit to be traversed by mule. To build the railway workmen were imported from all over the world—from England, Austria, Ireland, France, Jamaica, and from as far away as India and China. The death rate was appalling. It was said that one workman died for every tie laid on the roadbed, but the railway company denied the accusation, pointing out that there were altogether 74,000 ties and no more than 7,000 workmen had ever worked at one time on the railway. At least 20,000 workmen died. It was a foretaste of things to come.

In those years in the middle of the last century, the powers were still jockeying for position. The United States was establishing herself on the Pacific through her encroachments on Mexico. Already in 1846, before the discovery of gold in California, the United States had made a treaty with New Granada, by which she secured right of transit over the isthmus "upon any modes of communication that now exist or may hereafter be constructed." New Granada was guaranteed sovereignty over all the territories of the isthmus. It was this monopoly which enabled the railway company to extort a fabulous indemnity when De Lesseps attempted to build his canal over the isthmus.

Meanwhile there was trouble over Nicaragua, with Britain and the United States at loggerheads. Warships moved, ultimatums were delivered, and in 1850 the ugly situation was resolved by a treaty signed by Secretary Clayton and Sir Henry Bulwer, the British Minister in Washington. According to the treaty neither country could build a transisthmian canal without the assent of the other, and neither would ever "erect or maintain any fortifications commanding the canal, or occupy, or fortify, or colonize, or assume, or exercise any dominion over any part of Central America." Other countries were invited to sign the treaty, but none did. The treaty merely underlined the fact that the quarrel existed, and did nothing to remove the basic causes. Britain still cherished her protectorate over the Mosquito Coast, and though Palmerston fought to continue it, the protectorate was withdrawn in 1860. Nicaragua became a completely sovereign state. Palmerston thundered against the Americans. "Those Yankees are most disagreeable fellows to have to deal with," he said. "They are totally unscrupulous and dishonest and determined somehow or other to carry their point. The treaty opposes a barrier to the Yankees, and therefore they detest it." Yet the treaty remained in force, holding the two powers in a grip from which neither could escape. If the treaty was to be broken or abrogated, a force coming from an entirely unsuspected direction was needed. That force was Ferdinand de Lesseps.

When the Suez Canal was opened in 1869, De Lesseps possessed a moral force which few men have ever possessed. Like Schweitzer in our own time he represented in his own person the vast disassociated dreams of multitudes of people. France lay humiliated by the disastrous defeat of 1870, but De Lesseps was inviolate, the only Frenchman of untarnished fame and positive achievement. At geographical congresses held in Antwerp in 1871 and Paris in 1875 to examine proposals for the American canal, his name was on everyone's lips. In Europe, if not in America, he seemed to be the man destined to carry the Panama Canal through to a conclusion.

Secure in his fame, De Lesseps bided his time. Born in 1805, descended from a long line of minor French aristocrats, he had been appointed to consular posts all over Europe, in Algeria and Egypt, and might have continued all his life in the diplomatic service if he had not resigned in anger over French policy when he was appointed to Rome. Then for a few years he broke off all contact with public life, living quietly in the country. When Muhammad Ali became

Viceroy of Egypt, De Lesseps remembered how he had befriended the viceroy when they were both young: out of that friendship came the Suez Canal. His life had been a succession of fabulous accidents, and as he grew into old age he seemed to be waiting for one more fabulous accident to crown his career.

The accident came in the form of a young lieutenant of engineers with the improbable name of Lucien Napoléon-Bonaparte Wyse. Handsome and vivid, with a caressing manner, Lucien Wyse was the illegitimate son of Princess Laetitia Buonaparte, the daughter of Napoleon's brother Lucien. Princess Laetitia had married Sir Thomas Wyse, an Irish diplomat, but her son was born nineteen years after their legal separation. Lucien Wyse was twenty-eight years old in 1875, and like so many other members of the French aristocracy he had an incurable habit of meddling in dangerous affairs. He was a close friend of De Lesseps, and his brother-in-law was a certain General Etienne Turr, a Hungarian by birth and a major-general in the Italian Army. With De Lesseps' approval, Lucien Wyse and General Turr formed the Société Civile Internationale du Canal Interocéanique du Darien, with the intention of exploring the isthmus and obtaining a concession for a canal.

While General Turr remained in the background, Wyse set out for Panama late in the fall of 1876, with his chief assistant, Lieutenant Armand Réclus, and some fifteen technicians. In April, 1877, they returned to Paris with discouraging reports. There were mountains in the way; the cost of draining the marshes was prohibitive; and the best route involved a 2,300-foot tunnel through the mountains with five locks on each slope. De Lesseps pronounced that it was absolutely necessary to build a sea-level canal. He had built one at Suez. He could see no reason for not building one at Panama. Accordingly, he insisted that Wyse return and explore the isthmus again. Wyse returned to Panama, concluded that the best route would lie close to the railway, and on May 18, 1878, after a long nightmarish ride to Bogotá which he reached just in time, for the government was about to fall, he obtained a charter from the Colombian Government. The charter provided for a ninety-nine-year concession, with the company undertaking to complete the canal in seventeen years. The minimum payment due to Colombia in any one year was to be $250,000, the same amount paid by the Panama Railway Company. At the end of ninety-nine years the entire property, except 500,000 hectares of land leased to the company, would revert to Colombia.

With this bold stroke Wyse sealed the fate of France for the next decade and a half. Untold ruin and misery arose out of the strange contract signed at the last minute by the foreign minister of a government which was to fall ten days later.

De Lesseps was encouraged by the contract, and already saw himself as the acknowledged leader of the enterprise. But it was necessary to behave circumspectly. He spent the winter poring over the plans, and on May 15, 1879, he assembled in the great *palais* of the Geographical Society on the Boulevard Saint-Germain an international congress to study the canal. There were 136 delegates, of whom seventy-three came from France and her dependencies. There were eleven delegates from the United States, six from Britain, five from Spain, four from Switzerland, three from Italy and two each from Austro-Hungary, Portugal, Russia, and El Salvador. De Lesseps was chairman. He begged the delegates to conduct themselves in the American manner, "with speed and practicality, and with scrupulous care," and then vanished into the sidelines. General Turr and Lucien Wyse were given the task of explaining the sea-level canal across the Isthmus of Panama, to be built at a cost of about a thousand million francs. There were some objections, notably from Godin de Lepinay, a skilled engineer with a long experience of working in the tropics, who proposed to dam the Chagres River near the Atlantic terminus and the Río Grande near the Pacific, so creating an artificial lake eighty feet above sea level. It was a brilliant solution, but no one paid much attention to it at the time: many of the essential elements of Lepinay's plan formed the basis of the compromise plan later accepted by the French company, and his system of locks and dams and artificial lakes was adopted with only slight changes by the builders of the present canal. But De Lesseps had long ago concluded that a sea-level canal was practicable, and in the eyes of most of the remaining delegates—some 40 of them vanished before the two-week session was over—he alone possessed the authority which comes from accomplishment. Long before the ballots were counted, De Lesseps knew he would be the elected leader. "Two weeks ago I had no idea of placing myself at the head of a new undertaking," he said. "My dearest friends tried to persuade me, telling me that after Suez I should take a rest. Well, if you ask a general who has just won one battle if he will try to win a second, he cannot refuse!" He spoke while the ballots were being counted, in the full knowledge that he had won. He was seventy-four, but looked fifty, and there was a sprightliness about him which suggested that he was in full command of his faculties. In fact he was already failing.

Age, which embitters men, leads them backward along the paths of youth and tempts them to imitate their youthful feats, and the follies of their middle age. When Charles de Lesseps, his thirty-eight-year-old son and chief collaborator at Suez, asked him why he wanted to build the canal at Panama—was it for money or glory, when he had enough money and enough glory?—he answered that he had committed a few follies in his life, and Panama was another, but he hoped to live long enough to see his last folly revered and respected by everyone. So for the remaining years of his life De Lesseps laughed his fears away, until at last they overwhelmed him.

From the beginning there was trouble. First, an agreement had to be made with Lucien Wyse and General Turr for the transfer of the charter from the Colombian Government. Most of June was spent in discussions on how the transfer should be made and at what price. In the end it was agreed that the new canal company should pay Wyse and Turr ten million francs as soon as the company was organized. Then early in August, De Lesseps announced the formation of the Compagnie Universelle du Canal Interocéanique with a capital of 400 million francs. The press was hostile, and only 30 million francs were subscribed. To combat the press, he began to issue a fortnightly *Bulletin du Canal Interocéanique,* which became as the months passed a curiously strident, and often inaccurate, mouthpiece for De Lesseps and his closest followers. Here he published his appeals for funds. Here, too, he described the work in progress, always briefly and with an air of immense authority. He wrote in the *Bulletin:* "The Canal at Panama will be easier to begin, to complete and to maintain than the Suez." He was still thinking of a sea-level canal which would mysteriously find its way across mountains and raging torrents.

The press laughed at him, but he was a force to be reckoned with. His resilience—his ability by sheer persistence to wear his opponents down—remained as great as ever. Even at close quarters it was impossible to detect any failure of nerve. He went through all the proper motions, made all the proper speeches, and was buoyed up by a vast belief in his civilizing mission. His judgment however was clouded, and sometimes his behavior was senile.

The first signs of senility occurred during his first visit to Panama with his young wife and three of his young daughters. He arrived at Colón on December 30, 1879, accompanied by a small group of company officials, and immediately set out by railroad for Panama. The Iron bridge at Barbacoas had been washed away by heavy rains, but he was not in the least troubled by the absence of the bridge, laughed good-naturedly, scrambled across to the other side of the valley and joined another train waiting to take him to Panama. That night there was a banquet followed by fireworks in the plaza in front of the cathedral, and when anyone suggested there might be difficulties in building the canal, De Lesseps answered, "The canal will be built!" Everyone remarked on the beauty of his young wife and the good behavior of his children.

On the afternoon of January 1, 1880, the formal inauguration of the great work took place. A small steamboat was chartered to convey De Lesseps, his family, and his guests to a point in Panama Bay at the mouth of the Río Grande about three miles west of the city. A reception was held on board. There was a good deal of champagne, and the ceremony began later than expected. By the time De Lesseps was ready to deliver the first blow of the pick, the tide had receded, and it was discovered that the steamboat could not get within two miles of the place chosen for the ceremony.

As usual De Lesseps knew exactly what to do. All that was needed was a symbolic gesture. Accordingly he placed a champagne box filled with sand on deck, pronounced the inaugural discourse and gave the gleaming shovel and pickax brought specially from France to his daughter Ferdinande, who was seven years old. Ferdinande solemnly went through the motions of shoveling the first spadeful of earth, and the Archbishop of Panama bestowed his benediction. According to the *Bulletin* the affair was a resounding success. One by one the engineers, administrators, and officials had dug spadefuls of earth "on behalf of the alliance of all people contributing to the union of the oceans, for the good of humanity." Nothing was said about the receding tide or the champagne box.

According to Tracy Robinson, an American spectator, there was another contretemps a little later when De Lesseps ordered a heavy charge of dynamite to be placed near the summit of Cerro de Culebra. He hoped to blow off the top of the mountain. There were speeches by De Lesseps and others, a benediction from the archbishop, and once again Ferdinande was given the place of honor; but when she pressed the plunger of the detonator, nothing at all happened. "The crowd stood breathless," said Tracy Robinson, "eyes blinking half in terror lest this artificial earthquake might involve general destruction. Then a humorous sense of relief stole over the crowd. With one accord everyone exclaimed 'Good gracious!' and hurried away, lest after all the dynamite should see fit to explode."

So the six-week tour went on, with concerts, banquets, and more symbolic gestures, and nothing of any moment occurred except that the technical commission took samples of earth and rock, and the original prejudices of De Lesseps were reinforced. He kept saying that the canal would be easy to build—it was after all very short, less than the distance between Paris and Fontainebleau. As for those who thought the climate dangerously unhealthy, he said that this was simply an invention of his enemies. It was a wonderful climate, and he had not himself suffered a day's illness during all those six weeks.

From Panama De Lesseps went off to New York, where he was royally entertained and the New York Fire Department put on a special fire-fighting exhibition for his benefit. Eight thousand members of the French colony in New York invited him to dinner at the Lotos Club. He rode on the elevated railway and inspected the uncompleted Brooklyn Bridge, and then went down to Washington to confer with President Hayes, who addressed a special message to Congress declaring that "the policy of this country is to advocate a canal under American control," even while De Lesseps was in Washington. But the conference between De Lesseps and the President had been cordial, and De Lesseps was still living in a dream world. He believed he had the President's blessing, and announced in the *Bulletin* that the President had given personal assurances for the security of the canal, a phrase which meant whatever De Lesseps wanted it to mean. Wherever he went he was greeted with flattering attention, and as the triumphal tour passed through Chicago, Boston, and San Francisco he may have thought his star was still in the ascendant. But no American bankers offered to lend money for the canal.

It was a different story when he returned to France, spending the summer of 1880 in a triumphal tour which took him from one end of the country to the other. In November he opened a subscription, asking for 300 million francs. Twice that amount was subscribed. The first meeting of shareholders was held in Paris on January 31, 1881, with a second meeting two months later at which the new Compagnie Universelle du Canal Interocéanique was incorporated and its administration organized. There De Lesseps announced once again that the canal would be constructed with the greatest ease and would certainly be finished in eight years. Already the first detachment of workmen had been sent out, and all the French newspapers carried a cable message from the isthmus, dated February 1: *"Travail commencé."* But in fact no work had been done, and it was two years before the real canal digging began.

Trouble came from all sides—from the press, from the contractors, from the owners of the Panama Railroad Company, from inside the organization itself. Everyone had to be bribed. The Panama Railroad Company had floated 70,000 shares, which had a par value of $100. They were usually quoted under par. The company had De Lesseps at its mercy and insisted that he pay a bonus of $150 for each share, making a total of $17,000,000 for the 70,000 shares. In addition he was forced to pay a cash bonus of one million dollars to the directors of the railroad and buy seven million dollars of the company's bonds. To buy the railroad De Lesseps had therefore to pay 25 million dollars. So from the beginning he was forced to pour out money like water until it became a flood, and all of France was drowned in it.

Work started in earnest in 1883. It was inhumanly difficult work in a country where it was inhumanly difficult to keep alive. Yellow fever and malaria were rampant. Neither of the two large cities of Colón and Panama had sewers or water supplies, and the only scavengers were the huge flocks of buzzards wheeling interminably overhead. Panama was built of stone, Colón of wood, and both were inhabited by the dregs of humanity. No one knew that yellow fever was carried by the mosquito *Aëdes aegypti.* Because there were so many ants in the hospitals, the attendants put little cups of water under the legs of the beds, so that there were breeding grounds within the hospitals. The elusive and mysterious fevers of the place defied all precautions and laughed at all remedies. Vast numbers of Jamaicans who were immune to yellow fever were employed, but the French officials died off like flies. Continually in those early years the *Bulletin* announced that "the health of all our employees leaves nothing to be desired." In fact, the health of the employees left a good deal to be desired, and the most shattering of all the verdicts on the Panama venture was uttered by Dr. Gorgas when he said: "Probably if the French had been trying to propagate yellow fever, they could not have provided conditions better adapted for this purpose."

By the spring of 1885 it was becoming clear that things were not going well. In March there was a brief insurrection, put down by American warships, but there were things worse than insurrections, and worse than yellow fever. The very earth in Panama seemed to be in revolt against the canal. As they dug trenches, the earth came sliding in to fill it again. It was unstable earth, formed of two different kinds of soil without any cementing material. Excavating was like digging into wet soap, with the result that all the calculations for the number of cubic meters which had to be dredged were found to be sadly underestimated. At the beginning Lucien Wyse had estimated that it would be necessary to dig 50 million cubic meters. The French had already excavated 55 million when they were forced to withdraw, and the end was nowhere in sight. Before the canal was finished, the Americans had excavated 259 cubic meters, and nearly 120 million cubic meters came from the Culebra Cut alone.

By July, 1885, De Lesseps was announcing ominously that the canal might not be finished in eight years—it might in fact take nine years. Because funds were running out, he had already requested the French Government to grant him a lottery. The government decided to send Armand Rousseau, a former undersecretary of state for public works, to inspect the work. He was an exceptionally level-headed executive, and reported on his return that the undertaking had gone too far to be abandoned, if only because the prestige of the French was so deeply involved. He disagreed with reports in the French newspapers about the hospitals—he found them well kept—and about the flood of money which was being poured into houses and estates for the canal managers—he found them exaggerated. Rousseau was no partisan. It was simply that the matter had gone so far that it would be dangerous to stop. Privately, he informed De Lesseps that it would be necessary to keep better books.

Rousseau had hardly returned from Panama when De Lesseps decided to visit the isthmus again. This second visit, only a fortnight long, was another triumph. There were triumphal arches on which De Lesseps was acclaimed "the Genius of the Nineteenth Century." There were the inevitable colored portraits showing him in a gray frock coat, while Glory crowned him with laurel leaves. He was never tired, and always at the head of the cavalcade. He galloped up the hillside at Culebra on horseback amidst a storm of applause from blacks and whites, astounded by his youthfulness. Afterward, when the memory of his visit was growing dim, the Panamanians said he had come in a flowing robe of gorgeous colors, like an oriental monarch. He was eighty-one, and very tired.

When he returned to Paris, he must have felt the wind of failure in the air. Rousseau had approved the lottery, but the French Government remained undecided, voting to adjourn the study of his proposals by six votes to five, and so delaying a decision to the end of the year. De Lesseps knew he must raise money quickly to save the company from bankruptcy, and appealed once more to the French people over the head of the government. He wrote:

> True to my past, when they try to prevent me from going forward, still I go forward. Not alone, it is true, but with the 350,000 Frenchmen who share my patriotic confidence in the future. Although by their attitude six deputies are trying to prevent me from marching forward with you to victory in this peaceful work undertaken by France in the Isthmus of Panama, we shall overcome every obstacle yet. You shall march with me to a second victory by providing the 600,000,000 francs I need.

But already it was too late. The old man was dying, and the canal was dying with him. Only 200 million francs was forthcoming, and the sum was not enough. The year 1887 was the year of crisis, and soon he saw defeat staring him in the face.

Yet in Panama the work went on bravely. Fifty thousand workmen died, as though on the battlefield. Rousseau had proved to his satisfaction that France could not pull out, but others knew it was only a matter of time. It was not only that mistakes had been made and vast sums of money had been expended uselessly, but the whole original conception of the canal was wrong-headed. Brilliant young engineers like Philippe Bunau-Varilla, who acted for a brief space as director-general when he was only twenty-six, believed the canal could be saved by last-minute alterations in the general plan. He designed a system of locks with a high summit level, proposed the use of the latest labor-saving devices, including instruments for underwater dredging, and insisted continually against De Lesseps' objections that a lock canal was preferable to a sea-level canal. But the engineers on the spot were not in command; decisions were made in the Paris office, which was filled with young members of aristocratic families who cared little about the fortunes of the canal. They could see the doom moving toward them, but did nothing to prevent it. By July, 1887, over a thousand million francs had been poured by the company into the canal, into bribes to newspapers and government, and into the salaries of the officials in Paris, and now it was too late to save it.

Momentum kept the machine running for a little while longer. Occasionally there would pass over the face of De Lesseps an expression of intense pain and astonishment, as though he could not understand what was happening all round him: at such moments he would turn to his son Charles and ask whether anything had gone wrong. "Nothing has gone wrong," Charles would say. Coldbloodedly, ruthlessly, impelled by adoring affection for his father, Charles still supervised the canal and offered bribes to government officials. It was as though all the operators in that gigantic undertaking were forming a conspiracy to keep an old man happy.

Some men were not very happy. Among them was the most distinguished laborer in the canal zone, a handsome hawk-nosed ruffian of a man whose name will be remembered when De Lesseps is forgotten. Wearying of Brittany, Paul Gauguin sailed for Panama in April, 1887, with the vague intention of settling on the island of Tobago, which was in the possession of the canal company. He expected to find a tropical paradise, but instead found an island given over to hospitals and the estates of company managers. His money ran out after a brief stay on the island, and he went to work on the isthmus as a laborer. The hours were long, the heat was exhausting, and the company gendarmes were exasperating. Soon Gauguin was writing to his wife:

> Just because I urinated in a filthy hole full of broken bottles and excrement I was forced to walk all the way across Panama City under

arrest, and in the end I was fined 1 piastre. I felt like hitting out at the gendarmes, but the police here are very quick on the trigger, they follow you at a distance of five paces, and if you make a move they fire a bullet through your head. Tomorrow I am going to swing a pickaxe on the canal works for 150 piastres a month. As soon as I can put aside 150 piastres, which will take me two months, I shall go to Martinique. I have to dig from five-thirty in the morning to six in the evening, under tropical sun and rain. At night I am devoured by mosquitoes.

Gauguin was discharged a few weeks later before he had saved his 150 piastres, but he succeeded in making his way to Martinique, where he painted a few pictures, fell ill, and set out for Paris again, working his way as a common sailor. "I go to Panama to live as a savage," he said before leaving France, and he discovered that it was far more savage than he ever thought.

The end of the affair can be told briefly. De Lesseps professed to believe that his sea-level canal was practicable, even when he was faced with evidence that it was wholly impracticable. Though he was old and dying, there were people who still had faith in him. The government relented, and allowed him to issue a new series of bonds. The success of the issue was astonishing. In June, 1888, bonds to the value of 254 million francs were bought, and in the next month he bowed for the first time before the advice of the engineers who submitted plans for a lock canal. He hedged a little by adding that the new plan would not prevent the eventual construction of a sea-level canal. "The canal," he said, "will certainly be finished in 1891."

It was the beginning of the end. On January 26, 1889, the company met for the last time, and nine days later it was dissolved by order of a tribunal and placed in the hands of a liquidator. Heartbroken, De Lesseps sent off the telegram ordering all work to cease on the isthmus. Now the whole edifice came crashing around his ears. Lawyers went to work. Quesnay de Beaurepaire, the public prosecutor, ordered an inquiry into the tangled affairs of the company, and De Lesseps himself was ordered to appear before a councilor appointed by the court. He was ill in bed when the order came. He rose, dressed quietly, put on the sash of the order of the Legion of

Honor and presented himself at the councilor's office, where he remained for three-quarters of an hour, radiating charm and energy as in the days when he rode on horseback up the hillside at Culebra. The next day he fell into a decline. He whispered to his wife: "What a terrible nightmare I have had! I imagined I was summoned before the examining magistrate! It was atrocious!" For the rest of his life he never spoke about the canal again.

The losses were so vast and affected so many people that a trial became inevitable. Half mad, lost in his dreams, his strong body remaining alive long after the light had gone from his mind, he lived on quietly, tended by his wife and devoted children, who humored him and kept him from reading about the trials. There was evidence of stupidity, which is not a crime, and negligence, which is, and wholesale bribery, which is not necessarily criminal, particularly when bribes were demanded by government officials. The decision to hold a trial was taken by Louis Ricard, the new Minister of Justice who replaced Fallières in February, 1892.

In appearance De Lesseps represented all that was best in France: a solid, handsome, blunt, good-humored man with a sprawling mustache and twinkling eyes. Ricard was the opposite. Quesnay de Beaurepaire, who detested him, described him as a man who walked with the slow measured tread of a Supreme Pontiff about to bless the people, and there was something about him too which resembled a magician about to pull a pair of white doves from a chafing dish. He had a long, angular face, drooping mustaches, dull eyes, loose lips, and was consumed by vanity. "The words of others," said Quesnay de Beaurepaire, "glided over him like a pair of skates over ice; he sometimes listened, and seldom understood." To this man, whose nickname was *la belle Fatma,* the fate of Charles de Lesseps—his father, though named as a defendant, was never brought into court—was confided. The trial was an explosion which tore France apart, as only a few years later she was torn apart by the Dreyfus scandal.

As the full details of the financial operations emerged, it became clear that De Lesseps had walked waist deep through the muddy waters of the Paris money markets, the prey of sharks like Cornelius Herz and the sinister Baron Jacques de Reinach. Herz was the pure charlatan, a small dumpy man who had studied medicine in Chicago and who became a close friend of Clemenceau. For a while he was a deputy in the French parliament, and one of the men most concerned in the business of obtaining permission to hold lotteries on behalf of the canal company. He was continually blackmailing Charles de Lesseps. Once he sent off a telegram to the secretary-general of the company: "I shall wreck everything rather than be robbed of a single centime. Take warning: the time is short." Baron de Reinach—the title was Italian—was no better. A short, stout man, with a ruddy face and a thick black beard, he had amassed a considerable fortune by selling military supplies to the government, and he worked hand in glove with Herz. A third conspirator was a former coffee importer, Léopold-Emile Aron, who secured a position in the Société de Dynamite and sold great quantities of dynamite to the canal company. Quesnay de Beaurepaire was prepared to prosecute all three, but they escaped him. Aron fled to Germany, Herz to England, and Baron de Reinach took poison. On trial were Charles de Lesseps, Marius Fontane, Henri Cottu, and Gustave Eiffel, who later built the Eiffel Tower. Eiffel was implicated because he had contracted to build the locks. Fontane was secretary-general of the company, and Cottu one of the directors.

Eiffel was the only vigorous man among them: all the rest were sunk in weariness and despair. There were moments when Charles de Lesseps, bald and gray-bearded, with somber eyes below thick eyebrows, aroused himself and faced his accusers nobly, but then the mask would drop and the weariness break through. The story he had to tell sounded as though it were pure fiction. "Everywhere we looked," he said, "they came crawling out of the stones. Blackmail, libel, broken promises. . . ."

The trial dragged on through November and December, with Henri Barboux, the counsel for the defense, defending them brilliantly, pointing out that throughout the history of canal building all the preliminary estimates had been proved wrong. The Corinth

Canal was supposed to cost 24 million francs, but had cost 60. The Marseilles Canal was estimated at 13 million, and cost 45. Barboux was a small thin man with a bony face and mocking eyes, and he did the best he could, but the verdict went against him. All the defendants were found guilty. Ferdinand de Lesseps and his son were sentenced to five years' imprisonment and fined 3,000 francs each, Fontane and Cottu to two years' imprisonment and fines of 3,000 francs each, Eiffel to two years' imprisonment and a fine of 20,000 francs. Charles de Lesseps wept, and Cottu and Fontane collapsed in the arms of friends, but Eiffel remained calm. Though accused, Ferdinand de Lesseps remained quietly in his country house, too old to be concerned with the great events taking place in Paris, sunk in the senile apathy which remained with him until the day he died.

Exactly a month after the close of the trial, a second trial opened. The first was for fraud, the second for corruption. Once more Charles de Lesseps was in the prisoner's box. He was asked why he had paid 375,000 francs to Charles Baihaut, a former Minister of the Interior. Charles de Lesseps replied that he had no alternative; he was like someone standing in the woods when a cutthroat comes up to him and demands a purse or a watch. Asked why he did not call the police, he answered: "How could I? The policeman was holding me up to ransom." At the first trial the verdict was handed down by judges; at the second trial by a jury. De Lesseps was sentenced to a year in prison, but Baihaut was sentenced to five years, the forfeiture of civil rights, a fine of 750,000 francs and the repayment of the 375,000 bribe. Charles appealed against both verdicts: the first was quashed, but the Court refused to annul the second, and he remained in prison until September 12, 1893. He was allowed one brief visit to the bedside of his father. When Charles entered the bedroom, his father smiled and said: "Well, Charles, so there you are! Tell me, has anything new happened in Paris?"

Ferdinand de Lesseps lived on until the winter of 1894, dying at last a few days after his eighty-ninth birthday. He was buried in the cemetery of Père-Lachaise. He had left so little money that the Suez Canal Company paid his funeral expenses. Four year later, in the summer of 1898, the newspapers carried the announcement of the death in Bournemouth, England, of Cornelius Herz, the most infamous of the three scoundrels who blackmailed the Suez Canal Company. Of Aron nothing more was ever heard.

The second act of the story of the Panama Canal was over: there remained a third. While dredgers, railroads, and rolling stock were covered by deep jungles, interest in the Panama Canal remained. The French had built more than two thousand buildings in the canal zone, and much of their equipment was the best available. There were many who still hoped that something could be salvaged from the ruins.

Among those who clamored most loudly for the canal was Philippe Bunau-Varilla, the brilliant student from the Ecole Polytechnique. With his high forehead, heavy-lidded eyes and sharp nose, he resembled a small and effervescent eagle. Tireless in his advocacy of the canal, he even made a special journey to St. Petersburg in 1894 to interest Count Witte, and through him Alexander III, in the Panama Canal. The Trans-Siberian Railway had just been begun. Surely the interoceanic canal would complement the transcontinental railroad! Nothing came of the project, but the incident demonstrated Bunau-Varilla's determination. In the end this proud and entirely unscrupulous engineer became one of the three or four men most responsible for the canal being built.

American interest in the canal increased during the Spanish-American War. In March, 1898, the battleship *Oregon,* lying at anchor in San Francisco Bay, was ordered to make for Key West, and to get there it had to sail 13,400 miles round Cape Horn. Steaming at full speed the *Oregon* made the journey in a little over two months, arriving in time to participate in the naval victory at Santiago. The long journey demonstrated the need for a canal across Nicaragua or Panama, if the United States was to maintain a two-ocean navy. From the moment when the *Oregon* set out from San Francisco Bay, it became inevitable that the United States would have to take over the former concessions and assume full responsibility for the canal. She had become an imperial power: Cuba, Puerto

Rico, the Philippines, and Hawaii belonged to her: and in the dangerous world at the turn of the century she could no longer afford the risk of having a fleet divided into two squadrons which could be reunited only by a long voyage around South America.

But though the Americans had set their heart on a canal, they were still uncertain where it would be. Various champions urged the claims of Nicaragua and Panama. Even Theodore Roosevelt, later to become the most determined champion for Panama, wrote in 1894: "It is a great mistake that we have not started an interoceanic canal in Nicaragua." But others were just as ardently in favor of taking over the French concession and continuing the work begun by De Lesseps, and among these were William Nelson Cromwell, a shrewd lawyer, and Mark Hanna, a Republican senator who was one of the confidential advisers of President McKinley. Between them they were able to turn public opinion gradually in favor of the Panama Canal. But it is doubtful whether they would have won the battle without the aid of Bunau-Varilla, who sailed from France early in January, 1901, to launch his own private and well-thought-out campaign on behalf of the canal. A new company had taken over the concession, and Bunau-Varilla, as a representative of the company, hoped to sell the concession to the highest bidder.

In this affair all motives were suspect, for Cromwell and Bunau-Varilla had their own financial axes to grind and they were perfectly capable of using whatever weapons came to hand. Almost as soon as he arrived in America, Bunau-Varilla sought out Mark Hanna. They were in general agreement on the strategy to be employed. Bunau-Varilla was presented to the President, and went on to deliver a series of highly inaccurate lectures on the advantages of the Panama Canal. He issued a pamphlet *Panama or Nicaragua?* and spent some time closeted with Cromwell, who seems to have turned against him, for when Bunau-Varilla returned to France in the spring, he issued at a cost of $27,000 three advertisements proclaiming the need for France to resume work on the canal. Had France sunk into such a state of decadence and depravity that she could not see that her honor was involved? Suddenly he turned about-face, and the third advertisement was an appeal to the French to sell the concession to the Americans. It was an odd business altogether, and no one has ever been able to understand exactly what Bunau-Varilla was attempting to do, particularly since the last advertisement was published some ten days after the company had offered to sell the concession, together with all the standing equipment, to the United States for $40,000,000.

But though the offer had been made, the Americans were in no hurry to buy. In hot haste Bunau-Varilla returned to Washington, to argue the case. He was lucky in his timing. On May 6, 1902, the eruption of Mount Pelée on the island of Martinique destroyed the city of Saint-Pierre. Bunau-Varilla saw his opportunity. The Senate was debating the issue. The opponents of the Nicaragua venture had pointed out that there were volcanoes in Nicaragua which might endanger the projected canal, and unfortunately the Nicaraguan post office had issued some time previously postage stamps showing one of their volcanoes in process of eruption. Three days before the vote, each senator received in the mail a sheet of paper bearing the postage stamp and the typewritten inscription: *"Postage stamp from the Republic of Nicaragua. An official witness of volcanic activity on the Isthmus of Nicaragua."* The evidence was damning. On June 19, 1902, the bill in favor of the Panama Canal passed the Senate by a vote of 67 to 6, and a week later passed the House of Representatives by a vote of 259 to 8. Bunau-Varilla's successful trick—he called it "a broadside, loaded with explosive truth"—had helped significantly to win the battle.

With the passing of the bill in favor of the Panama Canal, the United States found itself for the first time committed to build the canal. The Clayton-Bulwer Treaty, which gave the British equal rights, had been abrogated the previous year; in its place was the Hay-Pauncefote Treaty, by which the United States was empowered to transform the Canal Zone into an armed camp, while keeping the canal open to all vessels on terms of entire equality. The French had abandoned their interest in the canal; so had the British.

It remained to discover whether the Government of Colombia would abandon theirs.

The Republic of Colombia was in no hurry to come to terms. The province of Panama was a small northern appendage to the republic, far from the capital at Bogotá. The Colombian Government was perfectly prepared to surrender a strip of territory on condition that it was amply rewarded. Negotiations were conducted by John Hay, Secretary of State, and Dr. Thomas Herrán, chargé d' affaires of the Colombian Government at Washington. The United States was granted a strip of land thirty miles wide between the two oceans on payment of $10,000,000 in gold and an annual payment of $250,000. On June 20, 1903, the Colombian Congress met in extraordinary session to consider the treaty. There were long delays. The Colombians hoped for more liberal financial concessions from the United States, and wrangled interminably among themselves. President Roosevelt, who had appreciated the strategic importance of the canal during the Spanish-American War, had no high opinion of South American republics, and flew into a tantrum. "These contemptible little creatures in Bogotá," he declared, "ought to understand how much they are jeopardizing things and imperiling their own future." He was prepared to use force, if necessary. The Colombian Congress adjourned in October, without coming to any decision on the matter.

It was a time when the least fanning of the flames might precipitate a revolution. Bunau-Varilla once again saw his opportunity. He decided to organize the revolt with the help of Dr. Manuel Amador Guerrero, the chief physician of the Panama Railroad Company and a popular figure in Panamanian social circles. The conspirators set to work in the Hotel Waldorf-Astoria in New York. With the help of a secretary who knew no Spanish, and who was therefore unable to understand the dimensions of the plot, Bunau-Varilla prepared the complete blueprint of a revolution, with a proclamation of independence, a cipher code, and a program of military operations. He offered to supply $100,000 from his own pocket on condition that he was appointed the new republic's minister in Washington, and he extracted a promise that the revolution would take place not later than November 3rd. As a parting gift he gave Dr. Amador a national flag, which his wife had hastily sewn together.

Dr. Amador hurried off to Panama, to discover that Colombian authorities had got wind of the plot. Two days later he sent a message in code to Bunau-Varilla, who was still in New York. The message read: "Fate news bad powerful tiger. Urge vapor Colón." Deciphered, the message meant that two hundred Colombian troops were expected to arrive shortly at Colón and it was absolutely necessary for the United States to send a warship.

A warship was sent. It was the *Nashville,* under orders to prevent the landing of "any armed force with hostile intent, either government or insurgent, either at Colón, Porto Bello, or other point." But Dr. Amador had underestimated the number of Colombian troops to arrive at Colón—there were altogether 450, many of them accompanied by their wives. They camped in the streets of Colón, while their officers took the train to Panama. Fifteen officers arrived at Panama at eleven o'clock in the morning, only to find themselves at the mercy of the insurgents. They were wined and dined. After lunch they asked to be taken to the fortifications and the seawall, presumably to signal to the three Colombian gunboats in the harbor and take possession of the quick-firing guns. It was a very hot day. General Huertas, in command of the insurgents, slipped out of the room and whispered to Dr. Amador. It was decided to pretend that everything was in order. The visiting officers were told that they could see the fortifications, but the moment they stepped into the courtyard they were surrounded by troops and taken to the police station. Then they were locked up.

At this moment there was very little the Colombian authorities could do. The 450 soldiers sent to quell the insurrection were still camped at Colón, without supplies and without money—it would have cost them $2,000 to travel by railway to Panama, and the railway officials refused to allow them to make the journey without

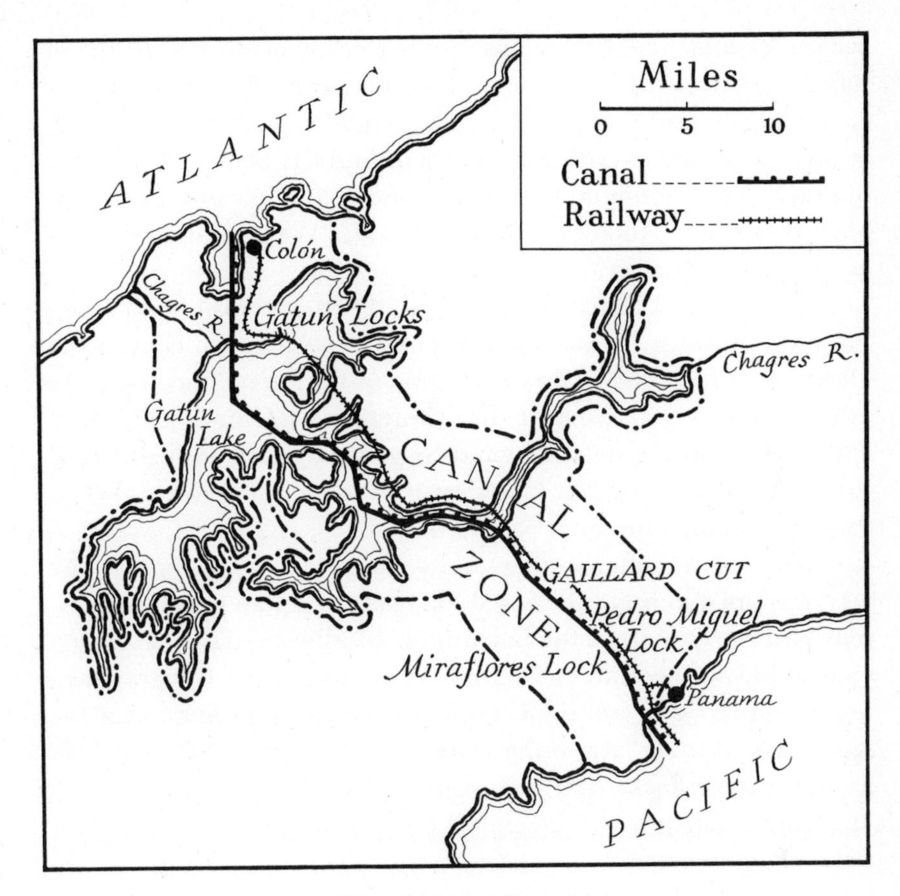

The Panama Canal

paying. In theory the Colombian Government could have sent an army overland to Panama, but that would have meant clearing a road for troops through impenetrable jungle inhabited by wildcats, anacondas and the untamed San Blas Indians. There was in fact nothing that the legitimate Colombian Government could do. It did nothing. The commander of the 450 troops sitting in the streets of Colón was given $8,000 to escape quietly to Jamaica, but the money was removed from him by his soldiers. One of the Colombian gunboats off Panama lobbed a single shell into the town, killing an unfortunate Chinaman. In Washington the Frenchman

Bunau-Varilla, acting as minister of the newly created Republic of Panama, presented his credentials to President Roosevelt on November 13th, and five days later Dr. Amador arrived to take part in the conversations with the President and the Secretary of State. But there was nothing to talk about. The revolution was an accomplished fact. Dr. Amador sighed and said, "Well, at any rate, yellow fever will disappear in Panama."

Years later President Roosevelt admitted that he had taken Panama at his own risk and without any attempt to consult the Congress. "If I had kept to the routine of traditional methods," he said, "I would have submitted to Congress a solemn document of 200 pages, and the debate would be going on yet! Instead I took the Canal Zone, and left Congress to discuss it afterward. While they are talking, the canal will be built."

Now at last, after so many false starts and false promises, the way was open to build the canal following the plan which De Lesseps had rejected from the beginning. In all essentials the Americans followed the plan of Godin de Lepinay at the Geographical Society in 1879. "Dam the Chagres and the Río Grande near the sea," he had said. "Raise the water level to eighty feet above sea level, construct locks, and then your cuttings in the Obispo Valley and across Culebra will be eighty feet less deep, thus enormously reducing your work."

So the backbreaking labor began, and it was ten years before the canal was built.

It began slowly with the inevitable hesitations and indecisions under a series of commissioners appointed by the American Government. Not until April, 1907, when George Washington Goethals was placed in command of the project, was there any great forward movement. Goethals was a career officer of Dutch descent, born in Brooklyn, tall, broad-shouldered, bronze-faced, gray-haired at forty-nine. He had been an instructor in civil and military engineering at West Point, and in charge of the Muscle Shoals canal construction on the Tennessee River. There was fire in the man. Shy, strangely humble, capable of sudden rages, he dominated the Canal

Zone from the day he took command. He regarded himself as the supreme commander of an expeditionary force sent to tame nature, and he succeeded brilliantly in doing what he set out to do. He liked to put aside part of the day for listening to complaints. Once a complainant said, "If you decide against me, Colonel, I shall appeal." Goethals answered simply, "To whom?" He was the whole court, counsel for defense, prosecution, and chief justice, and there was no court of appeal above him. He was a dictator with absolute powers, but there was never a dictator who acted so justly or so quietly.

Goethals had been in office barely six months when the full horror of the "expedition against nature" came to him. On October 4, 1907, a landslide began at the Culebra Cut during the night, spread across the gap excavated first by the French and then by the Americans, and moved steadily fourteen feet a day for ten days. Nearly 500,000 cubic yards of earth had to be removed until the unstable banks found their natural level of repose. There were more landslides later. In January, 1913, another slide started, and this time 2,500,000 cubic yards of earth had to be dug out. Even when the canal was completed, there were great landslides like the one which occurred in September, 1915, when the banks at East and West Culebra collapsed simultaneously, squeezing the canal bed upward 110 feet to form a ridge rising 65 feet above water level. Goethals was dealing with elemental forms of nature, with disease, with the difficulties of maneuvering a labor force in a tropical country, depressing, damp, miasmic, and intensely hot. William Crawford Gorgas, the Alabama doctor, had shown how yellow fever could be stopped, but the war against malaria was still continuing when Goethals took charge. Above all, there was the staggering difficulty of removing vast quantities of earth, and with every year the amount of earth which had to be removed grew larger. In 1905 an International Commission sent to Panama estimated it would be necessary to remove only 50 million cubic yards of earth. By 1908 the figure was 78 million, and by the time the canal was completed it was 100 million. The never ending work went on, and if a

Gates opening on Panama Canal (Pepsi-Cola International Panorama)

canal builder is measured by the amount of earth he excavates Goethals was the greatest of them all.

But in a sense the Panama Canal is not a canal at all: it is best defined as a flight of water steps divided into two sections at Gatun Lake and the Culebra Cut, with six enormous water elevators at each end. These locks are 1,000 feet long and 110 feet wide. At the Atlantic end there are three flights of three steps, while at the Pacific end two flights are separated from a third by the brackish waters of the Miraflores Lake. Into the lock chambers ships are drawn by electric "mules" or locomotives: then the huge steel gates, seven feet thick, close behind them. So with three steps upward and three down they climb the water bridge from sea to sea.

On August 15, 1914, with the war blazing in Europe, the canal was officially opened by President Belisario Porras of Panama.

There was almost no ceremony. The S.S. *Ancon,* belonging to the Panama Railroad, made the journey in just under ten hours. There were a few cheers, a few flags, nothing more.

A few weeks earlier another canal had been completed. This, too, had an ancient history, going back to 1784, when the old Eider Canal which started at Holtenau joined the Eider River at Rendsburg, so that ships could travel directly from the Baltic to the North Sea. The Eider Canal had six small locks, but was doomed by the coming of iron ships. In 1877 a new passage was begun, and completed in 1895. Twelve years later the canal was again taken in hand and reconstructed, being opened officially on June 24, 1914. This canal was the Kiel Canal, and through its 335-foot wide channels the Kaiser's battlefleet steamed out against the British Navy.

Today the Kiel Canal authorities claim that they have the busiest canal in the world. In 1956 one ship passed through it every eight minutes, while the Panama Canal has one ship every hour and the Suez Canal in normal times has one every thirty-six minutes.

Suez: the sea and the sands

Four empires—the Spanish, British, French, and American—contended over the Panama Canal, but the history of the Suez Canal goes back to remote empires of the past, so many that they are almost beyond counting. Like Panama, Suez is one of those focal points where the nerves of the world meet. Thousands of years ago men knew its value and counted the cost of constructing it. When it was abandoned by the Caliph al-Mansur, the sands swept over it and the great seaports built at both ends crumbled in the desert winds. In the time of the Renaissance the canal was no more than a legend, almost forgotten.

Occasionally, however, the memory of the canal returned to haunt the imaginations of conquerors. When Turkey captured Constantinople in 1453, Ottoman power controlled the overland route to Asia and possessed a monopoly on Red Sea shipping. So it happened that in the brief reign of Sultan Selim II, known as "the Sot," the Grand Vizier Muhammad Sokolli, then intent upon building a powerful navy, decided to cut a canal across the Isthmus of Suez to give his fleet undisputed control of the Red Sea and the Indian Ocean. He was one of the few Turkish generals who understood the need for canals. He even planned a canal to join the Don and the Volga, to enable him to attack the Persian province of Tabriz. To conquer Tabriz, he would have to seize the Russian town of Astrakhan, at the mouth of the Volga, but though his armies marched on Astrakhan in 1568, the Don-Volga Canal was never built by him, and he abandoned the idea of building a canal across the Isthmus of Suez when he heard of Arab disturbances in the Yemen.

Where Sokolli failed, Napoleon was determined to succeed. "He who is master of Egypt is master of India," he wrote, and the thought of converting the Indian Ocean into a French lake filled him with delighted enthusiasm. He made a special ten-day exploratory visit to the isthmus in December, 1798. He visited Suez, a small crumbling village ruined by three centuries of misrule by the Mamelukes and Turks, and upon his return to Cairo he summoned his chief engineer, Jacques-Marie Lepère, and ordered him to survey the isthmus. Lepère completed his survey in the following year and announced that the Red Sea was 32 feet 6 inches higher than the Mediterranean—a miscalculation accepted virtually without challenge, at a time when instruments for measuring sea level were notoriously inaccurate. Yet he was convinced that a canal could be constructed. He suggested that it should be cut along the path chosen by the ancient Pharaohs, joining the Red Sea to the Nile by way of the Bitter Lakes and Cairo. He suggested a width of 42 feet 6 inches at the bottom, and a mean depth of about 15 feet. Two years later Turkey and Britain combined to drive Napoleon out of Egypt, and once again the plan for a canal across the Isthmus of Suez slumbered.

Napoleon had thought to conquer Egypt; so had Britain; so had Turkey. But the true conqueror was the son of an obscure Albanian fisherman, Muhammad Ali Pasha, who rose to power by a series of brilliantly executed massacres. Treacherous, illiterate, astonishingly well equipped to lead his guerrilla armies, Muhammad Ali Pasha captured Cairo and, following a centuries-old tradition, led his armies across Syria in defiance of the Sultan of Turkey, to plant the Egyptian flag on the walls of Acre. He might have gone on to capture Constantinople, but the Great Powers intervened: it was a time when "the integrity of the Turkish Empire" was a basic axiom of European politics. Thereafter Muhammad

Ali Pasha, ruthless as ever, consolidated his power over Arabia and Upper Egypt, and showed himself the strongest ruler over the country since the time of the Ptolemies.

Like the Ptolemies and the Pharaohs, Muhammad Ali saw that the wealth of the country lay in her canals. He dug a canal between Alexandria and the western course of the Nile Canal. He made no surveys, provided neither transport nor accommodation, and sent 60,000 fellahin to shift the earth with their bare hands; and 15,000 died before the canal was completed. He built a barrage spanning two branches of the Nile at Rosetta and Damietta, and attempted to transform Egypt into his own private agricultural colony, exporting sugar and cotton. He cared nothing for the sacrifices entailed by his grandiose plans, but he was so successful in changing the face of Egypt that foreigners attributed to him some of the qualities they had attributed to Prester John in the Middle Ages. A fierce, beetle-browed man, who claimed to have modeled himself on Napoleon, he killed for pleasure. In the eyes of many Frenchmen and Englishmen this ruthless dictator who ruled Egypt with a hand of iron from 1805 to 1849 was a benevolent despot whose social program was slowly but surely lifting Egypt out of the misery of centuries of misrule. Egypt became the land of the future. People flocked to Egypt, as later they were to flock to the Soviet Union, seeing only what they wanted to see, mesmerized by the furious progress of the country which until recently had slept in the profound sleep of the Mamelukes.

Among those who were fascinated by the rebirth of Egypt were the followers of Comte Henri de Saint-Simon, who believed in "the redemption of human society through the dignity of labor." The Saint-Simonians formed a secret society devoted to the *mystique* of material progress. Saint-Simon himself believed that human welfare would increase immeasurably by cutting the canal at the Isthmus of Suez, and sent out a group of his followers to examine the project. Saint-Simon died in 1825, and nothing came of the first attempt to survey the land, but the dream of the canal continued to haunt his followers. It especially haunted Barthélemy-Prosper

Enfantin, a loyal follower of Saint-Simon, who succeeded in combining an acute business sense and an extraordinary knowledge of technology with a sacramental belief in visions. He believed in free love, and thought Jesus Christ was incarnate in him, and he lived to become the close friend of the German poet Heine and to be the director of the Paris-Lyon-Méditerranée Railway. To him, rather than to Ferdinand de Lesseps, should go the credit for bringing the Suez Canal to birth.

From the beginning the man who came to be known as Père Enfantin seems to have acted the role of fanatic with his tongue in his cheek. It amused him and served his purpose, but he was too intelligent to allow fanaticism to absorb him completely. Born in 1796, the year of Napoleon's victories in Italy, he became a brilliant student at the Ecole Polytechnique, the training ground of France's best engineers. It was a time of revolutionary ferment, with a bewildering succession of kings ruling over France: Louis XVIII, then Napoleon for a hundred days, then Charles X, then Louis-Philippe. Enfantin was tall and well built, inclined to fat, with large eyes and a fleshy mouth. He came to know the men in power, but he also knew the revolutionaries. He joined the secret society of the Carbonari, and about the same time he joined the Saint-Simonians. Soon he became one of the high priests of the movement, which was then in search of a leader to replace the late Comte Henri de Saint-Simon. One morning, at half-past six, before he was out of bed, he was visited by a hysterical member of the brotherhood, a converted Jew called Gustave D'Eichthal, who reported that during Communion at Nôtre Dame the night before it had been revealed to him that "Jesus lives in Enfantin." Furthermore, Enfantin was one of the holy couple, the Son and Daughter of God, whose coming had been prophesied in Revelation, Enfantin was pleased by the revelation, but decided to act cautiously. He explained that if he was the Bridegroom, it was necessary to await the coming of the Bride, and in the meantime he could not name himself nor could he be named. He begged D'Eichthal to let him go back to sleep. D'Eichthal left him, but returned almost immediately, insisting that the hour had struck and it was time for Enfantin to proclaim himself the Son of God. For a while Enfantin said nothing, calmly pulling on his socks. Then he said, *"Homo sum!"* The hysterical apostle was sworn to secrecy: no one must be told about the affair until the appearance of the Bride, who would no doubt soon reveal herself.

Though D'Eichthal had been sworn to secrecy, he was incapable of keeping the good news to himself. Soon all the Saint-Simonians were aware that the time of Revelation was at hand. Enfantin became "the elected one," "the Bridegroom," and was called "Jesus" and "Pope." He was believed to possess the power to regenerate the earth. He wore a beard and assumed the sacramental robe of Melchizedek, and with forty of his disciples retreated to Ménilmontant, just outside the city, where he established a monastery. The disciples wore vivid costumes of red, white, and violet, while Enfantin wore a costume consisting of a long, belted tunic with a low neckline and an embroidered silk scarf wound round the neck and cascading down to the knees, with the words *Le Père* written across his undershirt. All the disciples grew beards and wore sandals and worked with their hands, following the edict of the Comte de Saint-Simon: "Every man must work in a way useful to society."

No one paid very much attention to this strange society of dedicated workmen with their messianic beliefs until Louis-Philippe came to the throne. Then charges were brought against them: they advocated free love and scorned the public morality of the time. Enfantin was brought to trial. He appeared at court wearing a voluminous flowing velvet cloak trimmed with ermine, and announced that he was beyond the jurisdiction of the judges. He was a portentous figure, with his long hair parted in the middle, his long beard, his brilliant cloak and his Hessian boots, and he declared that he had appeared in court only in order that the judge might appreciate the beauty of his countenance and the majesty of his appearance. The judge was puzzled, and sentenced him to imprisonment in the terrible fetid prison of Sainte-Pélagie, where Alexandre

Dumas and the most brilliant of French mathematicians, Evariste Galois, were also prisoners. The society was disbanded. The government believed that the power of the Saint-Simonians had been broken.

But in fact the society was all the more alive with its messiah in prison, and its long shadow was to fall over the rest of the century. Its influence can be felt even in our own day, for Lenin read avidly in the works of Comte Henri de Saint-Simon and adopted many of his principles. The Saint-Simonians were the first to use the word "socialist," and the first to state that "the government of men will be replaced by the administration of things." And long before Marx, they foresaw the emergence of the industrial proletariat as rulers of the state. Yet still in those early years they were haunted by visions.

Released from prison the following year, Enfantin, still wearing his extraordinary costume, made his way to Egypt accompanied by a group of fervent disciples. He announced that the long-sought-for Bride was no woman of flesh, but Egypt herself, and his task, and that of his followers, was to transform Egypt according to the principles of the Comte de Saint-Simon. Not only would they cut a canal joining the Mediterranean to the Red Sea, but they would assume the burden of introducing vast public works in the Near East, which was sacred ground and clearly the source from which the redemption of the earth might be expected. They would build barrages, for that too was holy work; and many schools; and there would be great social and economic reforms. In one of those oracular statements which he composed in free verse Enfantin declared:

The task is ours to establish
Between ancient Egypt and age-old Judea,
One of the two new roads from Europe
Towards India and China,
And afterwards we shall cut the other
At Panama.
We shall have one foot on the Nile,
The other on Jerusalem,
Our right hand will reach towards Mecca.

Our left arm shall cover Rome,
Our left hand will rest on Paris.
Suez
Stands at the center of our work:
There we shall accomplish the act
Which the whole world is waiting for
To prove ourselves
Masters.

When Enfantin arrived in Egypt and sought an audience with Muhammad Ali Pasha, accompanied by an adoring group of technicians, he assumed two roles: he was the Son of God, and he was also the brilliant student of the Ecole Polytechnique. In the Near East, at that particular time, it was a dangerous and effective combination, and Muhammad Ali Pasha listened to Enfantin and allowed him to survey the isthmus. In Cairo, Enfantin met the recently appointed French consul, the young and aristocratic Ferdinand de Lesseps, who had already enjoyed tours of duty in Lisbon and Tunis. De Lesseps was twenty-eight, Enfantin thirty-seven. A close friendship sprang up between them. De Lesseps was impressed by Enfantin's technical knowledge, and seems not to have been unduly alarmed by the claims of messiahship. With the blessing of Muhammad Ali Pasha, Enfantin spent two weeks surveying the isthmus and laid his plans before the viceroy, who rejected the proposal chiefly on the grounds that it would offend Turkey. Enfantin remained for two years in Egypt, and then returned to France, where he gradually abandoned his claim to be the Bridegroom and took service in the French railways. By 1845 he became a director of a railway line, and two years later, having amassed a solid fortune and acquired some influence on Louis-Philippe, he set about organizing an international committee of engineers—the Société d'études pour le Canal de Suez—to study afresh the whole question of the canal and to enlist the support of European capitalists. The headquarters of the society was Enfantin's house in Paris, which was also the headquarters of the Saint-Simonian movement. Here hardheaded businessmen, skilled railway engineers, and devotees of the cult met to discuss the regeneration of the world in terms of engineering and economics. The Saint-Simonian fire was still burning.

Enfantin had failed to cut the Suez Canal when he visited Egypt because the time was not ripe. Linant de Bellefonds, a French engineer sent to Egypt by the Société d'études pour le Canal de Suez, reported that the plan was feasible. Enfantin brought the report to the attention of Louis-Philippe and sent emissaries to Muhammad Ali Pasha. France and Egypt gave their blessing to the work, and a company was duly registered with a capital of 150,000 francs. Elaborate plans were drawn up. They proposed that the Suez Canal should pass through the Bitter Lakes, joining Suez on the Red Sea with Pelusium on the Mediterranean. The canal would be ninety-one miles long, with a depth of twenty-six feet, and it would be provided with locks at each end. French engineers would be employed, and Enfantin would be controller-general of the whole enterprise.

Enfantin must have thought that the construction of the canal was almost within reach. Suddenly, one after another, the two powerful men who had backed the enterprise were removed from the scene—in 1848 Louis-Philippe was overthrown, and in the following year Muhammad Ali Pasha died, to be succeeded by his grandson Abbas Pasha, who disliked the idea of building a canal and favored the British, who wanted instead to build a railway between Alexandria and Suez. Construction of the railway began in 1851. In July, 1854, Abbas Pasha, a strange, unhappy recluse, was poisoned by his slaves. He was succeeded by his uncle, Sa'id Pasha, who weighed nearly three hundred pounds and kept a flock of French mistresses. He ate heartily, drank magnificently, and entertained visiting sovereigns with spicy stories. No one quite like him had ever appeared on the viceregal throne of Egypt. No one knew in which direction his agile mind might spring, for it might occur to him to load his visitors with honors or to cut off their heads. Once he entertained his governors by making them wade through loose gunpowder with lighted candles in their hands, to test their nerves. "Give him two hundred!" he would shout, without explaining whether he meant the whip or baksheesh. Few men had ever genuinely liked him. Among the few was Ferdinand de Lesseps, who had taken pity on the fat prince when he was a young consul in Cairo. They had become close friends and inseparable companions, but De Lesseps had gone on to more important consular offices and finally resigned from the foreign service in the upheaval following the 1848 Revolution. When he heard that Sa'id Pasha had come to the throne, De Lesseps was a forty-nine-year-old widower living in retirement, his only source of income coming from the management of his mother-in-law's estates.

De Lesseps was working on the roof of an old manor house when the postman brought news of Sa'id Pasha's accession. He immediately hurried down the ladder and wrote off a letter of congratulation, and requested an opportunity to pay homage to the viceroy in person. Quite suddenly he saw that fate was conspiring in his favor. Napoleon III had come to the throne of France, and it so happened that the Empress Eugénie was De Lesseps' cousin. Sa'id Pasha had been, and might be again, his closest friend. De Lesseps had no knowledge of engineering, but he knew Père Enfantin and many of the members of the Société d'études pour le Canal de Suez, and it occurred to him that with his formidable connections he was in a position to promote the canal, recoup his fortunes, and bring untold benefit to France.

On November 7, 1854, De Lesseps arrived in Alexandria, to be met by a viceregal carriage. A sumptuous palace was placed at his disposal. Servants, horses, washbasins of solid silver, a whole platoon of coffee makers—all these were given to him by Sa'id Pasha with the casual openhandedness of a man who wishes to reward the enduring loyalty of a friend. De Lesseps presented himself at the Gabbari Palace in knee breeches, gold-laced coat and cocked hat, assuming a consular uniform he was no longer entitled to wear. But the middle-aged monarch was overjoyed to renew his friendship with the retired diplomat, and a few days later De Lesseps was invited to join a military parade across the desert to Cairo.

Accompanied by an escort of ten thousand soldiers, Sa'id Pasha was about to show himself in the ancient capital.

Enfantin had his visions; so had De Lesseps; and they were the same kind of visions, and occurred at about the same hour of the day. On the morning of November 15th, as dawn broke over the desert encampment, De Lesseps stepped out of his tent wearing a bright red dressing gown. He returned to the tent, washed, put on warmer clothes, and then found himself looking up at the sky. A magnificent rainbow hung across the heavens. In the hush of early morning De Lesseps found himself strangely moved by this bright apparition, and repeated to himself the words of Jehovah: "I do set my bow in the cloud, and it shall be for a token of a covenant between me and the earth." Painted across the sky was the sign of inevitable success. He looked down to earth and saw the viceroy coming toward him with outstretched hands. He was tempted to talk about the canal at that moment, but shrewdly decided to postpone the discussion until later in the day. In the evening, at sunset, he was alone with Sa'id Pasha in the viceregal tent, sitting hand in hand with him on a divan. Then, very calmly, while watching the sun going down, De Lesseps expounded his plan. The viceroy listened attentively, raised some minor objections, and said at last: "I am satisfied. I accept your plan. For the rest of the journey we will concern ourselves with the means of carrying it out. You may regard the matter as settled, and trust to me."

A moment later the viceroy summoned his officers into the tent, and repeated in his own words all that De Lesseps had told him. He spoke quietly and slowly, like a man to whom a revelation has come, and sometimes the officers would raise their hands to their heads in sign of assent. Soon the dinner table was brought in, and they all dipped their spoons in the soup tureen; and this action, so solemnly performed, seemed to De Lesseps like the consecration of all that had gone before.

That night De Lesseps was too excited to sleep, and wrote out a long memorandum to be presented the next morning to the vice-

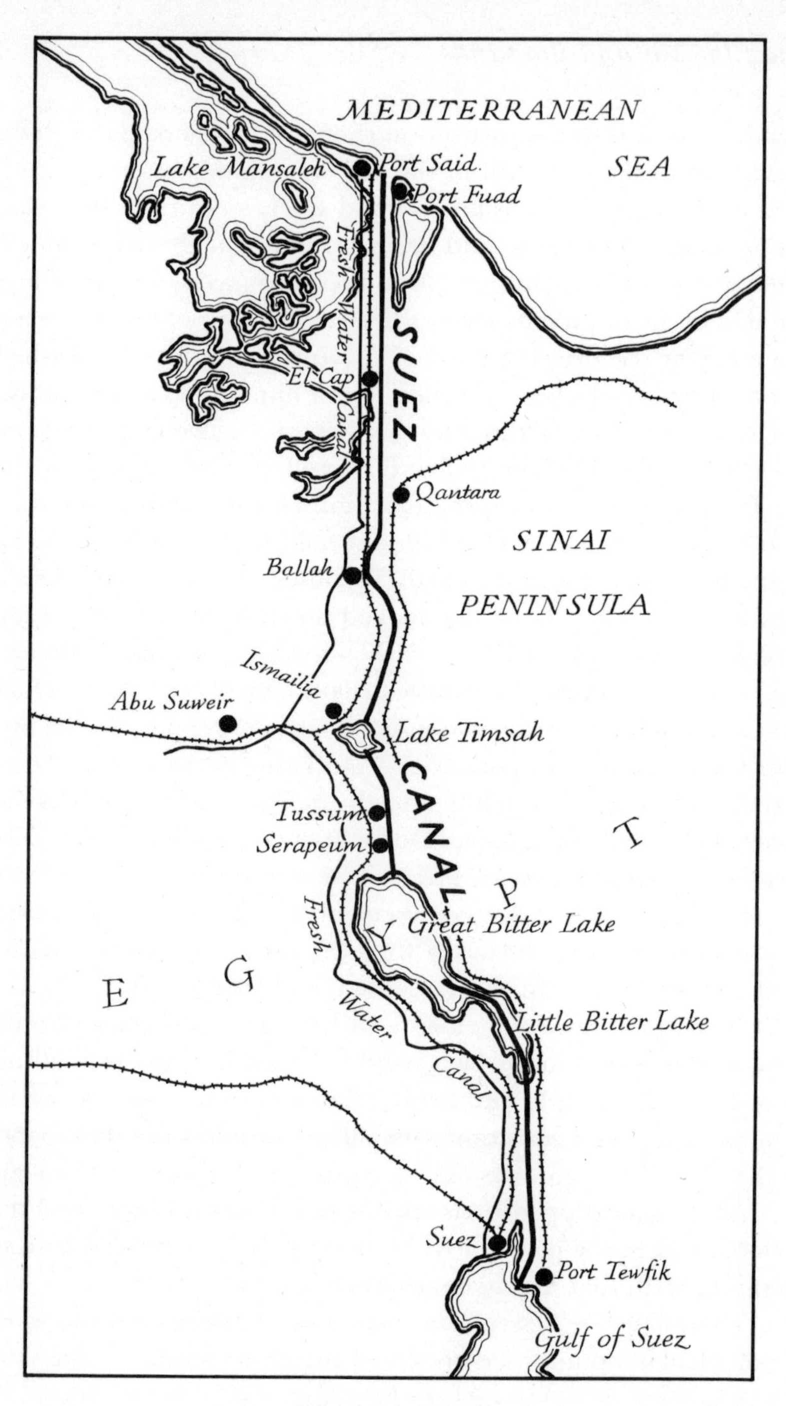

The Suez Canal

roy. The memorandum, which has survived, betrays the excitement of the hour. As he wrote, it seemed to him that there were no difficulties which could not be overcome, no technical problems which could not be solved with ease. "Success is no longer in doubt," he wrote, while describing the operation in the vaguest generalities. He was not at all sure where the canal would be cut—that was a matter to be left to the surveyors. He observed that "modern construction costs are likely to be high," but if only three million tons of shipping passed through the canal it would earn 30 million francs a year. All nations would applaud the construction of the canal; all would work to maintain its inviolable neutrality; no other labor of men's hands was so fraught with glory and the possibilities of great wealth. "For ages upon ages to come men will bless the name of the Prince who opens this canal."

So he wrote on in the night, dreaming of power, glory, and riches, dismissing briefly all the attempts which had been made to dig the canal in the past, searching for the arguments which would flatter the viceroy's vanity, speaking of the canal as only a few hours before he had spoken of the glittering rainbow which joined the east and the west together. Ten days later, in Cairo, the diplomatic corps attended the viceroy in the Citadel to present their congratulations on his accession to the throne, and the viceroy solemnly announced that he had decided after mature reflection to cut a sea-water canal through the isthmus. Furthermore, he had chosen "our friend Monsieur Ferdinand de Lesseps" as the promoter of the canal, empowered to float a company on capital from all the nations which desired to contribute, and De Lesseps alone would have the right to develop the enterprise. Only the English consul looked crestfallen.

The English were to be a thorn in De Lesseps' side for years to come. They objected strongly to the revival of French power in Egypt, cutting across their lines of communication with India and the Far East. They saw the possibility of vast changes arising from the construction of the canal. They feared, as they do today, the emergence of a foreign power on Egyptian soil. As far back as 1838

Lord Palmerston, the Foreign Secretary, had drawn the portrait of the nightmare—an awakened Egypt would declare its independence of Turkey, a weakened Turkey would invite a Russian attack on Constantinople and the Dardanelles, and the French, for all he knew, would support the Russians against the British. The power pattern of the Near East might change disastrously. Accordingly, the British showed no particular pleasure in seeing a French-operated canal in Egypt, even though De Lesseps continually proclaimed the neutrality of the canal, saying long before it was built that it would be open to all nations equally, in times of peace as in times of war.

Opposition to the plan came from other quarters. The Société d'études pour le Canal de Suez was still in existence, and Prosper Enfantin was now a powerful figure in French financial circles. Almost singlehandedly he had consolidated the Paris-Lyon-Méditerranée Railway in 1852. His company possessed prior rights over the construction of the canal, and there were members of the board of directors very close to Napoleon III. To the Saint-Simonians De Lesseps pointed out gleefully that he alone possessed an authentic firman from the viceroy, and in any event the Société d'études pour le Canal de Suez was no more than a company brought into being to survey the whole question: it was not in fact a construction company. When Prosper Enfantin threatened to bring suit against him, De Lesseps replied that it would be more sensible to bring suit against Sa'id Pasha. "As for myself," he wrote, "I am determined to keep the reins in my hands."

Until the canal was built, he never allowed the reins to drop from his hands. He assumed final responsibility. He surveyed the isthmus again, traveled all over Europe urging capitalists to extend capital to the company, of which he was the founder, chairman, and chief executive officer, and he drew up the terms of the concession, which was to run for ninety-nine years from the opening of the canal, with the net profits divided—15 per cent to the Egyptian Government, 10 per cent to "founders," 75 per cent to ordinary shareholders. The plan for the canal followed almost exactly the

Ferdinand de Lesseps

plan outlined by the Société d'études pour le Canal de Suez, joining Suez with Pelusium through the Bitter Lakes, with locks at both ends. An international committee composed of thirteen experts from seven countries was invited to examine the plan for the canal. The committee made slight modifications to the original plan and declared, in words that sound suspiciously as though they were written by De Lesseps, that "the execution of the work is easy, and its success assured."

It was not, of course, as easy as De Lesseps thought it would be. There were long delays, protracted battles. Lord Stratford de Redcliffe, Britain's ambassador to Constantinople, did everything he could to torpedo the scheme. For a while Napoleon III was undecided. Sa'id Pasha himself was in no hurry. But gradually, and with infinite patience, De Lesseps succeeded in countering opposition wherever it occurred. He bearded Palmerston in his den. He flooded England with propaganda in favor of the canal. The Empress Eugénie and Prince Jérôme Bonaparte became his willing helpers, and when the Sultan of Turkey refused to give his consent and Sa'id Pasha panicked and suggested it would be much simpler altogether to abandon the whole project, Napoleon III counseled patience, and still more patience, saying, "Be strong, and everyone will help you."

De Lesseps possessed the imperial temper. He was a man who combined ruthlessness and patience to an extraordinary degree. When everything went wrong, he held firm. He succeeded in obtaining a new concession from the viceroy. This document, dated January 5, 1856, provided that the company was to construct the canal "at its own risk and peril," four-fifths of the workers were to be Egyptians, and the project was to be completed within six years, unless unforeseen circumstances brought about interruptions. But the approval of the Sultan had not yet been received, and the British were still actively pursuing a policy against it. Once more De Lesseps approached the viceroy. He pointed out that a canal on Egyptian soil was a domestic operation, which needed only the viceroy's approval to be put into effect. The Sultan of Turkey had not been asked to approve the railroad which the British had built across Europe. Why wait? In a mood of desperation the viceroy, who had grown alarmingly fat, capitulated. He had given De Lesseps the concession, and he would not stand in his way. He was, besides, weary of the thunderclouds of international intrigue boiling all round him.

Once again, at a moment when all seemed lost, De Lesseps had found the words of the spell which opened the gates. The words were: "It is after all a domestic operation." They were wise words, carefully chosen, and when he saw the gleam in the viceroy's eyes, De Lesseps knew at long last that the canal would be built.

On October 15, 1858, De Lesseps issued his prospectus, inviting investors from all countries to take up "temporary certificates convertible to bearer bonds at a date to be announced later." Of the 400,000 shares on offer, 80,000 were set aside for the French people. The French oversubscribed to the extent of 207,111 shares. Mostly they were bought by people from the middle classes who shared De Lesseps' belief in the grandeur of the scheme and the expectation of quick profits. Four thousand shares were bought in Spain, where De Lesseps had family connections. Five were bought in Portugal, seven in Denmark, and fifteen in Prussia. De Lesseps' hope that the company would have international backing was sadly shattered. Except for a few shares sold on the Continent, the only investors were the French people and Sa'id Pasha, who made a personal investment of 177,642 shares, making him the largest single shareholder with 44 per cent of the total investment. The canal, if it was ever built, would belong solidly to France and the pasha.

The pasha was perturbed; so was De Lesseps. They expected to hear the thunder from the Sublime Porte and the still more resounding thunder from Downing Street. Surprisingly, the voices of international diplomacy were silent. De Lesseps had a brief meeting with Sa'id Pasha, and then left for Alexandria and Damietta. On April 25, 1859, he gathered his engineers and workmen on the shore of ancient Pelusium, drove a mattock in the earth, and pronounced that the excavation of the Suez Canal had begun. He named that desolate strip of coast Port Said, in honor of the monarch who had given him so much encouragement. But Sa'id Pasha was a sick and frightened man, so swollen that he could hardly stand, and when at last the long-delayed thunder was heard, he panicked again, refused to allow Egyptians to work on the canal, and only halfheartedly permitted the European engineers to remain.

Through the winter and the following summer work continued at a crawl, while De Lesseps sought to return to the good graces of the pasha. Napoleon III, fresh from his victories over the Austrians at Magenta and Solferino, was now a power in Europe; his intervention saved the day. Once again the fellahin went to work on the first stretch of the canal from Port Said skirting the eastern edge of Lake Mansaleh. They scooped up the sand in their hands and carried it in baskets. They were fed and housed and paid a standard wage, but they were forced to work: they were in fact slaves. De Lesseps saw nothing wrong in slavery. When the British objected to the employment of slaves, he suggested that the British Government might be better occupied in freeing the slaves of Russia and the United States. "In Egypt," he wrote, "slavery is the most normal thing in the world." He made a point of speaking with the workmen. "A hundred boys and girls from ten to thirteen years old are working here with remarkable zeal and energy," he declared, making no mention of their stern taskmasters who were provided with whips. He noted that the Arabs imported from Syria played merrily on their tambourines and flutes, and there were even a few dancing girls with them.

The work went on slowly. By the end of 1862 the fresh-water canal had been brought to Lake Timsah, and the waters of the Mediterranean were held back from the lake by only a narrow ridge of earth. De Lesseps liked pageantry. At eleven o'clock on the morning of November 18th, on a platform hastily erected and decorated with bunting and flags, surrounded by company officials and distinguished guests, he gave the signal for the workmen to break down the narrow barrier of earth, saying: "By the grace of God and in the name of His Highness Muhammad Sa'id, I command that the waters of the Mediterranean enter Lake Timsah!" The barrier gave way before the blows of an ax, and then the waters came boiling out of the cut, and soon everyone was shouting and the band was playing the Egyptian national anthem, while De Lesseps beamed, his right hand lying across his chest in the attitude made famous by Napoleon. Against all odds he had conquered; but there were still many more battles to come.

The news of the successful joining of the Mediterranean to Lake Timsah was flashed across the world. Napoleon III honored him with the rank of commander of the Legion of Honor. The Empress Eugénie and Sa'id Pasha sent their greetings. Only the British Government, concerned with the menacing growth of French influence on the isthmus, continued to show hostility. Sir Henry Bulwer Lytton was sent to interview Sa'id Pasha. He was amazed by the progress which had been made. "I have seen all this," he said, "and till I saw it, I confess I did not believe it." Sa'id Pasha professed to be indifferent to the whole operation. Aging rapidly, weary of the incessant diplomatic moves in London, Paris, Constantinople, and Cairo, he promised Britain that he would allow no more fellahin to work on the project, and a few days later explained to De Lesseps that his greatest ambition was to see the canal completed before his death.

Early in January, 1863, De Lesseps saw the pasha for the last time in a great tent erected near the Nile Barrage. The pasha was stricken by intense pains, and kept saying that death was near. To comfort him, De Lesseps said he was suffering from nothing more serious than sciatica. But the pasha knew better—obesity and high blood pressure were taking their toll. The pasha suggested that the time had come to arrange for the final settlement of his financial obligations to the company. Something must be done quickly, for the successor to the throne might fall under the domination of the British, and there was no time left to ensure the continuation of the company. "You must let me sign now, or everything will be lost," he said; and De Lesseps answered that there would be time enough when they met again. They never met again. By January 17th the pasha was dead, and his successor was his eldest son, Ismail, a short, blunt, black-bearded man, whose eyes never seemed to focus on the object they contemplated. The fortunes of the Suez Canal Company were now in the hands of an unprepossessing thirty-three-year-old wastrel, whose sympathies were closely allied to Britain.

De Lesseps fought back, as he had fought so many times before. When in April the Sublime Porte issued an order for the work to stop, he seemed unruffled. Turkey, to satisfy Britain, said the work could go on only if there was an end to forced labor. De Lesseps appealed to Napoleon III. Surprisingly, the Emperor of the French succeeded in imposing himself as mediator. In return for a waiver of 60,000 hectares of land and four-fifths of the laborers, the company was granted 84,000,000 francs. Ismail Pasha was pleased. All the land bordering the canal would now fall into his possession, to be used for raising cotton, soon to become the greatest single crop in Egypt. Formerly Egypt had grown wheat: now its entire economy was to be turned to cotton, with the result that Egypt was to become more and more involved in world economy and its attendant crises. With a stroke of the pen Napoleon III altered the landscape of Egypt.

When they learned that Napoleon had succeeded in imposing an act of arbitration, the British were alarmed, but De Lesseps had long ago prepared for just such an eventuality. Mechanical excavators were being used increasingly. Steam tramways supplemented the thousands of asses, mules, and camels now assisting the workmen who worked with their bare hands, rolling the mud into balls on their chests and then hauling it up the high banks. Workmen were already being imported from abroad—8,000 came from England, France, Greece, and Italy, and 10,000 more came from Africa, Arabia, and Syria.

There were still more crises to be overcome. Cholera broke out in June, 1865, and thousands of workmen fled. De Lesseps was in Paris. He feared neither cholera nor the British now, and hurried back to Egypt. Hundreds had died at Ismailia, and thousands of panic-stricken workmen were making for Port Said, but he moved among them like someone possessing the gift of immunity. His son Charles was the company manager at Ismailia. He had a son, Ferdinand, named after the grandfather, and the son was stricken. De Lesseps hurried to the bedside, too late to see his favorite grandson alive. Then for the first time his nerve failed. He collapsed completely. Six years later Robert Koch, working in Egypt, isolated the cholera bacillus.

Now the worst was over. One after another obstacles had been placed before them, but the engineers had surmounted them. In the relentless 120-degree heat the workmen continued to make their way toward the Red Sea. As always, the improbable attended De Lesseps. He discovered the remains of a granite stele marking the course of the canal dug by Darius. South of Lake Timsah he discovered and dug through levels of ancient clay containing the fossilized bones of elephants and dogfish. He noted that the workmen imported to dig through the clay came from Piedmont, which had seen the birth of the great Renaissance canals. Port Said, once a treacherous and waterless sandspit, had grown into a large town with schools, churches, mosques, hospitals, even a theater. When funds gave out and the company was on the verge of bankruptcy, the indefatigable De Lesseps appealed to the empress to help him rush a bill through the Chamber enabling him to issue preference shares. Then the work went on, as though there had never been any interruptions to its slow and ineluctable progress.

From all parts of the world people flocked to the canal, as they would flock to some fashionable event. Ismail Pasha arrived in state, to bless the undertaking and demonstrate by his presence his approval of the French. Soon he was to abandon the title of Pasha, which he shared with so many minor officials: the Sublime Porte granted him the use of the completely meaningless title of Khedive.

At long last, in the late summer of 1869, fifteen years after the concession was granted, the waters of the Mediterranean and the Red Sea merged in the Bitter Lakes.

At the ceremony De Lesseps presided with his usual aplomb, very quiet and calm, smiling at the workers, who had assembled from all directions, and behaving with his usual deference toward the Khedive Ismail, who sat on a small throne, his chest blazing with medals and his head protected from the sweltering August sun with an umbrella. The waters of the Red Sea were held back by a dike at the northern end of the Bitter Lakes. A mile away another dike held back the waters of the Mediterranean. De Lesseps planned to breach the Red Sea dike at a signal from Ismail. There were prayers from the mullahs, and then De Lesseps intoned the words: "Thirty-five centuries have passed since the waters of the Red Sea were hurled back by the order of Moses. Today, by the order of the Sovereign of Egypt, they return to their bed!" For De Lesseps it was a glorious moment, the fulfillment of all his dreams, and he was observed to wave his hands like a conjuror summoning the great flood of waters.

But he did not smile for long. The breach was made, the waters surged in, gleaming white in the sun, and moving with an appalling roar against the banks of the canal, flooding over them, overturning machinery and even threatening the place where Ismail and De Lesseps were standing. The workers screamed and ran to safety. The whole dike crumbled in the boiling waters. If the Mediterranean dike did not hold, then the work of years would be in vain. De Lesseps ordered every available man to hurry to the northern dike to reinforce it. They were only just in time. Night came, and they were still working. In the morning there were quiet waters on either side of the barrier, and De Lesseps sighed with relief. Then, without any ceremony at all, in the presence of only a few people, the last dike was breached, and for the first time since ancient geologic times the two seas were allowed to mingle.

Already De Lesseps was preparing for the grand ceremonial opening, to be attended, he hoped, by all the crowned heads of Europe. The Empress Eugénie, of course, would preside over the ceremonies. With pardonable pride he chose November 17th as the day when the canal would be officially opened, and since his birthday came two days later he might reasonably expect to be deluged with honors on his birthday. The empress made her leisurely progress to Egypt on board the steam yacht *L'Aigle,* visiting Venice, Athens, and Constantinople, where she charmed the sultan. Still young, still glowing with beauty, she enjoyed the illusion of power, the sense of her own magnificence; she could not foresee that in a few months she would be forced to leave Paris in disguise, to spend the rest of her life in exile. Crowned with diamonds, she entered Cairo like a conqueror, to find the whole city at her feet. It was a new city, remodeled by Ismail for her benefit: parks and public gardens had been built, palaces were restored, and gas lamps glimmered along the new boulevards. She visited the Pyramids. Six weeks before there had been no carriage road, but Ismail built one for her. He gave her the Guezireh Palace in Cairo, completely refurnishing it, painting the walls pale blue, her favorite color, and removing some of the marble nudes which upheld the gilded mirrors. Ismail himself had toured Europe, to invite the kings and potentates to the feast, together with five hundred chefs and a thousand servants, mostly from France. Bed linen, tablecloths, crystal chandeliers, damask curtains—everything was new. Floundering in luxury, he spent money so freely that it was estimated that the inauguration ceremonies alone cost Ismail four million dollars.

Neither the empress nor De Lesseps was in any mood to count the cost. *L'Aigle* steamed into Port Said on the morning of November 16th. It was a calm, summery day, with the waters of the Mediterranean a deep blue, and the fleets of half a dozen nations serenaded the empress and the other royal yachts all covered with bunting and flags. The British sent fourteen naval vessels, among them five ironclads. The harbor was crowded with ships of all sizes and colors, men-o'-war, launches, cutters, dinghies, rowboats, company vessels. The warships saluted the arrival of the empress with salvos, which were answered by Egyptian batteries on shore and the band playing *"Partant pour la Syrie."* Ismail had not succeeded in inviting all the crowned heads of Europe: the Czar of Russia and the Queen of England were notably absent. But the Emperor Franz Josef was present, and the Kaiser had sent Crown Prince Friedrich, and the Prince of Holland stood beside Prince Edward, the Prince of Wales, later to become King Edward VII. Islam was represented by the Grand Ulema of Egypt, and Christianity by the Archbishop of Jerusalem. To the very end there was to be a strange private quality to the proceedings, as though De Lesseps and his adored cousin were intent upon keeping the celebrations within the family, and so it was Monseigneur Bauer, the confessor to the empress, a strange twisted man who for many years had been the real ruler of France, who pronounced the solemn dedication.

Monseigneur Bauer was in his element. He delighted in great flights of passionate declamation, modeling his sermons on the funeral orations of Bossuet. But this was no funeral oration. Here was the triumph of one man and his empress against all the evil of the world! "The barriers are overthrown!" he cried. "One of the most formidable enemies of mankind—distance—loses in a moment two thousand leagues of his empire, and now the two faces of the world approach and feel only friendly feelings to one another, and in their exchange of greetings they recognize that all men are children of God, and recognizing this, they tremble in wonder at their mutual brotherhood."

There was a good deal more of it. The solemn incantations pronounced at the opening of canals form a peculiar addition to the crazier statements of men in love with their own handiwork. Monseigneur Bauer thought that the opening of the Suez Canal was as important as the discovery of America. "In the past," he declared, "all chronology was divided between the centuries before and after the discovery of America, but henceforth chronology will say: 'This was before or after the East and West met across the flank of Egypt!' In the future they will say such-and-such a thing happened before or after the opening of the Suez Canal!" It was an oddly blasphemous division of the earth's history under God, but the Monseigneur was in no mood to diminish the glory of the empress or her loyal servant De Lesseps. Her Majesty had worked silently for the completion of the canal—how silently and with what assiduity only De Lesseps and the Monseigneur knew—and the time had come when her name should be uttered to the four winds, so that everyone would know to whom the real credit should go. He said little about the Khedive Ismail, but much about De Lesseps:

Now that the incredible has become real, now that the chimera has become palpable, and the vast accomplishment lies before our enchanted eyes, what must be passing in the mind of him who was the soul of what we see? God knows! But as I look at him, I seem to see the glitter of tears in his eyes, and I would I could preserve those tears, for they belong to France and all humanity! So let me declare the name of the man who belongs to history, entering through her portals, by a divine privilege rarely accorded to those who are still living, while in the full enjoyment of his faculties. Let us declare to the world that France, though far away but in no way absent, is proud and happy in her son. And just as in the fifteenth century the discovery of the New World commemorates for ever the name of the great navigator, so too will the name of Ferdinand de Lesseps be for ever remembered.

Almighty and eternal God, creator of the world and Father of all creatures, bless this new highway which Thou hast permitted to be opened in the midst of Thy creation. Make of this river only a passage to universal prosperity, but make it also the royal road of peace and justice, and of the light, and of the eternal truth. O God, grant that this highway shall bring all men together and lead them to Thyself; and may it be a blessing for all men, in time and in eternity!

So, with considerable finesse, Monseigneur Bauer celebrated the world and the God who ruled over the world in the same breath; and sprinkled holy water on the canal; and then withdrew, so that Eugénie and De Lesseps could share the limelight. There were more salvos from the batteries, more salutes from the naval vessels; but the Khedive Ismail was seen to be bored, and soon preparations were being made for the more practical part of the ceremony —the long procession, led by the steamship *L'Aigle* with the empress on board, from the Mediterranean to the Red Sea.

This was the part which De Lesseps feared most of all, for there were ugly rumors of sabotage, and worse. On November 2nd a rock was uncovered in the canal. It broke the dredger's bucket, and De Lesseps called for gunpowder, saying ominously: "Heaps of gunpowder! If we can't blow up the rock, we'll blow up ourselves!" On the night of November 15th fire broke out among the fireworks stored at Port Said for the festivities. Nearby, were huge quantities of explosives, enough to blow the port sky-high. At the last moment two thousand troops entered the port and were just in time to remove the explosives to safety. At dawn, on the day of the official opening of the canal, De Lesseps was awakened with the news that there were unusual high tides and the platform where the religious rites were to be held was in danger. Again and again De Lesseps came to the conclusion that the fates were working against him.

But when the great procession of ships set out for the Red Sea, De Lesseps told himself he had calculated the depth and breadth of the canal to the last fraction of an inch, that all the fifty-two ships steaming a cable's length apart must surely reach their destination without grounding, and that the fates would not dare to imperil his handiwork. All the ships' captains had received their final instructions. The honor of leading the procession had been given to the Egyptian frigate *Latif,* which was steaming ahead at a cautious seven knots. It went aground after a few miles; a thousand workmen worked to free her, and De Lesseps was in despair. Accompanied by the khedive, he rushed to the spot. The khedive looked on grimly. De Lesseps suggested that there were two alternatives: to float her or to push her farther into the sandy shore. The khedive suggested a third possibility.

"Blow her up!" he shouted, and De Lesseps embraced him, saying, "Yes, yes, magnificent!"

Such easy solutions commended themselves to the canal builders, but in fact they were not necessary. The *Latif* was refloated just in time. The great procession sailed down the canal soon after dawn, with *L'Aigle* in the van. If *L'Aigle* was grounded, all the ships following her would be grounded. There was an extraordinary atmosphere of tension on the ship. The captain left the bridge. His place was a little perch above the starboard paddlewheel, from which he could look out on the banks. The empress, alternately elated and despairing, went below, saying she felt there was a circle of fire round her head, and every moment she expected the ship to come to a halt: France would be compromised, and the fruit of all their labors would perish. Standing outside her stateroom, De Lesseps heard her sobbing for the lost glory of France, though nothing had been lost, and the ship continued to steam cautiously down the canal, where the banks were lined by thousands of cheering Egyptians. At last De Lesseps could bear the tension no longer: he went to his own stateroom, lay down, and fell asleep from exhaustion, to be awakened by the empress herself when the ship reached Ismailia.

At Ismailia there were great bursts of applause, and the empress graciously showed herself on deck. Later there were celebrations on shore: triumphal archways, fireworks exploding in the night from the barges on the lake, parades of cavalry, and Arab sword dances, interminable salutes from howitzers. The khedive had built a palace at Ismailia for the occasion. Here, standing beside the empress, he received the felicitations of his guests, while Eugénie placed the sash of the Grand Cross of the Legion of Honor across De Lesseps' breast. Afterward, in a blaze of jewels, surveying his palace where the walls were made entirely of mirrors, listening to the gunfire on the sandy shores of Lake Timsah, the oriental potentate, descendant of an Albanian fisherman, reclined on a couch, placidly smoking a *hookah,* and seemed not to observe the discomfort of his five thousand guests, with seats for only half that number. Women screamed, men shouted, bedlam broke loose; and the Arabs gazing through the windows smiled to see the frenzy, and grew alarmed only when the tables were cleared, and dancing began. They thought dancing was fit only for dancing girls,

But the celebrations went on through the night, and all the next day. On De Lesseps' birthday, November 19th, the great flotilla of ships, carrying half of Europe's royalty—and the British ambassador from Constantinople—reached Suez. With the baptism accomplished, the flotilla turned about and made its way slowly back to Port Said. One day in Cairo, where she rested after her long ordeal, the empress complained that she missed the fragrance of orange blossom in her native Granada. By next morning there was a grove of orange trees outside her window in the Guezireh Palace.

In a sense it had been like that almost from the beginning. The magician's wand, so delicate and ethereal that it passed unobserved, hovered over the enterprise from the beginning. The fairy tale came true. The obscure ex-consul was acclaimed by Lord Mayo, the Viceroy of India, as a man who possessed "just title to the gratitude of all peoples," and Napoleon III offered him a dukedom with the title of Duke of Suez. He rejected the offer, perhaps because the canal alone was his greatest title to fame. Once, long before, Augustus Caesar had thought to reward Agrippa for his great victories at sea, and searching for something worthy of his friend he had given him—a blue banner of the purest silk! De Lesseps found his reward. At the age of sixty-four he married a girl of twenty, Louise-Hélène Autard de Bragard. The marriage took place quietly in the small chapel at Ismailia six days after the journey to Suez. It was a quiet wedding, with no crowned heads in attendance. Then there was a long honeymoon, with ovations in London and Paris, followed by the terror of the war of 1870. Napoleon III vanished into a German prison, and Eugénie into her English exile. It was the end of an era.

From the beginning De Lesseps had believed as an act of faith that the Suez Canal would be a financial success. He was soon disenchanted. He had calculated profits on the basis that a million tons of cargo would pass through the canal during the first year. In fact, less than half a million tons passed through; canal shares plunged from 500 francs to 272 francs; and once more the canal was faced with ruin. Two years later, in 1872, the canal showed a profit. Luck, the handmaiden of De Lesseps since the day when he wrote to Sa'id Pasha, once more turned in his direction, for quite suddenly shipowners began to see the merit of sending steamships through the canal—never before had East and West so dramatically confronted one another, at such speed, with such a saving of costs. With the coming of steamships the canal assumed vital importance. The mechanized dredger and the steamer saved the canal.

But though the canal was saved, Egypt herself was past saving, as she shuddered under the rule of her profligate monarch. The khedive poured money away impulsively, never counting the cost. He made war against Abyssinia, dug eight thousand miles of branch canals leading off the Nile, imitated the Pharaohs with a vast program of public works—docks, harbors, schools, railways, telegraph lines—and squandered immense sums on his own pleasures. In 1875 he went bankrupt. To stave off ultimate failure, he allowed it to be made known that he was prepared to sell his huge block of shares. A British newspaperman, Frederick Greenwood, learned of the khedive's decision and informed the prime minister, Benjamin Disraeli, who succeeded in borrowing from Baron Rothschild four million pounds sterling to purchase the khedive's shares outright. On November 24, 1875, Disraeli wrote in triumph to his queen:

> It is just settled. You have it, Madam: the French government has been outgeneralled. They tried too much, offering loans at a usorious rate which would have virtually given them the government of Egypt. The Kedive in despair and disgust offered Your Majesty's Government to purchase his shares outright: he would never listen to such a proposition before.

On the following day he wrote to Lady Blandford:

> After a fortnight of the most exacting labour and anxiety, I (for between ourselves, and ourselves only, I may be egotistical in this matter)—I have purchased for England the Khedive of Egypt's interest in the Suez Canal. We have had all the gamblers, capitalists, financiers of the world organized and platooned in bands of plunderers, arrayed against us, and secret emissaries in every corner, and have baffled them all, and have never been suspected.

Disraeli's brilliant stroke of diplomacy showed him to be the most resourceful politician in Europe. For a "bagatelle" of four million pounds he acquired 42 per cent of the shares, worth at least forty million. Sir Stafford Northcote, the secretary to the Chancellor of the Exchequer, pointed out that it was "not quite gentlemanly," and there were many other Englishmen who agreed with him; but Parliament approved the purchase, and even De Lesseps, smarting over the loss of so many shares to the nation which had done its best to ruin the canal, agreed that nothing was lost and that Franco-British solidarity would ensure the operation of the canal "on purely businesslike and peaceful lines." The presence of British directors on the board helped to cement the *entente cordiale*. The canal gained; so did De Lesseps; so did Britain and France. Only the Egyptians, suffering under the heavy taxes imposed by the khedive, their cotton crop at the mercy of international financial trends, their vast public works still unpaid for, lost, and lost hopelessly. The ruined khedive went into exile, to be succeeded by his eldest son, the Khedive Tewfik, an incompetent ruler incapable of stemming the tide of ruin which swept over the country.

At this juncture it was inevitable that the Egyptians should take the matter in their own hands. Out of the people there emerged Ahmed Arabi, a broad-shouldered peasant with dark eyes and massive forehead, and a fanatical determination to drive the foreigners into the sea. A soldier all his life, he forced himself into the position of Minister of War early in 1882. At one o'clock on June 11, 1882, an Arab donkey boy quarreled violently with a Maltese, a British subject. The quarrel ended with a flash of a knife, and soon all Europeans in sight were being massacred. By five o'clock in the afternoon two-hundred Europeans, including an English marine, lay dead. Arabi was not responsible for the massacre, but he did nothing to prevent it. London and Paris held their breaths. As June slipped into July it became clear that the only way the British and the French could protect their Suez Canal interests was by defeating Arabi's armies, or by placating him. The French, on the advice of De Lesseps, attempted to placate him. The British sent a punitive expedition to Alexandria and shelled the city, and then landed marines to restore order. But all this was only the prelude to more extensive military action, and soon a British fleet was on the high seas making its way toward Egypt with the avowed purpose of setting troops on the banks of the canal.

De Lesseps, when he heard of the coming of the British troopships, was in a quandary. He, better than any man, knew how easy it would be to disrupt the canal, and Arabi had promised to blow up the canal at the first sign of British interference. De Lesseps telegraphed to Arabi in haste: "The English shall never enter the canal: never. Make no attempt to block my canal. I am here. Not a single British soldier shall disembark without being accompanied by a French soldier. I answer for everything."

With that astonishing telegram De Lesseps showed himself at his best and worst. Never had he been so revealing of his own motives, his belief in his moral power and his unchallenged righteousness. Arabi telegraphed back: "Sincere thanks. Assurances consolatory but not sufficient under existing circumstances. Defense of Egypt requires temporary destruction of the canal."

Arabi's intelligence was strangely defective, for on the night of August 19th, thirty-two English warships and troopships steamed silently and with dowsed lights past Port Said and down the canal. At all strategic points small landing parties took over barges and dredgers, while the main forces went on to Ismailia. Arabi had lost his chance to destroy the canal. There were two English gunboats within four thousand yards of the vital lock gates of the Sweet Water Canal, which had been built to provide fresh water for the canal workers and followed the whole length of the canal. Sandhills stood between the gunboats and the Nefiche lock, but by emptying the boilers and throwing off every pound of ballast the captains had raised the ships high enough in the water to enable the guns to drop shells on the enemy. Arabi brought trainloads of troops up to the canal, but he could not blow up the lock. He decided instead to build a dam across the Sweet Water Canal. At a place called Tel-el-Mashkuta he filled the canal with reeds lashed together with telegraph wire, and soon the level of the water dropped, and the English troops were in danger of dying of thirst.

To win the canal the British had to act quickly. Fifty miles from Ismailia, on the Sweet Water Canal, not far from the River of Moses, Arabi built his defenses. He had seventy guns, 18,000 infantry and three regiments of cavalry. He stood on almost impregnable ground, with five miles of flat sand in front of him. Sir Garnet Wolseley, the commander in chief of the British forces, decided to employ the same tactics which were employed sixty years later by General Montgomery at El Alamein—a night march and an attack at dawn. In twenty minutes the battle was over, with fifteen hundred Egyptians killed and the rest in headlong flight. In the early morning of the same day, Arabi himself was a broken, huddled figure in the corner of a railway carriage bound for Cairo. The canal was saved. Seventy-four years later another Egyptian colonel modeling himself on Ahmed Arabi was to repeat the same order which had flown across the telegraph wires: "Defense of Egypt requires temporary destruction of the canal."

In the interval the canal remained a British lake, sometimes bitterly contested, but nevertheless securely held by British forces. Lord Palmerston had foreseen that the occupation of Egypt would become inevitable once the canal was constructed. Others, like Ernest Renan, foresaw that the canal would bring, not peace, but the sword. When De Lesseps was made a member of the French Academy in April, 1883, Renan followed the custom which attends such inaugurations by saluting the new member and all his works. He spoke of the universal admiration in which De Lesseps was held, of the glory he had brought to France, of the immense difficulties of the undertaking. He reminded his listeners that the Emperor of Abyssinia, the Lion of Judah, had said, "Lesseps is of the tribe of light," meaning that De Lesseps was one of those who march toward the light, as good soldiers march toward the guns. But he added the warning that in this case light and guns might be synonymous:

> You have cut the canal, the isthmus has become a defile, that is to say a battlefield. The Bosphorus by itself has been enough to keep the whole civilized world embarrassed up to the present, but now you have created a second and much more serious embarrassment. Not merely does the canal connect two inland seas, but it serves as a communicating passage to all the oceans of the globe. In the event of a maritime war it will be of supreme importance, and everyone will be striving with top speed to occupy it. You have thus marked out a great battlefield for the future.

But in the intervals between the wars, the canal lay quiet and peaceful under the Egyptian sun, strangely unaffected by the rise and fall of empires. It seemed to be, and was, hermetically sealed off from the fortunes of nations by the Convention of Constantinople in 1888, by which all the European powers guaranteed "free and open passage, in time of war as in time of peace, to every vessel of commerce or of war, without distinction of flag." For their own safety the High Contracting Powers placed the canal above national self-interest. But when this treaty was drawn up, De Lesseps was already dying, his health broken by the reverses which overwhelmed him after his attempt to build another canal in

Panama. He would have approved the preliminary invocation and the drum-roll roster of emperors and kings:

In the name of Almighty God

Her Majesty the Queen of the United Kingdom of Great Britain and Ireland, Empress of India; His Majesty the Emperor of Germany, King of Prussia; His Majesty the Emperor of Austria, King of Bohemia, etc., and Apostolic King of Hungary; His Majesty the King of Spain and in the name of the Queen Regent of the Kingdom; the President of the French Republic; His Majesty the King of Italy; His Majesty the King of the Netherlands, Grand Duke of Luxembourg, etc.; His Majesty the Emperor of All the Russias; His Majesty the Emperor of the Ottomans; wishing to establish by a Conventional Act a definite system destined to guarantee at all times, and for all the Powers the free use of the Suez Maritime Canal. . . .

The years since 1888 have dimmed the glory of the crowns, but the glory of De Lesseps remains undimmed. Three years after his death, in 1897, his statue was unveiled on the mole at Port Said, showing him with outstretched arm pointing toward the canal he

Monument to De Lesseps at Port Said

had constructed, and on the plinth, encircled by laurel leaves, were the words *"Aperire terram gentibus"* (To open the world to the nations). Until recently he stood there in massive bronze, a great cape flowing down his back, his head held high, with an air which somehow combined arrogance and benevolence.

The First World War left the canal unharmed. Britain proclaimed a protectorate over Egypt, swept the surrounding seas free of enemy ships, and patroled the banks of the canal. For a brief moment Jamal-ad-Din Pasha, commander of the Turkish Fourth Army, attempted to cut the canal, but in the short engagement between Tussum and Serapeum he was thrown back, and the Turks made no further effort to break through the canal, which had become the major route of Britain's supply line to the East.

In the Second World War Britain held more tightly than ever to the control of the canal. Vast numbers of antiaircraft guns were deployed along the banks. Suez was protected by a balloon barrage; false channels were dug; swarms of fighter planes ringed Ismailia. Ships moved through the canal in convoys, and while the Axis planes succeeded in dropping magnetic mines and four Allied vessels were sunk in the canal, normal traffic continued with only rare intervals when the canal was unnavigable. In February, 1941, normal traffic was held up for thirteen days—this was the longest delay throughout the whole course of the war. Ernest Renan had prophesied that the canal would become a battlefield: in fact it became the biggest military staging installation in history, with heavy guns and Sherman tanks streaming in from America. Field Marshal Erwin Rommel's thrust at the vital canal zone precipitated the great Luftwaffe offensive on the canal in the summer of 1942 with ferocious and uninterrupted raids on Port Said, Ismailia, Suez, and Port Tewfik. But the air raids never seriously disrupted navigation.

One day in the summer of 1942, just before the air raids reached their peak, President Roosevelt drafted a telegram to General Marshall: "On the assumption that the Delta will be evacuated within ten days and the canal blocked, I ask the following questions: What assurances have we that the canal will be really blocked? Do we know the specific plan? An effective blocking of the canal is essential." The British had already prepared a plan which would have effectively put the canal out of operation for six months.

With the rise of nationalism in Egypt and the surrender of the British mandate over Palestine in 1948, British control over the canal became increasingly tenuous. British troops still occupied the canal zone, with their camps stretching fifty miles along the canal's western bank, with their own airfields, assembly lines, and railroad repair yards, but they were foreigners in a country whipped up in a frenzy of fervent nationalism. The Egyptian Revolution of July 23, 1952, put an end to any hopes the British might have had of retaining the canal zone in their own power. On October 19, 1954, the British and Colonel Gamal Abdel Nasser signed an agreement providing for the evacuation of the canal zone by June 18, 1956. The long story of British control over the canal was coming to an end; and as the airfields and barracks were gradually evacuated the drifts of sand from the surrounding desert resumed their empire over the works of men. The Pharaohs and the Persians had had their block-houses along those strange desert paths, and these too had vanished. Soon there were only broken runways and crumbling towers, foundations rotting away, screen doors flapping in the wind. And then at Port Said, on the day when the last British soldier left Egypt, Nasser staged the triumphal procession which he had done so little to earn. For three days Egypt surrendered to such jubilation as it had not known since the day when the Allies hurled Rommel back from El Alamein.

Egypt was saved for the Egyptians, but the cost was not to be measured in the political violence of the times—the swarming crowds of fellahin who shouted and waved flags and paraded through the streets, conscious of their power, for the British had left only because Nasser had threatened a permanent guerrilla war against the British troops. The canal was Nasser's prize: after the Nile the second most precious thing in all of Egypt. With his command of the canal he could hold the world by the throat, and from the beginning he showed openly that this was his intention.

Forty-three days after the British troops left Egypt, Nasser seized the canal. For some weeks he had been speaking publicly about his determination to build a new dam at Assouan to harness the waters of the Nile, a far greater dam than the one built at the turn of the century, a little more than 120 feet high and one and a half miles long. The High Dam at Assouan, 364 feet high and more than three miles long, was to be the greatest the world has ever seen, the living monument of the new Egypt: "our new pyramid," as Nasser called it, containing seventeen times as much masonry as the Great Pyramid of Cheops. Behind the giant barrage, a lake stretching hundreds of miles and over the Sudan border would drown the ancient realm of Nubia and one-fifth of riverain Egypt. From this would flow life for the dead provinces, power to build an industrial empire, and wealth to combat Egypt's immemorial poverty. Such was the splendid dream which Nasser tossed into the sunlit air of Egypt until it seemed almost within his reach; and then it trickled away in violence and despair, and the larger dream of a United Arabic Empire.

Nasser was determined to bring this dream about, and he knew that in the money markets of the world bankers were prepared to extend vast loans for waterworks in backward countries. He might have obtained the loan, if he had not threatened to obtain the money from the Soviet Union. Nasser demanded from the Western powers the financial backing for his plan, as his price for obeying the 1888 Convention of Constantinople. The cost of building the High Dam would be $1,300,000,000. Ten thousand men would be employed for ten years.

Nasser's threat backfired when the State Department in Washington learned that the Soviet Union had no intention of paying for the dam. On July 19, 1956, the United States Secretary of State announced that no help would be forthcoming. Nasser, outraged, flew to Alexandria and delivered a three-hour tirade against the Western powers who were accused of conspiring "to trick Egypt into surrendering her sovereignty." He accused Washington of acting "without shame and with disregard for the principles of international relations." Shouting at the top of his voice, he said: "We are determined to live proudly and not to beg for aid. I look at Americans, and say: May you choke to death on your fury!" Not since Hitler had any responsible head of a government spoken publicly with such unashamed bitterness and frenzy.

Then he announced that the Egyptian Government had taken over complete control of the canal, vested in the Egyptian Cabinet and Council of Ministers. "Thirty-five million Egyptian pounds have been taken from us every year by the Suez Canal Company," he declared. "We shall use that money for building the High Dam. We shall rely on our own strength, our own muscle, our own funds. The money is ours, and the Suez Canal belongs to us. It was built by Egyptians, and 120,000 died in the building of it. We shall build the High Dam on the skulls of the 120,000 Egyptian workmen who perished in building the canal!"

These words were deliberately calculated to inflame an Egyptian mob. Nasser talked of skulls, of money, of foreign trickery, of all the sweat which goes into the building of great construction works. In simple mathematics he explained: "The Suez Canal Company's annual income is 100 million dollars, and so in five years we shall be able to acquire 500 million after the nationalization of the canal. All the money that belongs to the company will be consolidated. It will be frozen. It belongs to Egypt. A new Suez Canal Company will be formed, and it will be run by Egyptians! Egyptians! Egyptians!"

From this moment there was no turning back. Even before Nasser had finished speaking, Egyptian police and army officers swept down on the Suez Canal Company's offices at Cairo, Ismailia, and Suez, and all canal employees were ordered to remain at their posts or face imprisonment. By a single speech he had become for a while the undisputed leader of the Arab world, the *triumphator* who dared to hurl defiance at the Western powers. But these moments of glory are always precarious, and soon the Western powers were asking for explanations, especially of the mathematics of the canal. Nasser had promised that the total revenue from the canal would be spent on building the High Dam. Then what of operating costs, improvements, and indemnities? On what conditions would ships be allowed to pass through the canal? As the inflammatory speeches continued, it became increasingly clear that Nasser would employ the canal as a weapon. Soviet engineers were streaming into Egypt, while from behind the scenes Soviet advisers suggested that no indemnities need be paid, and that no foreigners other than Russians should be permitted to operate the canal. The British withdrawal had created a vacuum in the Middle East, and the Soviet Union was only too anxious to fill the vacuum. Nasser temporized, and in the intervals of making threatening speeches spoke as though nothing of any moment had occurred—all that had happened was that Egyptian sovereignty over the canal had been put into effect. The Western powers were alarmed. Nasser himself in a revealing passage of a book had proclaimed his intention of leading a jihad, or holy war, against the West, so uniting under his leadership all the separate Arabic states. He saw himself as the destined hero, a man who assumed his historic role because the role itself had searched him out. As the summer gave way to autumn, he began to wear his new robes more comfortably. He was aware of the risks—Soviet subversion, an invasion from Israel, the increasing danger of arousing the open hostility of the Western powers. He hardly cared. With the long blue sword of the canal he would split the world apart.

For years there had been border raids across the frontiers of Israel. On Thursday, October 25th, Israel mobilized, and four days later the first Israeli parachute battalion was dropped at Mitla, almost in sight of Suez. On October 30th Britain and France, the two powers most concerned over the safety of the canal, issued an ultimatum to Israel and Egypt to stop fighting and withdraw their military forces ten miles from either side of the canal. The Canal Zone of Panama extends for ten miles on each side of the canal, and Britain and France seem to have hoped that a Suez Canal Zone, protected perhaps by the United Nations, might come into being.

Suez Canal: northern entrance to by-pass

By this time Israeli forces were so close to the canal that the flash of gunfire could be seen from the waterway.

Israel agreed to the withdrawal, but Egypt refused, and the die was cast. The next day Britain and France bombed Egyptian airfields and prepared to assume control over the canal zone. With the help of Soviet engineers, Egypt put into operation a long-prepared plan for destroying the canal. At night some forty ships were moved into the main channel and scuttled, blocking the waterway and trapping thirteen vessels in convoy. Machinery for operating the canal was smashed to smithereens.

The British and French were faced with a dilemma. If they attacked defenseless Egypt, they would incur the moral obloquy of the rest of the world; if they failed to attack they would lose their lifeline to the East. While Sir Anthony Eden, the British prime minister, debated with himself whether he dared to launch an attack, the Security Council of the United Nations met in New York, and it became increasingly clear that the British and French had already lost the war, that nothing was to be gained by fighting, and that Nasser's control of the canal was so strong that any attempt to wrest it from him would only give him greater strength, greater reassurance. Nevertheless Eden decided to attack. On the morning of November 5, 1956, British and French paratroopers floated down on the Port Said region, and seaborne troops streamed ashore the next dawn. The Egyptians put up an unexpected resistance. While the aerial assault continued, advance forces struck south along the canal toward Ismailia, with the Egyptians steadily giving ground before them. The invasion, however, lasted only forty hours, for the Soviet Union had threatened to enlarge the scope of the war. On the evening of November 5th Eden received a note from Moscow, speaking of the determination of the Soviet Government "to crush the aggressors and restore peace in the Middle East through the use of force." Against that threat the British and French were powerless, and the next day they announced a cease-fire at midnight if the Secretary-General of the United Nations would confirm that a United Nations force would be sent to Egypt to protect the peace. Even then they hoped it might be possible to put the canal zone under supranational control. For a few more months they held fast to this hope, but with Nasser's authority restored it became evident that he would continue to use the canal as a weapon against the West. The French had made the canal, the British had wrested it from them, and now at last Nasser with the unconcealed help of the Soviet Union gave the canal back to the Egyptians.

The first chapter in the story of the Suez Canal was over. Long ago Ernest Renan had foreseen that until the end of history, or as long as the canal remained in existence, it would be a matter of "the world's debate." Now, at last, the canal designed to open the world to the nations had become a battlefield.

Blue waters and white seas

When Peter the Great constructed his new capital at St. Petersburg amidst the Finnish lakes, the peasants said he built it in the clouds and then lowered it on the banks of the river Neva, for how else could they explain why the young city never sank in the marshy ground? Peter himself was a little astonished by his success. Once, when he was surveying the marshes where the workmen from all corners of Russia were busily moving the earth in the skirts of their cloaks and in sacks made of coarse rags, for there were no wheelbarrows to be found, he remarked: "I see they are building in spite of everything. Strange how well our Russians work when they are under the leash!" And those words, echoing down the centuries, tell us as much as we shall ever know about the building of that capital of white marble and gilded spires on the shores of the Baltic.

Peter had no qualms in setting hundreds of thousands of men to work on his city. Men died like flies during the icy winters and in the long malarial summers, wading knee-deep in water. A German historian who was present during the early stages of the building of the city says that 200,000 died, and there is no reason to question his figure. To drain the marshes on the south bank of the Neva, Peter ordered two semicircular canals to be dug. One, the Yekaterininsky Canal, was named after Catherine, the Livonian peasant girl who became his empress and his successor to the throne. Two other canals, the Moika and the Fontanka, originally shored up with balks of timber, later with stone, remain to this day very much as Peter designed them, drawing his artless pencil across a sheet of paper and refusing to count the intolerable cost. He was in a rage to build his city quickly. Within a year the first timber houses were up, and within another year there were the foundations of the cathedral. He also drained Vasilievsky Island, which he had given as a present to his favorite, Prince Menshikov. Soon there were five hundred wealthy merchants and as many shopkeepers in business. The terrible-tempered emperor had accomplished what neither Sennacherib nor Darius had dared to do: he had built a city of stone on a marsh.

Once he had tasted the joys of canal building, Peter turned his attention to joining the Neva and the Volga, so producing a waterway which would reach almost to Moscow. Between 1703 and 1709, at enormous expense in human life, he constructed the Vishny-Volochok Canal, which joined the Neva to one of the tributaries of the Volga. This canal was important during the early days of Russian history, for it opened the way for maritime transport as far as Lake Ladoga. When Peter saw how difficult it was to cross the stormy waters of Lake Ladoga, he decided to construct another canal sixty-two miles long skirting the shores of the lake. The project was placed in the hands of Prince Aleksandr Danilovich Menshikov, Field Marshal, Prince of the Holy Roman Emperor, and Count of Kurland, who rose from obscurity to be the emperor's drinking companion.

Brilliant, affable, and unscrupulous, Prince Menshikov was the richest man in all Russia, the owner of so many estates that it was said of him that he could travel from St. Petersburg to the frontiers of Persia and never step outside his own property. Peter lived simply: Prince Menshikov lived in great state, riding in a golden carriage and eating off gold plate, attended always by thousands of servants. He was a disastrous choice as promoter of the Ladoga Canal. He wasted the eight million rubles set aside for the project, allowed the workmen to die of disease and hunger, and accomplished nothing. Peter himself had surveyed the canal and watched over its fortunes, but he seems never to have troubled to rebuke Prince Menshikov for his calamitous failure. All that remains of the Ladoga Canal are a few cuts on the rocky shore and a few mounds, which may be the graves of the workmen who died during the terrible winter of 1718.

Two years later Peter commissioned the Englishman William Henning to design a canal between the Volga and the Moscow River. Henning, a capable engineer who bore the rank of general in the czar's army, drew up a plan calling for the building of one hundred locks with a water level of not more than 6 feet 6 inches, and the canal was to be navigable for vessels with a deadweight of about 50 tons. He calculated that a journey along the canal would take at least three days. Though the plans were drawn up carefully, nothing came of them. They were put aside and forgotten until the nineteenth century when Nicholas I decided to build the great Cathedral of Christ the Savior in celebration of the Russian victory over Napoleon. In Milan at the time of the Viscontis the Church authorities had made use of canals to bring stone to the site of the cathedral. So now in Russia Nicholas I approved the plan of digging a canal for the sole purpose of transporting limestone and granite from the upper reaches of the Volga to Moscow. But once again nothing came of the plan: the huge cathedral with its walls of sheer marble and its granite stairways was built without benefit of canals at a cost of fifteen million rubles. According to Henning, the gunnery expert who was chief inspector of foundries and chief canal engineer to Peter the Great, the canal could have been built for half that sum.

Yet slowly and almost imperceptibly the Russians were making progress with canals. Along the banks of the Volga, on obscure estates where the landlords were cultivating their land, small canals were being dug. In the technical colleges of St. Petersburg and Moscow canal engineering was being taught. In the reign of Alexander I, during the brief period of peace between the Treaty of Tilsit and the invasion by Napoleon, an attempt was made to join the rivers with a complete canal system. The first, called the Mariinska, joined the

Neva to the headwaters of the Volga, and was completed in 1810. In the following year the Tikhvin Canal joining Lake Ladoga to the Volga was completed. Tikhvin, the birthplace of Rimsky-Korsakov, was an old Russian town lying some seventy miles from the lake on one of the tributaries of the Volga. These canals were used for floating timber from the northern forests and for turning the water wheels of factories on shore, but they were little more than tentative experiments. Peter the Great had dreamed of a time when all the riches of that amazingly productive land would flow to the capital by canal. Somehow, by some means unknown, he would make St. Petersburg the center of a vast radiating canal system which would link the capital with the rivers of Central Asia.

While he was studying a number of canal projects, a report reached him that somewhere in Central Asia a great dam had been built—where, and by whom, no one seemed to know—which turned the Amu Darya, the ancient Oxus, once known to have fallen into the Caspian, into the Aral Sea. Determined to know more about the mysterious dam, and realizing the great significance the river would have for trade between Russia and the Central Asian khanates, especially if it returned to its old course, he sent a special mission to Khiva, supported by picked troops, with the task of negotiating for the destruction of the dam. The ill-fated expedition set out, bearing presents and a letter from Peter to the Khan of Khiva. Many years later it was learned that the mission had struggled with difficulty through the desert, and had been massacred to the last man by the treacherous khan. Two hundred years passed before it was discovered that the great dam was a fiction of some geographer's imagination, for the river had simply changed its course, as rivers sometimes do, leaving its trace in the great depression known as the *uzboi.* The Amu Darya still flows into the Aral Sea, and so far no one has succeeded in changing its course.

From the time of Peter the Great to the time of the Bolsheviks the desire to tame the rivers exercised men's minds, but only very short canals were built. Perhaps the most useful of the canals built during this time was the Morskoy Canal, which was not in a strict sense a canal at all, but a dredged channel joining the fortress and naval base at Kronstadt with St. Petersburg. This channel was 17 miles long, 23 feet deep, and was built between 1875 and 1888 at a cost of ten million rubles.

With the coming of the Bolsheviks to power the dreams of Peter the Great at last became reality. For the first time in Russian history the central government was able to set up a planning board with the task of controlling the rivers and devising a complex system of canals. The task was made all the easier by the employment of millions of political prisoners, whose lives were of no importance to the ruling régime. Once again, as in the time of the Sumerians and the Egyptians, slaves were employed to dig the canals.

The first great project was the Baltic-White Sea Canal, connecting Povenets on the northern tip of Lake Onega with Belomorsk on the White Sea. This stupendous canal followed the line of the railway across a range of granite hills for 140 miles: it is unlikely that any other canal ever built involved so much hardship, or so many lives. From Lake Onega it was cut through to Lake Vyg, where the water was raised 19 feet by a dam and dozens of islands disappeared. In the south it was linked to Leningrad by a system of waterways joining the Neva to Lake Ladoga, the Svir River and Lake Onega. Year after year the prisoners were sent north to work on the canal, and more than half of them are believed to have perished during the fierce winters. Nineteen locks were constructed, and at last in May, 1933, a squadron of the Red Banner Baltic Fleet steamed for the first time through the newly opened canal.

Nothing quite like this canal had ever been built before, and Stalin was so pleased with it that he allowed it to bear his name. The official name for the canal is the Stalin Baltic-White Sea Canal. An official account of the building of the canal contains the revealing words: "Stalin it was who started the idea of building the Baltic-White Sea Canal with prisoners, because under his leadership such a method of reform seemed possible."

The building of the canal was a feat comparable to the building of the pyramids. Most of it was carved out of the living rock with picks and shovels, by gangs of prisoners who lived in desolate huts on the bleak granite ranges. Yet no one could deny the advantages gained by the canal, which shortened the stormy seventeen-day voyage around Norway to six days or less. During World War II, when the German armies reached the southern end of the canal, one dam was blown up and the waters rushed in a flood into Lake Onega, cutting a new path which was in some places fifty feet deep. By desperate efforts, and despite fierce frosts, the canal was reopened for navigation by August, 1946. This time German, not Russian, prisoners were employed.

The next attempt to tame the rivers occurred in the Ukrainian Republic with the building of the Dnieproges dam near Dniepropetrovsk. The dam raised the level of the river by 120 feet, and thus put an end to the dangerous sixty-two-mile stretch of rapids, which could be navigated in the past only by the most skillful pilots. The dam fed the largest hydroelectric station in Europe, which was destroyed during the German invasion. The Germans had proclaimed that a new dam would not arise for twenty years, but by 1947 a new and more powerful station arose on the ruins.

To tame the Dnieper more dams were built at Kremenchug, Prodzerzhinsk, Zaporozhe, and Kakhovka, near the Dnieper's mouth on the Black Sea. From Kiev to the Black Sea the river was tamed.

The Dnieper was the ancient historic waterway of the Russians, but it was the Volga with its innumerable tributaries which broke men's hearts and summoned to its banks nearly a third of all the people in the Soviet Union. Rising as a small village spring near Kalinin, it wanders eastward north of Moscow for nearly two-thirds of its 2,290 miles. Shallows and shoals made the river impassable except in spring. In 1901 the czarist government ordered dredgers to dredge out the river, hoping to let larger boats navigate the headwaters, but little came of it—the river was fickle, and as fast as the dredgers removed sand from one place the current piled it up at another.

The Soviet Government inherited the large-scale plans already in existence, and improved on them. It was decided to reconstruct the entire river route. Not only did the river have to be shortened and deepened, but the current had to be slowed down to facilitate upriver traffic. In addition, the Volga had to be joined to the White Sea, the Baltic, the Black Sea, and the Sea of Azov.

The Greater Volga scheme was launched during the years of the First Five-Year Plan. First, the Mariinska, joining the Neva to the Volga, was reconstructed. Then at Ivankovo, on the upper reaches of the Volga north of Moscow, a dam was built, forming a lake which entirely covered the town of Korcheva and sent waters southward toward Moscow. The lake, known as the Sea of Moscow, covers 126 square miles. Moscow itself was eighty miles away, and separated from the lake by a range of hills, and so it was decided to build a canal from the lake over the hills to feed the Moskva River, which was proving inadequate to meet the water needs of its citizens and industry—statisticians calculated that Moscow was using 1,250 million liters of Volga water every day, which was twice the volume of the Moskva River.

Because Moscow was the capital of the Soviet Empire it was decided to build the new canal in style. It was to be 280 feet wide to allow simultaneous two-way passage of the largest river vessels, and 18 feet deep. There were to be 11 reinforced concrete locks 950 feet long and 98 feet wide, and 8 hydroelectric stations. Since there was no natural water to feed the canal by gravitation, five pumps were installed. These pumps, which replenish the top level of the canal, turn turbines as the canal flows down toward Moscow, and are used to feed electrical power to Moscow during the day and evening hours: during the nighttime hours they provide the power to fill the canal. Finally a dam was built on the Moskva, raising the water level at Moscow by ten feet, thus enabling large ships to moor directly in the port of Moscow. On May 2, 1937, after four years and eight months of work, and after 7,120 million cubic feet of earth had been dug out, a flotilla of motorships moved down the canal and anchored opposite the Kremlin.

Two more dams were built: one at the ancient Russian city of Uglich, the other at Shcherbakov. The Uglich dam produced only a small lake, but the Shcherbakov dam produced a lake, called the Rybinsk Sea, which covers a territory of 1,800 square miles, eight times larger than Lake Geneva. The Uglich dam was opened in 1940, and the Shcherbakov dam in November, 1941, just after the German invasion.

These three man-made lakes transformed the upper reaches of the Volga. Where cows once used to ford the rivers and quails called in the sedge water meadows, there were deep waterways for seagoing ships. The recurring spring floods and the shallow shoals of the hot summer months were now things of the past.

Just before World War II another canal of an entirely different kind was completed. This was an irrigation canal 170 miles long, taking water from the headwaters of the Syr Darya which flows into the Aral Sea. This canal, said to have been constructed by 160,000 people and completed in six weeks, was built to irrigate the Ferghana Valley in the Uzbek Socialist Republic. It is known as the Stalin Great Ferghana Canal.

The war interrupted a plan to link the Volga and the Don. Work was begun in 1938, abandoned during the war years, and resumed in 1947. Between the two rivers lies the Yergenei range, waterless and treeless. These were the hills which prevented the Volga from falling into the Sea of Azov.

The engineers had worked out a sixty-two-mile route from Stalingrad to Kalach on the Don. The Don is a higher river than the Volga, by some 145 feet. There were no sources of water on the hills, and so once again it was necessary to build pumping stations to lift water from the Don to the highest locks. Construction was difficult. It was necessary to install altogether 13 locks, with lifts of about 30 feet each. On the Volga side there was a climb of 286 feet to the top of the canal.

The Lenin Volga-Don Canal

The Volga-Don Canal was opened on June 1, 1952. Then for the first time Moscow could claim that it was a port of the five seas—the White Sea, the Baltic, the Black Sea, the Sea of Azov, and the Caspian.

This, however, was only the beginning. All over Russia plans were being made to harness and canalize the rivers. In the Turkmenian Republic, the most arid of all Central Asian republics, work went on with the Great Turkmenian Canal, cutting across the immense desert of Kara-Kum, linking the Amu Darya and the

Caspian. For two-thirds of its length it will flow along the ancient bed of the river, Peter the Great's *uzboi.* This time there will be no imaginary dams, but real ones. According to recent reports the main canal will be 680 miles long with 745 miles of branch canals. Though scheduled for completion in 1957, it has not yet been completed.

Already Soviet engineers are planning canals and hydro-electric stations in northern Siberia. From the Altai Mountains flows the 3,300-mile Yenisei with its tributary the Angara, the 2,700-mile Ob and its tributary the Irtysh. These rivers, too, are about to be transformed into inland seas and canals. Two hydraulic engineering projects are under way on the Angara, at Bratsk and Irkutsk. The Angara itself will become navigable for its whole length. In time it is hoped to provide transverse canals across the whole length of Russia, so that a ship may set out from Moscow and reach Peking without once going to sea.

The astonishing successes of the Russians are about to be equaled in the New World. The St. Lawrence-Great Lakes Seaway will create a fourth North American coastline 2,687 miles long, opening the heartland of the United States and Canada to ocean-going shipping by providing a twenty-seven foot channel from the Atlantic to the Great Lakes.

The Canadian and American engineers working on the Seaway have been faced with very much the same problems as the Russians, and in the same kind of climate. But there was one essential difference between Russian and American methods: the Americans never had any need to employ slave labor. Nor was there any need for employing picks and shovels when walking dragline diggers, shaped like enormous beetles and weighing up to 650 tons, could pick up 20 tons of earth with every bite, and do this every 48 seconds. The dragline digger can excavate an acre of ground to a depth of eight feet in 24 hours. A thousand slave laborers might do the same work in the same time.

The story of the Seaway goes back to the short, stocky, bearded sailor Jacques Cartier, who sailed out from Saint-Mâlo in Brittany and found himself coasting off the shores of Labrador southward toward the estuary of a river, which he discovered on St. Lawrence's day in 1536. The river was not marked on any maps, and seemed not to be a river at all, but a great bay. He turned westward into the bay, and six weeks later he was still sailing—a thousand miles from the Atlantic. Even there the bay was a mile wide. He believed he had entered a passage which would lead to the Orient. Far ahead of him he could see the great waterway between the mighty forests, leading toward the coast of China. He disembarked, parleyed on a small island with the Red Indians who told him there was no end to the waterway, and then he found himself confronted with a great swirling rush of broken water. Today the rapids are called by the name he gave them—la Chine, meaning China. He was still far from the Great Lakes.

Other Frenchmen came, but few penetrated deep into Canada. The first sailing ship to reach Lake Michigan belonged to Robert Cavalier, Sieur de La Salle, who in the spring of 1679 built his ship the *Griffin,* a vessel of some forty-five tons, one-fourth the size of the *Mayflower,* in a clearing near the Niagara Falls. She had two square sails, a high poop, a gilded eagle on the quarterdeck and a griffin on the prow. The white flag of France with the golden lilies hung from her jackstaff. In August he returned from Fort Frontenac, bringing an anchor which required four men well laced with brandy to haul up the Lewiston heights near the Falls. Then all hands joined to tow the ship upstream, and on August 7, 1679, she sailed with thirty-four men into the wide reaches of Lake Erie. With bared heads the crew sang the *Te Deum* and thundered a salute from their five small cannon. Well she might thunder, for this prophetic ship was to sail deep into the remote recesses of Canada and open the way for millions who came after her.

There were three extraordinary men on the *Griffin.* One was La Salle, the clear-eyed conquistador determined to blaze a path through the wilderness at all costs. Another was Henri de Tonty, a heavy-built dark-browed man who had hacked off a maimed hand with his own sword on a battlefield in Spain. The third was Father Louis Hennepin, fresh from France, a quiet and cautious man, who was perfectly prepared to enter an Indian camp unarmed. All these men possessed vivid characters and a longing to lay down their lives for France.

But in the beginning they were aware only that they were sailing through a kind of paradise. A fresh breeze sprang up as they entered the unknown waters of Lake Erie; for three days they held their course and on the fourth turned northward into the Strait of Detroit. There they found wild turkeys feeding on the grapes which hung festooned from the oaks; herds of deer, flocks of swans, and gentle lumbering bears. The bulwarks of the *Griffin* were hung with game.

A furious storm struck them in Lake Huron, but the ship came safely into the cove of Michilimackinac, where once again they fired their cannon, to the astonishment of the Indians on shore. At anchorage, the *Griffin* was surrounded by more than a hundred bark canoes—"like a Triton among minnows." Then they went on to Lake Michigan (which La Salle called the Lake of Illinois), and early in September they sailed into Green Bay, where La Salle found the agents sent from Fort Frontenac the previous year. He had hoped to go on farther in the *Griffin,* but a great quantity of furs had piled up and he needed to satisfy his creditors. Accordingly, he filled the *Griffin* with the furs and sent her back on September 18th, having decided to continue the journey to Illinois, and, ultimately, the Gulf of Mexico with fourteen men in four canoes. The *Griffin* set sail in an icy calm. That night a sudden storm rose, and the ship was never seen again. It was a hundred years before another vessel of her size was seen on the lakes.

For nine years La Salle continued his explorations, dying at last on the shores of Texas at the hands of his own rebellious countrymen. But the memory of the famous journey remained in the minds of the French, who flocked into Canada and founded settlements on the Lakes and along the banks of the St. Lawrence River until the British with the help of a few seasoned troops acquired the

Canadian empire which the French had fought so resolutely to build. Canada became British, and most of the land south of the Lakes fell into American hands.

Almost from the time of La Salle there was talk of improving the narrow waterways between the Lakes and the rapids of the St. Lawrence. In 1700 the Sulpician monks who ruled over the island of Montreal decided to build a canal beside the worst of the Lachine rapids. The canal was to be a mile long, 12 feet wide and not less than 18 inches deep, deep enough for a fur-laden canoe. A contractor was engaged, but he failed financially and was unable to complete it. The Sulpicians appealed to Louis XIV, who promised his help, but died before he could make good his promise.

Shortly after the British took Canada from France in the Seven Years' War (1756–1763), they were confronted with the American War of Independence. Once again an attempt was made to carve a canal past the Lachine rapids, and so in 1780, and again in 1804, short side canals were built with a depth of two or three feet. Meanwhile, in 1797, the Northwest Fur Company decided to dig a shallow half-mile ditch past the Falls of St. Marys, where Lake Superior makes a twenty-one-foot drop into Lake Huron. There were then two widely separated canals on the St. Lawrence and the Great Lakes. Together, they amounted to just over a mile, and at their best they could carry only ships' dories and the fur-laden bateaux of the fur traders.

In England the great days of canal building were almost over when the Canadians started to dig seriously. First, they widened and deepened the Lachine Canal, carrying it from Montreal harbor to Lachine on Lake St. Louis. Work on the first Welland Canal, intended to conquer the 326 feet of the Niagara escarpment, was begun in November 1824. The Welland Canal linked Lake Erie to Lake Ontario. It was eight feet deep, had forty wooden locks, and was completed five years later. Originally it ran from Port Dalhousie on Lake Ontario to Port Robinson on Chippewa Creek, and so to the Niagara River. In 1833 it was extended to enter Lake Erie, and then its length was 27½ miles. In its time it was the largest of Canadian canals, and the first which could be regarded as a feat of engineering, for the other canals had been little more than ditches.

The Erie Canal provided cheap water transport from the Great Lakes to the Port of New York, and soon the attention of the people of Michigan, who entered the Union in 1837, was attracted to a waterway round the Falls of St. Marys on the American side of the border. Almost the first action of the new Governor Stevens T. Mason was to call for a canal system linking Lake Michigan, Lake Huron, and Lake Superior. He proposed a canal around the falls of the St. Marys River with three locks, and estimated the cost to be $114,000. His appeal to Congress for help was refused, and the State of Michigan decided to raise the money and let out a contract.

The first attempt to build the American Soo—the name derived from the French name for the falls, Sault Sainte Marie—was a total failure. On May 11, 1839, the eighty-ton schooner *Eliza Ward* arrived at the Soo with fifty laborers and a great quantity of horses, barrows, and shovels. The canal line ran directly across the grounds of a United States army post at Fort Brady. The contractor hitched up his teams, rolled his wheelbarrows along the Fort Brady millrace, and ordered his men to start digging. The commandant of the military reservation was determined to protect military property and marched his thirty regulars toward the diggers. The contractor, who had already visited the fort and knew exactly what would happen, explained that he was under orders of the Congress of the State of Michigan to dig the canal, and that he intended to continue digging whatever happened. While the workmen leaned on their shovels, the commandant barked an order and the thirty regulars cocked their rifles. On the whole the contractor was pleased. The bid he had submitted was too low, and he stood to lose a good deal of money if he built the canal. Soon the horses and the wheelbarrows, the picks and shovels, and all the laborers were back aboard the *Eliza Ward.* They sailed down the St. Marys River and amused themselves by catching whitefish.

For thirteen years the canal at the Soo was forgotten. Occasionally there were debates in the Federal Congress on the necessity for appropriating Federal funds for the canal, but the debates led nowhere. The Soo was a long way from Washington. Henry Clay took it upon himself to denounce the project, saying it was "a work beyond the remotest settlement in the United States, if not in the moon." The remark only proved his lack of knowledge of geography. Already copper and iron outcrops on the shores of Lake Superior had sent men swarming past the Falls of St. Marys. The tide was slowly turning. In 1851 President Fillmore announced that "a ship canal around the Falls of St. Marys of less than a mile in length, though local in its construction, would be national in its purpose and benefits." In the following year a bill was passed granting 750,000 acres of Federal land to Michigan as a subsidy for the canal project and granting a 400-foot right of way through the Fort Brady Reservation.

Even then nothing might have been done, if it had not been for a twenty-four-year-old salesman of weighing scales who had been wandering through the iron and copper towns selling his scales. He was at the Soo, recovering from a severe bout of typhoid, when he heard of the projected canal, which was to be 12 feet deep, 100 feet wide, and 5,400 feet long, with two locks, and costing about half a million dollars. The Yankee salesman, Charles T. Harvey, was sufficiently excited by the reports to write off a letter to his company in Vermont and suggest that they enter the business of canal digging. The company evidently had faith in his judgment, for on April 5, 1853, the company formed the St. Marys Falls Ship Canal Company and Harvey was appointed general superintendent in charge of operations at the Soo. Less than two months later, on June 1st, the chartered steamer *Illinois* brought four hundred men, together with mules, horses, lumber, drills, blasting powder, and supplies to the Soo, and four days later he thrust the first spade in the ground.

Before the work was over, Harvey had shown that he belonged to the race of great canal builders. Even when he was laid low by

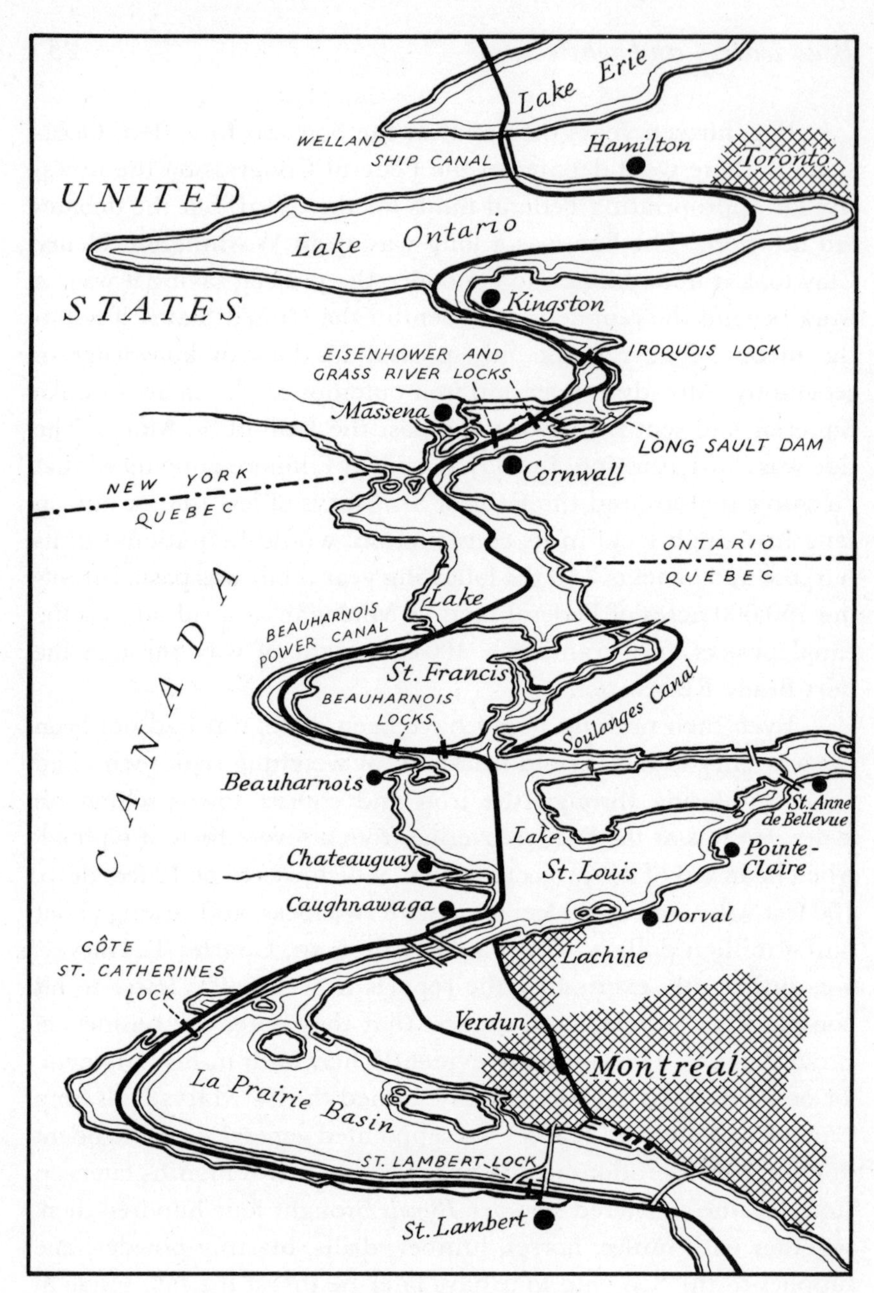

St. Lawrence Seaway

fever, he remained in command. He kept the supplies moving. He wore out three horses a day galloping over the canal works. For ages the northern winters had remained silent, in the grip of ice. Now they were loud with the pounding of the horses' hoofs and the swinging of the picks. No one has told the story better than Walter Havighurst, who learned to splice a rope on Great Lakes ore boats before becoming the historian of the Lakes:

> That winter two thousand men were working in the frozen pit that would receive Lake Superior water. The temperature dropped below zero and stayed there for bitter weeks. Down in the pit the mules breathed jets of steam from their nostrils, the picks rang on the frozen ground, and the drills punched into the rock with a slow, cold din. A watchman was posted at the head of each wheelbarrow runway to rub snow on the gray faces that betrayed frostbite. For one stretch that winter it was 35 degrees below zero. In the mess barracks the meat froze solid. The cooks chopped it with an ax and rammed it into their ovens. They dug vegetables from frost cellars in the ground.
>
> In the winter of 1854 typhoid and cholera struck the camp. Then a new pit was dug, out of sight in the woods. Burials were held quietly at night, to keep the knowledge of epidemic from the men. At the same time hundreds of workmen were lured by high wages to the copper and iron country, and scores went out to seek their own homesteads. To keep his gangs working Harvey sent company foremen to New York to board immigrant ships in the harbor. They signed on Irish and German workmen, herded them into trains for Detroit and delivered steamer loads of them to the growing excavation beside the rapids. The picks kept swinging.[1]

They kept swinging until April, 1855, when a last powder blast broke through the wall of earth which separated the canal from Lake Superior, and ships might have passed along the canal the same day if the walls had not begun to give. It was decided to delay the grand opening until the walls had been strengthened. Then at last, on June 18, 1855, the steamer *Illinois* which had brought the first load of workmen to the Soo headed the procession of ships which made their way through the canal, and two months

[1] Walter Havighurst, *The Long Ships Passing* (New York, The Macmillan Company, 1956), p. 203.

later came the first ship laden with red iron ore from the north. Without the Soo the ore from the vast Minnesota and upper Michigan iron mines could not be shipped cheaply to the steel mills of Indiana and Ohio. From the beginning, traffic on the Soo was prodigious. In 1952 it amounted to 94,889,000 long tons. In the same year 83,448,000 long tons passed through the Suez Canal, and 33,611,000 long tons through the Panama Canal.

Within twenty years Harvey's canal was widened and deepened, and new locks had to be built. Twin locks, 1,200 feet long, were built in 1914 and 1919. Improvements went on year by year, and in 1943 the great MacArthur Lock was built on the site of Harvey's old locks. In all of America there is no place where so many ships pass, or where there is so much quiet history.

While the Americans concentrated on improving the Soo, the Canadians concentrated on the Welland. In 1841 the entire canal was purchased by the Legislature of Upper Canada, and the original forty wooden locks were reduced to twenty-seven. Twelve years later the banks and the walls of the locks were raised to ten feet. In 1870 a special commission met to plan a new cut. This third canal, partly following the original cut, provided for a fourteen-foot draft, and by 1901 all the canals on the St. Lawrence between Montreal and Lake Ontario had the same depth.

Around the Soo and the Welland grew the legend of a deep-water channel which would allow ocean-going ships to sail right up the St. Lawrence to Duluth and Chicago at the head of the Lakes. With the Soo in American hands, and the Welland in Canadian hands, it was clear that the deep-water channel above Montreal could only be made if there was agreement between Canada and the United States. That agreement was long in coming. The first discussions between Canada and the United States took place in 1895, but little came of them. In 1918 the International Deepwater Commission met at Ashland and heard the wheat farmers clamoring for a deep-water canal, pointing out that half the cost of shipping grain from Duluth to Liverpool, England, was incurred between Buffalo and New York Harbor. Iron shippers spoke of how

St. Lawrence Seaway: Côte St. Catherines Lock
(Photo by Hans van der Aa)

iron ore could be shipped directly to Bethlehem and Philadelphia, while paper manufacturers from Wisconsin argued for a seaway to allow them to import foreign pulp and pulpwood at water level. In the following year the Great Lakes-Tidewater Association came into existence as an association of seven Great Lakes states to deal with some practical problems of the continuing conference. It was decided to build a new deep lock at the Soo, and enlarge the locks at the Welland Canal and the new canals around the rapids of the St. Lawrence. With these improvements the Atlantic would be brought 1,500 miles inland, and farmers and manufacturers of the Midwest would be able to ship directly to the world's markets. The Welland Canal was deepened to twenty-five feet and provided with locks carrying thirty feet of water on the sills. When it was opened in 1930, it was evident that the construction of the Seaway could not be long delayed.

Objections against the Seaway came from the American side of the border. Shortly after the renovation of the Welland Canal, in 1932, a treaty for the construction of the Seaway was concluded between Canada and the United States. The treaty, however, was couched in general terms, and lobbying against the Seaway continued. The Eastern railroads, the Atlantic and Gulf ports, coal miners and shippers in the Great Lakes opposed it on the grounds that they would inevitably lose their vested interests. Not until 1954 did Congress finally authorize United States participation in the project, and even then opposition continued.

But in fact, without the help of Congress, the Seaway was already in existence except for a short link between Lake Ontario, 246 feet above the ocean, and the sea-level harbor of Montreal. A ship can travel from Chicago across Lake Michigan, Lake Huron, Lake Erie, and Lake Ontario in a continuous deep-water passage for 1,134 miles. The trouble lies with the complicated, confined channels in the 183-mile section which includes Lake St. Francis and Lake St. Louis and stretches from the Thousand Islands to Montreal. Canadian authorities have long since divided this section into five strips—the Thousand Islands, the International Rapids, Lake St. Francis, Soulanges and Lachine. The main work has fallen on the 47-mile International Rapids strip, the 18-mile Soulanges strip, and the final 24-mile strip leading into the harbor of Montreal. The International Rapids strip includes three locks, the Iroquois Lock recently completed by the Canadians, and the Eisenhower and Grass River Locks which are being built by the Americans. The four other locks being built by the Canadians are the Upper and Lower Beauharnois Locks on the Beauharnois Power Canal, and the Côte St. Catherines Lock and the St. Lambert Lock and on the 27-foot channel on the south bank of the river curving round the Laprairie Basin. When completed in the spring of 1959, this new series of canals will enable ships carrying cargoes from 7,000 to 10,000 tons to move with only moderate delays from

St. Lawrence Seaway: site of Upper Beauharnois Lock
(Photo by Hans van der Aa)

the Atlantic to the Great Lakes. There will still be fifteen locks to pass through—the seven locks between Montreal and Lake Ontario and the eight locks between Lake Ontario and Lake Erie forming the Welland Canal, which circumvents the falls and rapids of Niagara. Each lockage will consume about fifty minutes, and there will be a total delay of only twelve hours.

The Seaway is nearly complete, but it is only a beginning. As new towns, new industries, and new centers of hydraulic power, like the International Power Station at Massena overlooking the Eisenhower and Grass River Locks, spring into existence, the Seaway itself will change. It will be widened and deepened, and the number of locks may be reduced. Today it is closed by ice for four months of the year, but already experiments are in progress to ensure that the St. Lawrence will be kept open for all-year shipping as far as Quebec, and in time the whole Seaway may be kept open all the year round. With improvements and enlargements, trade and industry in the Midwest will inevitably expand, and the character of the Midwest will change.

But it should not be forgotten that much of the driving force for the Seaway came from Canada, where for more than 260 years —ever since the Northwest Fur Company dug a canal round the Falls of the St. Marys River—men have hacked their way through the reefs and rapids of turbulent rivers. American objections to the canal were powerful and deep-rooted. American reluctance was finally overcome only after Canada's decision to build the Seaway alone, if necessary. The honor belongs largely to Canada.

The area affected by the Seaway is larger than all of free Europe. A third of the combined populations of Canada and the United States live in the province of Ontario, which stretches across all the Great Lakes, and in the American states bordering the Lakes in the south. Here are the major production centers of steel, automobiles, and machinery. Here are most of the nation's coal and iron mines, the wheat and corn belts, and the bulk of the dairylands. Rubber from Akron, clothing and photographic equipment from Rochester, chemicals from the Eastern waterways and meat from Chicago—all these will soon flow out cheaply along the Seaway to the ports on the high seas; and the richest hinterland in the world will grow still richer.

Long ago Frontinus, *Curator Aquarum,* pointed to the great Roman aqueducts and boasted that Roman skill and enterprise had triumphed over the pyramids of the Egyptians and the temples of the Greeks. It was a legitimate boast, though perhaps a dangerous one. Today the Americans, Canadians and Russians can boast of feats which would have appalled the Romans and reduced them to shame. The pygmies have been followed by giants, and these in turn will be followed by still greater giants. But there is a sense in which nothing has changed. Though the scale is immeasurably increased, the problems remain largely the same: men depend upon water for their very lives, and though the rivers may be tamed in time, for many years to come we shall continue to live at the mercy of its unpredictable powers. In the Valley of the Nile and of the Tigris and Euphrates men still fear its relentless ferocity and placate it with gifts. It is possible that our quarrel with water will be endless.

In the Near and Middle East farmers still dig their little irrigation ditches as they did thousands of years ago, with the same tools and the same hope of fertile fields. They know, as we know, that canals are the containers of an explosive element, to be treated with care and reverence. Modern water engineers speak of water as though it were at once the most commonplace and the strangest thing in the world; and their attitude is not far removed from that of the ancients. "Yielding and unyielding, soft and hard, very bright and dark as shadows, such is water," said the Chinese philosopher, who added that of all things it was closest to the Way of Heaven.

Select bibliography

"Scorpion and Labyrinth"

Breasted, J. H., *A History of Egypt.* Charles Scribner's Sons, N. Y., 1956.
———, *Ancient Records of Egypt.* University of Chicago Press, 1906.
———, *The Dawn of Conscience.* Charles Scribner's Sons, N. Y., 1939.
Campbell, Joseph, *The Hero with a Thousand Faces.* Meridian Books, N. Y., 1956.
Frankfort, Henri, *Before Philosophy.* Penguin Books, Harmondsworth, England, 1951.
———, *Birth of Civilization in the Near East.* Doubleday, N. Y., 1956.
Ghirshman, R., *Iran.* Penguin Books, Harmondsworth, England, 1954.
Kramer, Samuel Noah, *From the Tablets of Sumer.* Falcon's Wing Press, Indian Hills, Colo., 1956.
Lloyd, Seton, *Ruined Cities of Iraq.* Oxford University Press, N. Y., 1945.
Pope, Arthur Upham, *A Survey of Persian Art.* Oxford University Press, London, 1938.

"The Ancient Waterways"

Chi, Chao-ting, *Key Economic Areas in Chinese History.* George Allen and Unwin, London, 1936.
Gest, Alexander Purves, *Our Debt to Greece and Rome: Engineering.* Longmans, Green & Co., N. Y., 1930.
Olmstead, A. T., *A History of the Persian Empire.* University of Chicago Press, 1948.
Petrie, Sir Flinders, *A History of Egypt.* Methuen & Co., London, 1918.
Philostratus, Flavius, *Life of Apollonius,* tr. J. S. Phillimore. Oxford University Press, London, 1912.
Winston, Richard, *Charlemagne.* Bobbs-Merrill, Indianapolis, 1954.

Wright, F. A., *Marcus Agrippa, Organizer of Victory.* George Routledge & Sons, London, 1937.

"An Experiment in Lombardy"

La Lande, Joseph, *Traité de canaux de navigation.* Paris, 1778.
McCurdy, Edward, *The Notebooks of Leonardo da Vinci.* Reynal & Hitchcock, N. Y., 1939.
Parsons, W. B., *Engineers and Engineering in the Renaissance.* Williams & Wilkins, Baltimore, 1939.
Zonca, Vittorio, *Novo Teatro di machine e edificii.* 1607.

"The Canals of England"

Evans, George Ewart, "Myddleton's Glory," in *Life and Letters,* October, 1947.
Eyre, Frank, and E. C. R. Hadfield, *English Rivers and Canals.* Collins, London, 1947.
Hadfield, Charles, *British Canals.* Readers Union, London, 1952.
Newton, H., *British Canals.* Ian Allan, London, 1948.
Rolt, L. T. C., *The Inland Waterways of England.* George Allen and Unwin, London, 1950.
Smiles, Samuel, *James Brindley and the Early Engineers.* John Murray, London, 1864.

"America Pushes Back the Frontiers"

Adams, John Quincy, *Diary,* ed. Allan Nevins. Charles Scribner's Sons, N. Y., 1951.
Bobbé, Dorothie, *DeWitt Clinton.* Minton, Balch & Co., N. Y., 1933.
Buley, R. Carlyle, *The Old Northwest.* Indiana Historical Society, Indianapolis, 1950.
Crouse, D. E., *The Ohio Gateway.* Charles Scribner's Sons, N. Y., 1938.
Eckman, Jeannette, *Delaware: A Guide to the First State.* Hastings House, N. Y., 1955.
Hatcher, Harlan, *The Buckeye Country.* G. P. Putnam's Sons, N. Y., 1947.
Havighurst, Walter, *Land of Promise.* The Macmillan Co., N. Y., 1947.
———, *The Long Ships Passing.* The Macmillan Co., N. Y., 1956.
Hislop, Codman, *The Mohawk.* Rinehart & Co., N. Y., 1948.
Hulbert, Archer Butler, *The Great American Canals.* Arthur H. Clark Co., Cleveland, 1904.
Langdon, William Chauncy, *Everyday Things in American Life, 1776–1876.* Charles Scribner's Sons, N. Y., 1949.

Savage, Henry, *River of the Carolinas: The Santee.* Rinehart & Co., N. Y., 1956.

Wildes, Harry Emerson, *The Delaware.* Rinehart & Co., N. Y., 1940.

Wilson, Mitchell, *American Science and Invention.* Simon & Schuster, N. Y., 1954.

"Panama: The Sea and the Jungle"

Anderson, Charles L. G., *Life and Letters of Vasco Núñez de Balboa.* Fleming H. Revell Co., N. Y., 1941.

Bishop, Joseph Bucklin, *The Panama Gateway.* Charles Scribner's Sons, N. Y., 1913.

Haskin, Frederick J., *The Panama Canal.* Doubleday, Page & Co., N. Y., 1914.

Mack, Gerstle, *The Land Divided.* Alfred A. Knopf, N. Y., 1944.

Mills, J. Saxon, *The Panama Canal.* Thomas Nelson & Sons, London, 1914.

Romoli, Kathleen, *Balboa of Darien.* Doubleday, N. Y., 1953.

Siegfried, André, *Suez and Panama.* Jonathan Cape, London, 1940.

"Suez: The Sea and the Sands"

Beatty, Charles, *De Lesseps of Suez.* Harper, N. Y., 1957.

Hurst, H. E., *The Nile.* Constable, London, 1957.

Lesseps, Ferdinand de, *Recollections of Forty Years.* D. Appleton & Co., N. Y., 1888.

Longgood, William F., *Suez Story.* Greenberg, N. Y., 1957.

Roux, Charles, *L'Isthme et le Canal de Suez.* Hachette et Cie, Paris, 1901.

"Blue Waters and White Seas"

Galaktionov, V., *The Dawn of a Great Project.* Foreign Languages Publishing House, Moscow, 1953.

Grunwald, Constantin de, *Peter the Great.* Douglas Saunders Publications, London, 1956.

Komarovsky, A., *The Moscow-Volga Dam.* Foreign Languages Publishing House, Moscow, 1939.

Mikhailov, Nicholas, *Soviet Russia: The Land and Its People.* Sheridan House, N. Y., 1948.

Index